"*Not Your Shoe Size* is a definite must-read! From the poignant and entertaining dialogue to the vivid imagery and scene-setting, Jennifer DiVita's creativity and storytelling are at a level most authors reach only after releasing multiple titles, not on a first book." ~Terri DeBoer, author of *Brighter Skies Ahead*

"This delightful story is very relatable; however, it is anything but predictable. Written in such an inclusive way, I honestly felt like I was walking alongside the main characters as if I were the third friend. I smiled with the turn of every page. A feel-good, what-will-they-get-into next, can't-put-it-down read that will captivate you from cover to cover." ~Contessa, author of *Innamorata*

"*Not Your Shoe Size* is one delightful journey to the ripe "old age" of 100 through the eyes of best friends! It will make you laugh, cry and relate to this wonderful art of aging. I LOVED it!"
~Shelley Irwin, On-air Host & Producer, NPR Radio and PBS

"I found myself relating to both characters with the challenges and joys we share collectively as women. I laughed and cried at times while reading their stories, and I move forward with a renewed love for the journey ahead of me in life." ~Paige Rubleski, Miss Michigan '22

"Jennifer DiVita is a brilliant writer, fluent, precise, crisp, and in full command of the music of words. Get ready for a genuine experience that acknowledges the future that is bright and glorious. It is a true work of art."
~Bob Israels, Celebrity Designer

"What a lovely book about lifelong loyal friendship and aging gracefully. I couldn't turn the pages fast enough to find out what happens next in Julia's and Colette's lives!" ~Kelly the Kitchen Kop, Foodie & Influencer

"*Not Your Shoe Size* is a fun and touching novel about relationships and life and captures the true essence of friendship through the years. The end will not disappoint." ~Lisa Novosad, Senior Realty Specialist

# Not Your Shoe Size

a novel by
Jennifer DiVita

Published by Hummingbird Book House

ISBN: 979-8-9881264-0-9

For Julie, my BFF. Her life-long loyalty and friendship inspired some of the vignettes. May this book be a tribute to her memory and her life which was cut too short. I know our friendship would have endured like Julia's and Colette's. I wonder which one of us would have the larger shoe collection.

For Ava, my daughter. I hope this story gives you the courage to embrace who you are at every stage in life. In a society that's harder on women than men to age gracefully, be true to yourself, and love the skin you're in. You are beautiful!

# Denarians

## Ages 10 – 19

**C** OLETTE, 10

I was ten years old and writing my own obituary. Not because I was dying, but because I was living—to one hundred! I had to make up the story of my life and share what I hoped to accomplish by the time I was dead. It was homework for the one-hundredth day of school. It was assigned by my ancient history teacher, Mr. Hendricks. And let me clarify; I didn't mean as in ancient history; I meant that *he's* ancient. He was old as dirt.

Dinosaurs like Mr. Hendricks must wonder about dying a lot. It's what they did after school. They thought about becoming worm food during their short time left on Earth before going under the earth.

He was really, really old. He had bushy white eyebrows and a bald head, except for the u-shaped fuzzy gray hair that swooped from ear to ear around the back. He had deep wrinkles near his eyes, especially when he smiled. All signs pointed that he was an old fogey—a geezer. He must be like one hundred years old. It was a wonder he could even stand up in class and teach. Maybe we should know how old he was to prepare ourselves for his imminent death. We were going to need a substitute teacher.

"Mr. Hendricks, how old are you?" I blurted out in class one day.

"I'm sixty-five," he confidently replied.

Yep. Ancient. That's close enough to one hundred. This could very well be his end, and he needed us to help write his life story. At the rickety old age of sixty-five, he was ready to keel over any minute. In fact, I couldn't believe he was still alive.

To appeal to his apparent last dying wish, he made us write out our obituaries. I didn't even know how to spell oh-bit-choo-air-ee. And as my grandmother preached, "If you can't spell it, don't use it." So now I had to write about something I couldn't spell. Or pronounce.

How was I supposed to know when I would die? I chewed on my yellow #2 pencil, trying to wonder, but instead staring blankly at my ancient teacher. I tried hard to imagine my life at death. It was impossible to see. I was ten years old and in the fifth grade. I didn't even know what I was having for dinner tonight, let alone what my last meal would be.

Mr. Hendricks offered to help us get our "creative juices flowing," a phrase I didn't understand but that he explained as brainstorming. He drank a bottle of prune juice daily, which was probably why his brain was so juice-logged. In his attempt to help our brain juices flow, he gave us clipped newspaper oh-bit-choo-air-ees of old people who had died. Some clippings showed side-by-side pictures of the people from when they were young and beautiful to now when they were old and pruny. It didn't seem very nice to show what time had done to someone. Those victims of old age were unrecognizable from the beautiful pictures taken in their youth. So why even show the pictures? It was cruel and thoughtless. Is that what life would do to me? I didn't want to get old and look like that.

So I decided I wouldn't do that for my oh-bit-choo-air-ee. I would only show a picture of me as a sweet, chubby baby. Babies are cute, not like wrinkled old people. I wanted people to remember me as a button, you know, cute just like I was. There would be no picture of me with thin gray hair, skin peppered with brown spots, and a face that resembled shriveled fruit. Besides, I would never look like that at one hundred. I would age more responsibly and carefully. These people surely didn't know what they were doing to age like that.

The newspaper clippings were full of big words like preceded, visitation, and interment. Again, words I couldn't pronounce. I wouldn't use them because my grandmother said so.

Our teacher told us to work slowly, reading through each person's story and jotting down simple questions for ourselves, like the what and where of our lives. The questions were supposed to help us figure out what we wanted our story to say and where our lives would lead us. I began mapping out my fabulicious life based on my favorite board game, the Game of Life. The point of the game was to get a career, get married, get kids, and get as much money as possible to retire. That must also be the point of life, so I based my obituary on it.

I thought about jobs that paid like a bazillion dollars. I'd buy fancy cars and houses all over the world. I'd definitely buy the dream dollhouse my parents refused to get me. I'd buy anything I wanted because luck would give me loads of money. I smiled, knowing my husband would be like the prince from Cinderella.

*Will I have children and grandchildren?* I wondered. I decided I'd have five children. No, make it six. And more grandkids and great-grandkids than I could count. They'd get all As on their report cards. They'd be pretty, with sparkly white teeth. And they'd be sweet as pie and thoughtful and caring like me. "Enough about them," I said aloud under my breath. "I need to think about myself."

*Who would be survived by me?* I pondered silently. I had to think about this one. I wasn't even sure what that meant from the oh-bit-choo-air-ee. I figured it was all the people left behind who would be lonely after I was gone, leaving a giant hole in their lives. They would miss me so much. But there would be too many survived by people who loved me, so I better only name my best friend, Julia.

*How will I die? When will it happen? And where?* Yuck, these were yucky questions. I squirmed uncomfortably in my desk chair. Who wanted to think about death anyway? But I had homework to finish, which required asking gross questions and giving gross answers.

I finished the questions about my deadness. Now I was ready to write. Mr. Hendricks gave us the whole hour in class to do it. I gnawed on my pencil as I struggled to put words to paper. It took the entire time, and I didn't get to go out for early recess like the other kids who raced through their life stories. I finally dropped my chewed pencil on my desk, satisfied with my oh-bit-choo-air-ee. I felt good about the next ninety years of my perfect life and the decisions I made for my future.

The next day Mr. Hendricks announced we would have to read our homework to the whole class. It was bad enough that we had to plan our deaths, but now we had to listen to how everyone else would bite the dust, too. I didn't care about how dead as a doornail the other kids were or how their lives turned out—except for Julia.

The first student got up in class and read the story of his life and death. It was awful. Were we supposed to clap for that? Everyone shifted nervously, looking to our teacher for a cue.

Mr. Hendricks began to clap his hands together and shout, "Bravo!"

Of course, he would be the one to like it. That was his job as a teacher. He went through the rest of the class, calling up each student to read their deadly autobiographies. They were as varied as the students in class. Then Julia went up. She hesitantly stood from her chair and walked timidly toward the front of the room. Her face burned red. She carefully pulled a wadded-up piece of paper out of her pocket and unfolded it. Her hands shook. She began to read, stressing every syllable, giving way to the nervous crackle in her voice:

*"Julia, whose name means 'youthful,' lived to be one hundred. Julia spent her life in service to others. She enjoyed doing ordinary things. Nothing was exciting about her life. It was simple, but she was happy. She married young, had many kids, and spent time with her grandkids, watching them play. When she retired from a chocolate factory, she spent her retirement reading books and knitting baby booties. Rocking in her rocking chair gave her great satisfaction. She never moved away from her hometown. She stayed married to her husband for seventy years. They died hours apart, still happily married because they couldn't live without each other. Her lifelong best friend Colette was at her bedside holding her hand when she died. She had a content life, and it all went according to plan."*

Julia ran back to her desk in the back of the room and buried her face. The spotlight wasn't her thing.

I was called up last. But I didn't read my oh-bit-choo-air-ee. When Grandmother Imelda, my dad's mom, learned about our assignment, she was mortified and said I shouldn't be subjected to this morbidness. So she wrote a letter for me to give to Mr. Hendricks instead. I read it out loud.

*"Dear Mr. Hendricks (aka Grim Reaper), I'm utterly appalled you would have these innocent children write such an abominable assignment. It's distasteful to ask ten-year-olds to think about their deaths. They don't need to worry about old age and death until they're there. I'm much closer than they are and don't think about old age or death. Protect their innocent minds from reality. Regretfully, Colette's Grandmother, Imelda"*

Nobody clapped. Not even Mr. Hendricks. Like Julia, I wanted to run back to my desk and throw my head down. But I stood frozen. I was humiliated that I didn't get applause. I wasn't sure if I'd return to fifth grade tomorrow. Grandmother Imelda had just ruined the rest of my life.

"Well, that wasn't quite the assignment," Mr. Hendricks said. "It's not about your death but how you choose to live your life. I respect her opinion to not let you read it. However, I still expect you to turn it in for a grade."

"I can still read it," I said, knowing Grandmother Imelda wouldn't be happy. But I wanted applause, too. I unfolded my oh-bit-choo-air-ee and carefully read it to the class.

*"Sadly, Colette died at one hundred years old but looked decades younger. Her beauty lasted as long as her age. She peacefully nodded off for an eternal dirt nap. She was very popular. She is survived by many admirers who thought she was amazing, including her gorgeous, devoted, rich, loving, charming husband, six adoring, well-behaved children who minded their manners and never talked back, and her wonderful parents who gave her almost everything she asked for. She lived an exciting life. She was an accomplished opera singer, Oscar-nominated actress, Pulitzer-prize-winning author, even a gifted scientist who discovered all kinds of scientific things, and ~~vetaranarian, vetranaryan,~~ animal doctor. Her charm and brilliance were a breath of fresh air to all. Donations may be made to a charity of your choice as long as it's the 'Colette Piggy Bank Fund' of which she was a devoted supporter. Colette will never, ever, ever be forgotten."*

Everyone clapped enthusiastically this time. I was sure my oh-bit-choo-air-ee got the loudest round of applause. I curtsied to the class, celebrating the perfect life I would have.

• • • • • • • • •

## JULIA, II 1/2

I started driving today. Ignore the fact I was only eleven-and-a-half. Not sixteen and legally qualified to. But as I said, I started driving today. Really, what's the difference between eleven-and-a-half and sixteen?

Colette and I took Papa's car out for a joy ride. I knew how to drive. *Abuelo*, my grandpa, taught me how to drive his old beat-up pickup truck on dusty back roads when I was really young—like six months ago. Never mind, I sat on his lap while he drove and simply steered. But I considered this enough driver's training. Abuelo always taught me well, and I trusted everything he said. And he said I was a good driver. I decided to test my newfound driving skills because Colette wanted ice cream, and she said we were too cool now to ride our bikes to the ice cream parlor. She dared me to drive and said she'd buy me an ice cream sundae if I did it.

I took the dare and jumped in the driver's seat while Colette took command as my copilot. We felt so grown-up. Driving was something adults did, and here we were, taking the wheel by the horns. Or was it the bull by the horns? I didn't know. I was just a kid.

I was a bit too short to reach the gas pedal, so I adjusted my seat forward. I still sat too low in the driver's seat, so I stuffed my backpack under my bottom to boost me up. I could barely see above the steering wheel. I turned the key, and the engine rumbled to life. It was a thrilling and terrifying sound. I nervously gripped the steering wheel and backed out of the driveway. I slowly inched the car up to the intersection at the end of our street. No cars were coming from either direction. I was relieved. The ice cream parlor wasn't far. *You can do this*, I told myself. *You're like the little engine that could.*

Colette sat in her seat motionless. She was as pale as Abuelo's transparent skin. I couldn't look at her because she made me feel jittery and lose confidence in my driving ability. My knuckles turned white like Colette's face. I gripped the steering wheel so hard that my hands went numb. As we made a jerky snail's pace down the road, people passed by us fast. Some blew their horns and shouted obscenities at us. The nerve of people!

"Get the *bleep* off the road, ya old fogey!" one man yelled. (I can't say the bleeped word because I wasn't allowed to swear).

"Stupid geezer!"

"Move over, granny!"

"Crazy old driver!"

The verbal assaults fired away. Abuelo would not appreciate these insults. I guess other drivers thought I was elderly because I could barely see above the dashboard and was driving ever so slowly. Who else drives this way except senior citizens? Illegally driving kids, I guess.

When the ice cream parlor came into view, I breathed a sigh of relief. Our journey was half over. I felt victorious. But I rejoiced too soon. As we turned into the parking lot, I was besieged by cars coming and going. Backing out and pulling in. Going this way and that. It was a parking lot, but it felt like a chess match on wheels. Who would make the next move? I had driven on country roads but not in parking lots.

I panicked in confusion and hit the gas pedal instead of the brake. The car lurched forward. It rammed through the yellow picket fence, over the flower boxes, and into a picnic table outside the ice cream parlor, missing the patrons by the length of an ice cream cone. I finally slammed on the brakes and stalled the car, but not before hitting the outside soft-serve ice cream machine. The car stopped amidst chocolate and vanilla ice cream swirling onto the hood. The bumper was seriously bruised. And so was my ego.

"WHAT DID YOU JUST DO?" Colette screamed.

"This is all your fault!" I yelled back at her. "If you hadn't dared me, I wouldn't have done it."

The terror on her face shook me back to the reality of how much trouble I was in. Her reaction was only a preview of what I expected to encounter with my parents.

I was right. After the police told them the story, they said they were grounding me for life. I knew it wasn't possible to ground me for life. But they might ground me until I was fifty. I had never been in so much trouble. I was a goody two shoes and had always worked hard not to misbehave.

Believe it or not, I did minor damage to Papa's car. But I wrecked the fence and flowers. I would be forced to pay the owners out of my piggy bank by doing chores for years. I pinky-promised I wouldn't drive again until I had my license, which Mama and Papa pushed back until I was eighteen years old as a punishment. I wouldn't rat out Abuelo. I didn't want him to get in trouble for teaching me to drive. I was afraid he'd go to jail, so I stayed silent.

"What compelled you to do such a mindless, stupid thing?" Mama asked.

The shrug of my shoulders must have convinced my parents of my ignorance. Abuelo was off the hook. I would defend him until the day I died. I also vowed I would never get in trouble ever again. I always followed the rules, except this once, and it cost me a lot of piggy bank money.

Because of my joyriding, I was ordered to do community service and help at the senior center where Mama worked as a chair aerobics instructor. Colette's parents gave her the same punishment for being an accomplice. They wanted to scare her so bad that she wouldn't drive before she got her license. It worked—she was scared to death to be near the old people at the center.

"I'd rather crash into another building than sit with old crazy coots," she declared.

But I was tickled with the idea of providing company to lonely seniors. Mama said they needed young blood to connect with their youthful inner selves. Whatever that meant.

On our first day, I joined right in. For me, it was entertainment. For Colette, it was like being hung by her eyelids.

When bingo started, I gave Colette the easy task of calling numbers. I wanted to help the seniors place plastic chips on their cards. They smiled at me a lot and liked to call me "dearie." They seemed so happy to have young people in their presence.

Colette's voice monotonously droned on as she called bingo numbers.

"B-5... O-64... N-44..."

The tedium caused many seniors to fall asleep sitting up, so I played their cards for them. *What makes old people sleep so much?* I wondered.

Bingo went on all afternoon. They sure liked it. When the final bingo was yelled, an old woman waved me over to her table. She bore a delightful resemblance to Mrs. Claus. She had white, fluffy hair like cotton balls. And her face was covered with deep folds, which gave away the secret that she had lived a long life.

"Hi, Florence," I said, reading her name tag.

"I've not seen you here before, young lady. What's your name?" she asked sweetly.

"I'm Julia, and I'm eleven-and-a-half." It was important she knew I was eleven-and-a-half and not just eleven.

"What brings you to this place meant for old folks?" Florence asked.

"I got into trouble," I confessed. "So I have to do service hours and work here at the center." My face must've shown the regret I was feeling.

Florence smiled. "But that means you're a very lucky girl."

"How's that?" I wondered.

"If it weren't for that, you wouldn't be sitting here next to me right now," she teased. I so wanted to hug this Mrs. Claus. She was bubbly and cute.

"But what I did wasn't so lucky," I insisted.

"You'll make all kinds of mistakes in life, but that's how you learn and grow," she said. "It's okay to fail at things. What'd you do anyway?"

"I stole Papa's car and went out for a joyride to get ice cream," I explained. "And I lied about it."

"Oh dear," she replied, smiling sympathetically. "You'll save yourself regret in life by being honest, and you'll truly enjoy a life of freedom."

"I feel terrible about it."

"I bet you do," Florence agreed. "It's your inner guidepost warning you to live your life with integrity. Don't bend the rules or take shortcuts; you'll sleep soundly with a clear conscience every night. What's hard to understand at eleven-and-a-half," she explained, "is how far-reaching dishonesty can spread. As you get older, you can see the ripple effect of your actions more and more."

"Thanks for sharing with me," I told her. I liked Florence.

"I've learned all kinds of lessons in my ninety years," she said. "I only wish young people wanted to hear my pearls of wisdom. It's difficult to share the lessons of life with adolescents. They think they're know-it-alls. They aren't interested in listening."

I was interested. I wanted to keep talking with her, but it was time to go.

"If you return, I'll share more," Florence promised. "But the true teacher is time and experience. You'll only be able to grow wise as you grow old. Wisdom doesn't come from lectures by fogeys like me. It comes from living."

Her eyes twinkled as she passed her life lessons on to me. I couldn't wait to return and talk with Florence. I loved the influence the elderly could have on my life.

• • • • • • • • •

## COLETTE, 12

"You're a woman now!" Mom proudly proclaimed, crouching over me as I sat on the toilet.

I shrieked when I used the bathroom and discovered I was bleeding. It was my first period. I was taught about menstruation in health class, but though I was prepared for this moment, experiencing it for the first time was shocking. Mom had heard my yelp echo from the bathroom and rushed in. When she saw the red-stained toilet paper, she awkwardly hugged me as I sat indiscreetly on the toilet. Mom's eyes welled with big, juicy tears.

"I'm so proud of you," she continued to gush. "This is an important rite of passage into womanhood. You're not a little girl anymore. This is a big moment."

Exactly. This was a big, dig-a-hole-and-disappear moment. I didn't want this ridiculous attention. And while I sat in total vulnerability on the toilet seat, she took the next twenty minutes telling me about the birds, the bees, the flowers, and the trees.

I knew about this gross life transition, but she didn't care when I told her I'd already learned about "the change" at school. She explained things I didn't want to hear ever again as I sat exposed on the porcelain throne with my pants down to my ankles. She still hadn't given me a chance to move off the seat as she blabbed and cried.

But I should've braced myself. It was nothing compared to what came next. I overheard Mom call my grandma on the phone and proclaim the good news that I had joined the sisterhood of fertility. I slammed the bathroom door, hoping she'd get a clue as to how humiliating this was for me. It was too subtle a hint.

At dinner, the conversation turned from discussing everyone's day to Mom proudly discussing the events of mine. Was this walk of shame ever going to end?

"Colette's a woman now. She's menstruating," Mom declared to Dad as she cleared away the dinner plates and put dessert on the table. "We're going to celebrate with a good old-fashioned cherry pie."

I would rather celebrate by becoming a worm, crawling into the cherry pie, and shriveling up into a crisp-fried invertebrate than be subjected to this torture. What was she doing to me? This would be my undoing if she continued to celebrate this most unwelcome milestone. Was she trying to scare me away from actually becoming a woman?

"My big girl has started her feminine cycle," Mom gushed, addressing me. "You're a modern woman now. You're privileged to have reached menarche."

"What's menarche?" I asked.

"Let me tell you where babies come from," Mom said. "It's like the sausage we had for dinner. It starts with a man's..."

I was sorry I asked. I tuned her out and gulped down the cherry pie. I was mortified at being taught sex education after eating Polish sausage for dinner—and in front of my dad, of all people! Dad squirmed in his chair, as uncomfortable as me. I ran out feeling sick. My stomach hurt. Was it embarrassment or cramps? I wasn't sure. I did know this was the worst day of my life. Worst. Day. Ever.

"I'm proud of you," Mom yelled after me as I raced upstairs to my bedroom. I threw myself down on my bed and sobbed. I wouldn't be able to show my face to my family again. Why would she be proud of me for this? It's not like I did anything. I didn't choose this. I wouldn't wish this on anyone.

From what my friends told me—and I believed everything they said—menstruating would be a miserable experience for the rest of my life. I would bleed for a week every month until I was an old lady. I did the math on this. If I had a period until I was fifty—the age of an old lady—that meant I'd have this curse for thirty-eight years. That was a total of 456 visits from "Aunt Flo."

How depressing was that? Maybe I could just adopt a kid if I could trade in this privilege. Fertility, when you're an adolescent, is not a privilege. Why couldn't I be given this so-called privilege when I was actually old enough to get pregnant and have kids? There was no point in starting my period when I was just a kid. It seemed as if God had acted prematurely in wanting me to become a woman.

"I want the men to pause now," I cried, burying my head in my pillow. I had no idea what the men-pause was, except my mom said that's when periods would finally stop around fifty. The next four decades would drag by, waiting for men to pause. Starting today, I'd count the days, months, and years until they did. Oh, how I wanted to be the little girl I was yesterday before men ruined everything with men-arche and men-pause! This was a bloody awful start to womanhood.

• • • • • • • • • •

## JULIA, TWEEN

The elementary years flew by. We had nearly reached Queen of the Hill status—eighth grade. This was a big milestone in any kid's life. The principal, Mr. Patrick, held an assembly every spring to celebrate the incoming eighth graders since we would rule middle school next year. We packed into the gym bleachers and rearranged our seating to sit close to our best friends and avoid the gross, stinky boys. It was noisy and chaotic.

Mr. Patrick yelled into the sound system to get us unruly kids to settle down. As part of the assembly, he handed out pretend paper flames to symbolize passing a torch. We found it corny, but this was a school tradition for whatever reason. Mr. Patrick explained that he also had a gift for each of us.

"I want to teach you how little time you have to live," Mr. Patrick said.

How little time we have? I've got so much time ahead of me I can hardly wrap my juvenile mind around it. Was he confused? Is this what they meant when someone was having a senior moment?

"Life goes by at a breathtaking speed," Mr. Patrick explained. "And the older you get, the faster it goes. At the mere age of twelve, it's hard to imagine life going fast when the days seem to drag by. But trust me; you'll wake up one day at fifty and wonder how you got there."

My thoughts zoned in and out. I glanced at other students in the gym, and they seemed as bored as me. One girl scribbled pictures on her hand; a boy chewed the eraser off his pencil; and Colette counted ceiling tiles.

"I'm telling you this to help you prepare for your future—to help you make the most of your time, make smarter choices, try new things." Mr. Patrick's voice crackled through the microphone. "Your years on this earth are numbered, and we don't know if you'll have fifteen years or 115 years. So stop and smell the roses! Enjoy every moment because they'll soon be memories."

His speech over, Mr. Patrick instructed us to file out of the bleachers. One by one, like lemmings at the edge of a cliff, we obediently jumped off to receive a long-stemmed rose. This was an exciting change to the usual format of past years. I guess the adults were as bored as us with the paper-torch passing ceremony.

Colette was ahead of me in the rose-receiving line. Following closely behind her, I nervously walked to the middle of the gym floor. I didn't like being the center of attention. It made my hands sweat.

I stared at Colette in front of me. She always kept calm. We were so different from each other. But we had become soul sisters when we were babies because we were born on the same day, just hours apart. Colette was technically older since she was born first on our birthday. Our appearances were also very different. While Colette was tall and lanky with long flowing blonde hair, I was short and somewhat chubby. And my dark chocolate, almost black, wavy locks could not be tamed no matter how hard I tried. Colette was the graceful swan. I was the ugly duckling.

My turn came to be given the long-stemmed white rose. And then, like soldiers, we walked in single file and returned to the bleachers. I opened the card attached to my rose. It read, *Stop and smell the roses.*

Mr. Patrick had to quiet us down since we'd gotten rowdy again. "This is to remind you to take in every moment and live life to the fullest," he rambled. "To stop and smell the roses means to enjoy life every day, even the boring parts."

I looked around at the assembly. The boys were using the roses as swords on each other. The girls were plucking the petals, reciting, "He loves me, he loves me not." I don't think this was what Mr. Patrick meant for the flowers. Somehow, we all missed the point of his lesson.

"These roses are my gift to help you enjoy the simple things in life," Mr. Patrick said earnestly. "Whenever you see roses, pause and appreciate where you are instead of racing to get to the next best thing. It's important to recognize it's times like this you'll always remember."

"Grownups are so weird," Colette whispered to me.

I had no idea what Mr. Patrick was talking about either, but I appreciated his intentions. I was relieved when the bell rang, and we all ran out of the school to board buses. We were even noisier than in the assembly.

As we stepped off the bus in front of our homes, Colette whacked me over the head with her rose.

"Act your age, *chica*," I said, poking her in the ribs.

"Not your shoe size," she countered with a laugh. This was our signature sign-off whenever we parted ways. It was like our own secret handshake. We giggled at our silliness.

I brought my rose home. I was about the only one who hadn't plucked mine apart. Mama said Mr. Patrick's gift was a beautiful gesture. She wanted to press it and dry it for a keepsake. Great, now I'd have a dead rose that I didn't understand the meaning behind.

• • • • • • • • •

## COLETTE, 13 (GOING ON 30)

It was my thirteenth birthday, and it was going to be the best. I loved birthdays. I didn't understand why grownups dreaded their birthdays so much. I wanted a birthday every day of the year. I couldn't imagine not being excited for this day to come, no matter how old I was. And today, I wasn't a child anymore. I was a teenager. It was a big deal.

As a passage into my teen years, my mom finally allowed me to get my ears pierced. Until now, she'd said I was too young for earrings. She said they made girls look too mature and that I didn't need to look older than my age.

I begged for makeup. I could be prettier with makeup. I always felt plain, especially compared to Julia. She was a natural beauty with thick, wavy dark hair; mine was straight and limp. Funny, she always said I had the better hair.

She also had smooth, light-brown skin, and I was fair-skinned with acne. She was athletic and the right height for seventh grade. I was too tall and stood out like a giraffe.

Mom put her foot down with the makeup request, arguing that I was too young and that it was for grownups. She said I could start wearing a little makeup when I got into high school. I couldn't wait to be older to wear rouge and lipstick like everybody else. I swear I was the only girl on the face of the planet besides Julia, who wasn't allowed to wear makeup.

Since I was now a teenager, I begged to have my bedroom changed over to teenage décor, too. I wanted to get rid of my little girl's room and buy new furnishings and bedding to make me feel like the teen I now was.

Mom threw me one last birthday party. Apparently, I was too old now for birthday celebrations but not old enough for makeup. Parents made no sense. She decided that after this year, it would be time to put these parties to rest. Is that why adults didn't like birthdays—because they didn't have parties?

Gram and Gramps, my mom's parents, and all my aunts, uncles, and cousins came. Julia couldn't come because her family was throwing her party at the same time. Mom baked my favorite chocolate cake, frosted with pink icing and marked with thirteen candles. My family sang "Happy Birthday." I made the two biggest wishes—that I would stop getting pimples and that my bust would fill out. I wanted to look like a real woman to stop stuffing my training bra with socks. I blew out the candles, confident my wishes would come true—that I'd get clear skin and boobs.

Mom and Dad followed through with my birthday gift list and surprised me with the bedding and accessories I had chosen. But as expected, no makeup. I was so excited about the new room décor. My room was finally going to be redecorated to match my teenage maturity. But that wasn't the only surprise.

"We'll redecorate for you, except it'll be in your new room," Mom said, avoiding looking at me as she said it.

"My new room?" I asked. "Are we moving?"

"Sort of. Not we. But *you*. You're moving into the attic," she announced. "Gram and Gramps are coming to live with us, and they're going to stay

in your room. We feel you're old enough now to have the attic for your
bedroom. You'll have your own space on another level of the house."

Her smile was forced. Was she trying to convince herself that this was a
good thing?

"Are you kidding me?" I yelled. "This is so not fair! What if the house starts
on fire, and I'm trapped in the attic?"

"Well, dear, that's exactly why we don't want Gram and Gramps up there,"
Mom teased. "If there were a fire, we'd lose all their knowledge and wisdom.
That's very valuable."

Everyone else laughed—everyone except me. There was nothing funny in
any of this. I screamed, throwing the bedspread across the room.

"Antiques are supposed to be stored in the attic, not young girls," I shouted, pointing at Gram and Gramps. "They are the antiques. Not me."

Everyone looked at me as if I was supposed to be happy. This was dooms-
day. Not only were my grandparents moving in with us and stealing my
room, but I would also become like the rest of the storage items in the
attic—discarded—taken out only when needed.

I reacted like any typical thirteen-year-old. I unleashed a full-blown temper
tantrum. I threw accent pillows across the room, forcing my family to dodge
the shrapnel of my outburst. I stormed out of the room and charged upstairs
to my bedroom, my family watching in disbelief at my hissy fit. I didn't care.
I cried so hard I was heaving. I collapsed to the floor and pounded my fists
on the carpet. Mom came into my room and yelled at me for my despicable
juvenile behavior. My sobs only grew louder.

She didn't understand. My life was over. Her very old parents were coming
to live with us. I was losing my bedroom and being forced to live hidden away
like a prisoner in the attic. How could she not be sympathetic? Instead, she
was angry at me for reacting like anybody would under this kind of torture. A
bomb just went off in my life. This was the worst birthday ever in the history
of the universe! No wonder adults didn't like birthdays. Birthdays ruined
everything.

Mom scolded me, telling me to grow up and stop acting like a child. I
found it ironic that I was supposed to act like a grownup, but I wasn't
allowed to wear makeup like a grownup. She grounded me for a week. That
was going to feel like a lifetime.

I slammed my door behind her, determined I was never coming out. I'd stay there forever, even if it meant never eating or playing outside with friends again. I was not giving up my room. I wouldn't do it. I could hold out for days. I felt the anger boiling up inside me. So I trashed my room. I yanked every shirt and dress off the hangers and started building a mountain of pink and purple outfits. I pulled out every piece of clothing stuffed in my dresser drawers and added them to the pile. I was justified in doing this. If they were going to throw me out of my room, I wasn't going out easily. Gram could put my clothes away in my new room up in the attic. I wasn't lifting a finger.

I cried myself to sleep on top of the pastel mountain. Later that evening, Dad came into my room. I thought he was going to apologize for the terrible mistake and tell me I could keep my room, and Gram and Gramps would move up into the attic. But my fantasy didn't last long. Dad hadn't come to apologize. He had come to straighten me out.

"I see you've gotten a jumpstart on moving your clothes," Dad surmised soberly. "Your grandparents will be here in two weeks, so you can start packing your stuff and hauling it up anytime. I think you'll like your new room."

"Doubt it," I huffed under my breath.

"You want us to treat you like you're a mature young lady, yet your attitude was anything but," Dad lectured. "If you want respect, then you need to earn it. You will help your grandparents settle in because of your behavior. And you'll do it graciously. Do you understand?"

"Great!" I snapped, rolling my eyes in disgust. I slumped on the pile of clothes with my arms crossed and lips pursed, waiting for him to finish. Instead, he turned and walked out. I wanted to scream once again. But I wouldn't be doing myself any favors. How about Gram and Gramps show *me* respect and not force me out of the bedroom I've had for the last thirteen years? They were squeezing me out like they squeezed their denture paste from a tube.

For the next week, I worked on setting up my attic prison. I put every single item away in my new closet by myself. Then when Gram and Gramps moved in, I had to hang up all their clothes, too. They smelled like musty mothballs. It was punishment for trashing my room. Where was the justice? I was never going to adjust to this new arrangement. Never, ever, ever.

My grandparents' presence was a rude awakening. Maybe Mom and Dad didn't care, but I was annoyed by all the visual reminders of having old fogeys take over our home. The toothbrush cup I used for my retainer was also used for their fake teeth in the bathroom. Next to my feminine pads was a box of adult leak-guard pads. Plus, my one bottle of gummy vitamins was lost in the medicine cabinet among ten medication bottles. This juxtaposition was an assault on my youth. And my ego.

•••••••••

### JULIA, 15

I was a second-generation American born to Mexican parents. While my parents were 100 percent Mexican, they were selective in what they passed down to me from their Hispanic heritage. They didn't purposely teach me Spanish because they wanted me to assimilate into American culture. But they spoke it often, so I learned it naturally. Yet Mama still fully expected me to carry on certain Hispanic traditions like a *quinceañera*. Mama had been planning my quinceañera—my fifteenth birthday party to celebrate my rite of passage from childhood into adulthood. It was a big deal, and it took Mama a year to plan it. Every generation of women in her family celebrated this milestone, and she expected I would, too—even as she tried to morph me into a typical American girl.

Our family from Mexico was traveling up for this significant birthday. Mama had invited nearly one hundred people for the celebration, which would be held at our home. And to Papa's chagrin, the guest list kept growing. It was important they didn't miss my day as I transitioned from being a girl to a woman.

For months Mama and I had carefully shopped for the perfect ball gown. This was as big of a deal as shopping for a wedding dress. It was a process not to be rushed. I tried on dress after dress. After a seemingly endless process, I fell in love with a light pink satin gown with layers of ruffles. The sleeves were puffed, and the bodice was stitched with pearls and crystals. I felt like a princess wearing it. Mama approved. Finally. She also picked out a crystal tiara as a gift for me, and we bought two pairs of shoes for the ceremony: a pair of white ballet flats and a pair of white heels.

On the day of my quinceañera, I got to shave my legs and tweeze my eyebrows. These were big things in a girl's life. Mama took me to the beauty salon to get my hair set. It was pulled up high on my head, with big ringlets of dark-brown curls cascading around the tiara. Mama also had the beautician apply makeup. It was my first time wearing makeup—another significant moment to mark the day. The beautician spun me around in the salon chair, and I gasped at how grownup I looked with makeup.

My day would be like a fairytale, perfect in every way. As part of her Hispanic culture, Mama was superstitious, and she warned me not to jinx the day by proclaiming it to be perfect beforehand. And then I was jinxed. I didn't know if it was just the stuff of life—I hadn't learned enough about life yet—or if superstition was coming to get me because I had said it would be perfect.

First, I woke up with a giant pimple on my forehead. It was the size of a bowling ball. Then Colette called with the worst news in the history of the world. She had come down with chickenpox. The chickenpox, today of all days! She was too sick to come to my quinceañera.

"But you have to come!" I demanded. "You can't miss this milestone birthday we share."

"I want to come," she cried. "But I can't make it. I've got blisters covering my entire body. And I've got a fever and a sore throat."

This was devastating.

"But you're a *dama* in my court. You're like a bridesmaid. How could you not be there? This is the most important day in my entire life!" I broke down sobbing, making a mess of the freshly applied makeup.

"I know. It's the saddest thing in the world to miss," Colette said, sniffling. "But you won't even notice I'm not there. It's going to be an amazing day for you. You get a fiesta. Remember, my mom celebrated my passage into womanhood by buying me tampons. Your mom bought you a tiara."

That made us both laugh.

"I'm so sorry I can't be there for you or to see you in your fancy dress," she said.

"Well, I'm sad you'll miss my party, but I won't let you ruin it by spreading chickenpox," I said. "I promise to show you all the pictures the photographer takes."

I hung up. I looked in the mirror to see dark mascara smudged under my eyes. I carefully wiped away the evidence of disappointment, a river of black tears sliding down my cheeks. I forced myself to be happy. *Abuela*, my grandma, always said happiness was a choice. I had to choose this now despite not spending my special rite of passage with my best friend.

The festivities began with a Catholic mass at church. I felt the butterflies flutter in my stomach as I watched my *familia* file into the pews. Beads of sweat trickled beneath the layers of pink satin. I was so nervous. I was afraid my sweaty armpits would ruin my beautiful dress. I still didn't like to be the center of attention. I tried to look past the staring faces and focus only on Abuelo and Abuela. They beamed at me with pride, which pushed the butterflies out.

The event officially began with the crowning ceremony. Mama placed the tiara squarely on my head and announced I would always be God's princess. It felt rather dramatic with such pomp and circumstance. Her eyes filled with tears as she adjusted the tiara into place with countless bobby pins that stabbed into my head. She had fretted all morning that it would fall off, so she made sure to secure it tightly. She did!

During the ceremony, I was presented with even more gifts—including a rosary, a book of prayers, and countless keepsakes to commemorate the day. After mass, we returned to our house, where the reception was held. All the guests would indulge in scrumptious Mexican fare and dance to the music of a mariachi band.

A childhood boy friend (not boyfriend, silly) escorted me into the party as part of the grand entrance. He was a pimple-faced, clumsy kid. And dirt always jumped up onto him. But today, he was dressed in a dapper tuxedo. Everyone cheered at my arrival, and Papa greeted me with a kiss on the cheek. He smiled a big toothy grin. I felt so special watching Papa look upon me with endearment. He took me by the hand and walked me into the living room, where everyone waited in anticipation for the *brindis*—or toast. Papa handed each guest a fancy decorated goblet filled with champagne to make his speech.

"Welcome, everyone, to this spectacular day," he began the brindis, scanning the group of guests. "Juliana's fifteenth birthday celebration with all of you is a beautiful event—her passage from a little girl to a young lady. I couldn't be prouder of her, and I'm so grateful you could all be here to share this moment.

"Fifteen years ago, I held this delightful bundle of joy in my arms, and today she's already grown into a lovely woman. How did she grow up so quickly?" Here he turned his attention to me. "My brindis today is that you use your life to do good, to live well and mature into a beautiful woman. You have your whole life ahead of you, and I pray it's blessed with happiness and love. I love you, Julia."

Papa lifted his champagne glass into the air to salute me and then poured the champagne into his mouth. Everyone followed his lead, drinking the champagne. They let me have a sip, too. The bubbles tickled my nose.

As ballroom music filled the air, Papa clasped my hand gently in his and whirled me around the living room. This would be our first dance together for the family to see. We took dance lessons for a month to learn the waltz. Even this was a big deal. I was officially given permission now to dance in public as part of the rite of growing into a woman. It was so Cinderella-esque.

When the music quieted, Papa walked me over to a chair. It was now time for the ceremony of the shoes. As I sat, the plume of pink ruffles ballooned around me like a cloud of cotton candy.

As is custom after the first waltz, Papa knelt before me for the "Changing of the Shoes"—another sign of my maturity into womanhood. He marked this tradition by replacing the girlish white ballet slippers I wore at the start of the day with the pair of womanly white high heels. He carefully removed my right slipper and then my left. He held up the high heels for all to see and then gently placed one on my right foot and the other on my left. Papa's eyes flooded with tears, and everyone cheered. I was officially a woman now. This was the last step of the quinceañera that made my transition complete. The ceremony was a beautiful symbol of my transformation. I was now officially an active adult in society. The shoes proved it.

• • • • • • • • • •

## COLETTE, 17

Though it had already been four years, it seemed like Gram and Gramps had just moved into our house yesterday. As I got used to them taking up space in our house, I felt sorry for them. They were nearly blind and wore bifocals. I think they were deaf, too, since I had to yell to get them to hear me. They ate weird food like prunes and fruit cake. I'd notice them do gross things, too. Gram would take her dentures out of her mouth and leave them on the dinner table. And Gramps would put powdery fiber stuff in his orange juice at breakfast and then pass gas the rest of the day.

Gramps began to sleep most of the time and didn't go anywhere. When I asked Mom about this, she said not to concern myself with it. It was grownup business. They never let me in on grownup business. Even though I was in high school, they still treated me like a child. I hated it. That left me having to eavesdrop and put the pieces of the story together myself.

Mom and Gram vaguely shared about Gramps' illness. They said they couldn't take care of him. He was too sick. Gram cried a lot, saying it was too tiring and too much work. They agreed it was time to put Gramps in a nursing home. I overheard Gram say she felt like she abandoned him, but Mom said it was for the best. I wondered who it was best if Gram didn't want him to go and Gramps didn't want to go, either. I wasn't sure why they made him move. It seemed to me he was being held hostage by a nursing home. I would convince them to bring him home quickly. Despite my rebellion when he and Gram first moved in, Gramps and I had grown close over the past few years. Now that I had adjusted to them living with us, I wasn't ready for Gramps to leave.

Mom wanted me to visit Gramps as soon as he got settled in. I was nervous. Visiting an old folks' home meant watching people do weird things like what Gram and Gramps did. From what I overheard while eavesdropping, the nursing home didn't sound very good. They described it as a hospital with a bunch of old, sick people. I didn't want to see old, sick people, but I did want to see Gramps.

When we arrived at the nursing home, I read the sign on the entrance: *Heritage Manor.* The place looked nice enough on the outside. It was a three-story brick building with lots of flower boxes that hung beneath the windows. The landscaping was well-kept, and the grass was lush and green. There was a big turnaround drive under a covered roof to drop people off. Mom parked in the lot, and we walked toward the main doors.

I noticed the first old person. She was sitting in a wheelchair outside the entrance. It made me a little jittery seeing her. I had never seen a lot of old, sick people in one place, so I didn't know if they would all be passing gas like Gramps. Mom had given me a lecture in the car ahead of time to be polite and not stare. I decided the best way to handle it would be to act like they were invisible.

We walked inside the first set of doors. There were so many old people. Most of them were staring at us. But as Mom reminded me, I couldn't stare back. Some had smiles on their faces. Others blankly gazed forward, not looking at anything in particular. They were all withered and wrinkled and sad.

We walked to the second set of doors, and Mom rang the buzzer. As we made our way in, a few nurses stood guard. Probably making sure the geezers didn't run away from this place. Not that they could run, but they might try if they wanted to escape badly enough. I hoped I wouldn't be like them when I got old—caged in a nursing home. I made a pact with myself to stay young and never end up in a nursing home like Gramps.

"May I help you?" a voice echoed through the intercom.

"We're here to see my dad," Mom said.

The door clicked to allow us in. There were even more decrepit people lingering in the lobby. One old woman sat in a wheelchair, shuffling her feet to move around. But she only went in circles. An old man slowly pushed a walker, taking one feeble step at a time. A few more shuffled down the hall, gripping the railings for support. Others slept in the lobby chairs.

I instantly loathed this place. The people were sick, and the place smelled like decay. Mom and I finally reached the elevator, and she pushed the up arrow. I prayed the elevator doors would open quickly so I could get away from all these people staring at me.

"It's okay, honey. These people aren't going to hurt you," Mom assured me, reaching out to stroke my cheek. "You look frightened, and you don't need to be."

I didn't realize fear was showing. I didn't know what I was afraid of. I knew they couldn't hurt me when they could barely even stand up. It was just the scariness of seeing many people so frail and ill. Death lingered here. Were all these people on their way out to kick up dirt? It creeped me out thinking about them becoming worm food. I just wanted to see Gramps, bring him home, and get out as fast as possible.

The elevator doors opened. A nurse stepped out backward, pulling a man in a wheelchair. Another man followed, hobbling with a cane. The old folks were multiplying and coming out of the woodwork. Mom pushed the button for the third floor, and the elevator closed.

"Mom, when can we bring Gramps home?" I asked in concern. "I don't think this is the best place for him."

"He won't be leaving, dear," Mom replied, tears welling up in her eyes. "Gramps is really sick and will live here until he dies."

"He's going to die here?" I asked in disbelief. "When?"

"The doctors aren't giving him much time, but nobody knows for sure," Mom explained. "He'll be more comfortable here than at home because Gram can't take care of him, and neither can we. He needs a lot of help. So, the doctors will take good care of him."

A lump swelled in my throat, and tears burned my eyes. Gramps was dying. Nobody told me that. I wasn't ready for Gramps to die. He wasn't like the rest of the people here. I wanted to scream, throw myself on the elevator floor, and sob. I fought back my tears, which made my throat ache and my forehead throb. I tried to be brave and not a sissy.

The elevator doors opened on the third floor. We walked down a long corridor lined with rooms. Most doors were open, and when I looked into the rooms, I saw lots of people sleeping in hospital beds. Some rooms had two people in them, with a curtain separating the beds. Other people had a room to themselves. They were lucky.

We got to Gramps' room. He was sharing it with someone else. But he got the bed near the window, at least.

"Dad, look who's here to see you," Mom said to Gramps. "Colette is here today. She came by to give you hugs and kisses."

Gramps was resting with his eyes closed. He slowly opened them to focus on us.

"Come sit next to me, apple dumpling," Gramps said. He had many pet names for me, usually related to fruits like cherry blossom or peach cobbler. He patted the blanket spread over him to get me to sit by his side. He looked visibly frail, like all the people here. I didn't remember him looking like this at home. How did he get so sickly so fast?

Mom pulled up a chair next to the bed and held his hand. She asked him how he felt and if he was in any pain. I tuned out their words and zoned in on his appearance. For the first time, I saw him as he really was. Dying. He had dark circles under his eyes, and his cheeks were gaunt. He was pale. And very thin. His face was bony. His skin was wrinkled and saggy and covered in brown spots. His hair was thin and matted down. I saw him not as Gramps but as a dying old man. It scared me. I wanted to run out of the room. But that would be worse. Then I'd have to find my way out of the building with all the other dying people surrounding me.

I felt panic rise in my body. I couldn't breathe. I quickly jumped up and headed back toward the elevator, crying as I ran. Mom hurried behind to catch up with me. She held me in her arms.

"I don't want Gramps to die," I sobbed into her chest.

"I know, dear, but he's very ill," Mom shushed me, stroking my hair. "We need to prepare ourselves. We don't want him to suffer. Doctors are taking good care of him to make sure he dies comfortably. Let's say goodbye to Gramps for today, and we'll come back another time."

We returned to Gramps' room. I bent down to him and hugged his frail body under the hospital blankets. When I kissed Gramps' cheek, I took in his familiar scent. He wore cologne every day of his life, and even today, as he lay dying, he still seemed to be accessorized with it. I buried my face in his shoulder. I stayed there for a long time until Mom finally pulled me away.

"I love you, my lemon meringue," Gramps whispered with difficulty into my ear. He lifted his frail hand to my cheek, wiping our tears that blended into a salty sea of sadness.

As we left his room, I glanced back. Gramps was smiling at me. I felt my chest suffocate, and I tried to catch my breath. I sobbed all the way home.

After that day, I didn't want to return to the nursing home. It scared me. And watching Gramps wither away made me too sad. I wanted to remember how he used to be, not how he was now—decaying in a hospital bed. As it turned out, that would be the last time I saw him. He died one week later. Gram, Mom, and Dad were at his bedside when he took his last breath.

While I tried to forget what Gramps looked like in the nursing home, I couldn't. The look of impending death burned in my mind. It was then that I vowed I would never end up in an old folks' home. I was afraid of what I saw and terrified of aging and dying. I would make my future husband and kids promise me they would never put me into a nursing home. I didn't want to get old and frail like those people. I wouldn't let it happen to me. I didn't want this to be the ending of my story. That day, I declared war on aging. I would go to my grave fighting it.

# Vicenarians

## Ages 20 – 29

### C OLETTE, 20

"Shriveled raisins, listen to this," I said, out of breath, flopping onto the lower bed of my dorm bunk. "I learned in class our skin is already aging. We're withering up!"

Julia was humming along to a music record and clearly not listening.

I was in a tizzy. I had just come from health class, and the professor had lectured about why our skin wrinkles, develops brown spots, and sags. "Our skin is already deteriorating even though we can't see it," I repeated gloomily. "But it's happening, Julia. It's happening."

Julia still ignored me.

I inspected the dry skin on the top of my hands, checking carefully for signs of early aging. Panic grew in me. Was that a brown spot? I inspected. It was only a freckly, thankfully. But Julia didn't seem alarmed. How could she remain so calm with this impending doom upon us?

"Julia, this is bad," I said, now looking specifically for brown spots on my skin.

"Hmmm..." Julia replied, disinterested. Relaxing in a beanbag on our dorm room floor, she fixed her eyes on her record album. I read aloud from my textbook:

*"Wrinkles are an inevitable part of the natural aging process. As we age, our skin becomes thinner, dries out, and loses elasticity, causing wrinkles. Because of the loss of fatty tissue and the effects of shrinking bones, our skin sags. This process starts internally in our mid-twenties."*

I paused to see if Julia was listening yet. She wasn't.

"We can't stop it, Julia," I persisted. "It's like a vulture preying on decomposing roadkill."

"Okay, but when will we even begin to notice?" Julia mumbled, finally responsive but still not looking up.

"Not for decades," I admitted. "But we're getting old, Julia, right now. Our genes play a role in how we age, too. There's nothing we can do about the genes we've been given and how they may affect us."

I continued to read with panic. My textbook said 25 percent of aging was genetic, and 75 percent was determined by lifestyle. I had better get this right. This was serious stuff if my life choices dictated how I aged.

"Don't you want to know what you *are* able to control to slow down the aging process?" I asked.

"Hmmm..." Julia mumbled again, non-committed.

"Well, in addition to the intrinsic aging factors, which we can't control, there are also extrinsic factors. Those we can control," I elaborated. "We need to stop sunbathing. And we can't smoke."

"We don't smoke." Julia chuckled at me, raising her eyebrows.

"But we can't start. It will make us old and turn our skin yellow," I paused to glare at her. And DON'T DO THAT!"

"Do what?" she asked, confused.

"Raise your eyebrows like that," I said. "Repetitive facial movements cause wrinkles. You'll get *wrinkles on* your forehead."

"Well, you shouldn't smile, either, because you'll get wrinkles around your mouth," she suggested.

"You're absolutely right," I squealed, jumping off the bed to peer into the vanity mirror and examine my mouth up close. "I smile too much."

"And you better not laugh or squint in the sun."

"Julia, you're on to something. I need to make a list of all the things that will lead to wrinkles so we can stop doing them immediately to prevent long-term damage."

"Could you be any more ridiculous?" Julia asked, taking a sip from the straw tucked in her can of soda. She wasn't hiding her amusement.

"Give. Me. That," I said indignantly, yanking the can out of her hand. "Drinking from a straw is like smoking a cigarette. You're making the same puckering face that leads to fine lines around your lips."

"Gravity causes our skin to sag, too," Julia remarked. "Standing is causing you to get old, too. Oh my gosh, I can see it starting. Colette, you're hideous." She covered her face to shield herself from my impending ghastliness.

"Maybe we need to do handstands each night to reverse the effects," I suggested.

I reached down to the floor and took a headstand position, my legs stretching up the wall. I continued the conversation upside down, reading from my textbook right side up—or was it upside down now? I rattled off a list of factors that cause wrinkles: not getting enough sleep, dehydration, medications, and sun damage.

"Colette, I've got an idea," Julia offered. "Let's do a twenty-year science experiment with this."

"Okay, what do you have in mind?"

"I'll do all the terrible things that cause wrinkles, and you do a handstand for the next twenty years. And when the experiment is over, we'll see who looks worse."

Julia stood up from the bean bag chair and headed for the door.

"Where are you going?" I asked. The blood rushing to my head was making me dizzy. I didn't know how long I could stay like this.

"I'm leaving you here upside down until you come to your senses or pass out, whichever comes first," she said. "In the meantime, I'm going outside to develop sunspots by baking myself in the sun with baby oil and tin foil. And maybe I'll even smoke."

"You're too straight and narrow to do anything that reckless," I laughed. "Where are you really going?"

"I'm going to the library to study. I can't get straight As in this environment," she said. "While I'm gone, have fun turning the world on its head and testing my theory." Grabbing her can of soda, Julia laughed and walked out of the dorm.

"People will think you're my grandmother if you don't heed my warning about straws!" I yelled from my upside-down position. "Don't say I didn't warn you!"

• • • • • • • • •

## JULIA, 21

I had been in college for two and a half years and was still floundering on what to do in life. How do you know what to do with the rest of your life when you're only twenty-one? That's a lot of pressure to put on someone who's lived only two decades and has to decide on a career for the next forty years. I didn't want to get it wrong.

How could some people just *know* what they wanted to be? It was overwhelming to figure out the *rest of your life*! That decision determined the entire trajectory of your life and money-making opportunities. Mama said I just needed to meet a handsome, rich man and settle down, and then I didn't need to worry about working. I could stay home, raise babies, and cook my husband dinner.

But I had to figure out something until Mr. Handsome Rich Man appeared. So I scheduled an appointment with my professor. I figured he'd tell me how to spend the rest of my life since I didn't know.

"Welcome. I'm Dr. James," he said, shaking my hand.

"You're going to be my miracle worker, right? My career fortune teller?" I joked with him as I entered his stately office in the academic building on campus. The room had crowded bookshelves and dark wood paneled walls adorned with plaques and certificates to prove he had the credentials to shape my future.

"What do you mean?" he asked.

"You'll look into your crystal ball and tell me what amazing line of work will get me out of bed every day."

He laughed. "If I had a nickel for every time someone thought I had that power, I could retire."

Dr. James was distinguished-looking, somewhere settled in midlife. He had salt-and-pepper hair with swatches of gray above his ears that looked as though they were deliberately painted there. When he smiled, the laugh lines appeared around his mouth, and crow's feet showed at the edges of his eyes. He was very handsome for his age, whatever that was. I wondered how old he might be. Maybe he was in his fifties or even sixties. I realized I was moving my eyes to check him out. I felt an attraction for him welling up inside me, which surprised me. He was old enough to be my dad! I blushed when my eyes locked on his.

*Pay attention, Julia,* I thought. *This is only the rest of your life he's trying to discuss with you here.* Rest of my life? Oh, I could stare at him for the rest of my life.

The flirtatious internal monologue troubled me. This was more like Colette to be flirting with a professor. I couldn't pull my thoughts away from him. I had to bite my lip to stop the smirk from ruining my stoic face.

"Miss Julia, in deciding what to do with your career, the problem isn't because there are too few options. The problem is there are too many," Dr. James explained. He talked very articulately, like how a wise professor should.

"The first thing I always tell students is to pick wisely. Choose a career path you're passionate about, not what will bring in the biggest paycheck or what people say you should do."

He paced back and forth across his office. I watched him intently, moving my eyes from his face down to his waist, then his legs, and finally his ankles. He was sexy for being a dad figure.

"Choosing something that gives you meaning and purpose is important," he said. "I want you to wake up every day excited to go out and do the job. You'll be miserable if your only motivation is to make money or bide your time until you're married. I want you to be happy in whatever you do."

He wanted me to be happy? Maybe he was feeling something for me, too. My thoughts trailed off as I fantasized in my head. He peered at me as he sat back down in his leather chair. He ran his hands through the sides of his hair and rested them on the back of his neck, cradling his head. He had charisma and an air of calm intensity. I felt more flushed the more I looked him over. Could he see my cheeks burning red?

"Finding meaning in your work will be important to your career success," he continued. "If you do what you're passionate about, you'll never feel like you're working a day in your life. You'll automatically be successful. When you do what you love, you'll love what you do."

He paused for effect, giving me time to think about his brilliance. I could tell I wasn't the first student on whom he used this philosophical jargon.

"So, what do you love doing?" he asked, leaning toward me. I could smell his cologne.

"I like visiting with senior citizens, but that's volunteer work. I can't exactly pay the bills when I'm socializing with the elderly as an unpaid volunteer," I teased, trying to be charming.

"Well, says who?" he asked. "Gerontology is a growing field."

"Geron-what?"

"Gerontology. It's the study of the social, psychological, cognitive, and biological aspects of aging. A whole new industry will explode in meeting the needs of the elderly," he explained.

Dr. James was fascinating. *Can I take care of you when you're old?* I thought. But I didn't say it. Instead, I asked, "What can I do with a degree in gerontology?"

"A lot," he replied. "You can work in assisted living or nursing homes, dementia, long-term care. Even develop new products and services for older folks. The possibilities are endless. Would waking up every day knowing you could help seniors be rewarding?"

"Yes. Working with seniors would pull me out of bed," I said.

"Then the field of gerontology is the one!" he proclaimed, slapping his leg confidently.

*Oh, baby, you're the one.*

"Remember, your first job might not be your dream job," Dr. James cautioned. "Take a few entry-level jobs that you may not love. There's nothing wrong with being in an imperfect job. Staying in it—that's the problem. So decide what you'd like to be doing in the next five to ten years and work toward that."

"Is it okay to try something, fail at it, and then try something new?" I asked.

"Of course. Plan on it. Take risks early in your career to try new things. You'll find out what you love and what you don't. You'll be just as successful in your failures because you're learning from those, too."

"What happens if I'm in a job I hate and not making money?"

"Find something you love about the job. Look for one thing to keep you motivated," he spoke encouragingly. "You've got a long road ahead of you to work. You'll have your ups and downs in your career. Expect it, and you won't be so disappointed with the less-than-stellar jobs."

"What? You mean to tell me the next forty to fifty years of work won't always be fun?" I joked. I smiled brightly for him, hoping he'd pick up on my flirtatious cues.

"Definitely not. But I promise it will be an adventure."

I appreciated his sincerity in helping me. But if he had known what was going through my head, he might've thrown me out of his office.

"The point is to make the best of it," he said. "You've got many years ahead of you. I want you to enjoy your career. And I say all this from my heart."

*Oh, I'd like to capture your heart.*

He suddenly seemed to notice the seductive way I was gazing at him, and it made him uncomfortable. He nervously cleared his throat and stood up to indicate the meeting was over. Darn, I wanted to keep admiring him. But I took his hint and got up from my chair.

"I just need to hug you," I gushed, throwing my arms around his neck. I didn't care if this crossed the line. "You just helped foresee my future."

"I guess I did look into my crystal ball and find your career, after all," he admitted, untangling my arms from his neck.

"Thank you," I said. A hint of disappointment trailed in my voice, ending the fantasy of seducing my silver-streaked professor. It was then I knew I'd marry an older man.

"Best of luck to you for a long life of success," Dr. James concluded with a smile as I walked out of his office toward my future.

I had found my destiny. I would devote my life to the elderly.

• • • • • • • • • •

**COLETTE, 22**

It was winter break. Julia and I had very different plans lined up for our twenty-second birthdays. Julia was going to Fort Lauderdale, Florida for a week of fun and sun. I was flying to blustery Minneapolis, Minnesota—which was even colder than Grand Rapids, Michigan, where I lived—to help Grandfather and Grandmother Imelda, Dad's dreadful parents, pack up so they could enjoy the fun and sun, too. They were moving to the old person's section of Florida (definitely not Fort Lauderdale) to spend their retirement years on the sandy beaches of Punta Gorda. Grandfather had retired, cashed in his retirement nest egg, and was heading to the land of the retired with Imelda.

While Julia would sip frilly drinks with umbrellas and celebrate our birthday with suntanned, muscular men, I would hang out with pasty, flabby grandparents. Pack boxes—me. Six-pack abs—Julia. I was the one who was supposed to have fun, not Julia. Julia didn't even like to have fun. I tried negotiating with my parents to let me go to Fort Lauderdale, but they wouldn't hear of it.

"Why do I have to go to Minneapolis when Mom isn't even going?" I whined to Dad.

"Because it's not her parents who are moving," Dad said. "Besides, she needs to stay home and watch Gram. Have you forgotten Gram still lives with us and can't be left alone?"

"You just need to put Gram away for the week so Mom can help you, and then I can go on vacation with Julia," I suggested unapologetically.

"You better rein in your tongue before you say something you'll regret," Dad warned.

"Everything always revolves around old people in our family!" I yelled. "My break is a bust because of old farts. They're a nuisance!"

My voice raged with anger, and my eyes burned from fresh tears. Old people had a way of ruining my life.

"I will not tolerate your disrespect for the elders in our family!" Dad yelled back. "Because of your attitude toward your grandparents, you've created more work for yourself when we get to their house."

"Does it matter? My break is already ruined."

"You'll learn to honor your grandparents one way or another," Dad retorted unsympathetically. "They've earned it. They deserve your respect. And you will show it to them when you get there. Do you understand me, young lady?"

"Of course, Father. How could I be so insensitive to the decrepit?" I replied in a sweetly affected tone, feigning respect.

Grandfather and Imelda didn't deserve my respect. Why should I give them any respect when they didn't show me any? Imelda wouldn't even let me call her Grandma, or endearing names like Mimi or Grammy, because she didn't want people to know she was old enough to have grandkids. As if her blue hair and baggy elephant ankles didn't give away her advanced age. She made me call her by her first name and call Grandpa "Grandfather" because it sounded more formal. She pretended she was a spring chicken when she was, in fact, an old stew hen.

Imelda was very eccentric and ostentatious. She wore bright floral muumuus wherever she went. Her hair was always stiffly coiffed. A windstorm couldn't move that haystack of hair. Her spidery fingernails were painted a ghastly orange color. Her face was layered with thick poorly-matched makeup. She wore bright orange lipstick that matched the gaudy nail polish. She sprayed expensive perfume on her wrists multiple times throughout the day to keep a cloud of wealth encircling her.

They drove a big, luxurious Cadillac even though Imelda didn't drive. She had Grandfather drive her everywhere. Their enormous house was like a museum. They had white carpeting throughout, but guests were only allowed to walk on the plastic runners. They also had clear plastic slipcovers on the furniture so nothing could get dirty and worn out. Their lifestyle did not make room for kids. I barely saw them growing up because Imelda said I "was as delightful as a mosquito buzzing in her ear on a hot summer night."

She even had the audacity to say it to me. She didn't feign her dislike for me. So I stopped pretending to like her, too. While I was a toddler, she told my parents I "was meant to be seen and not heard, and even that should be kept to a minimum." She didn't mince words. She was an old crony who gossiped over mint juleps while playing bridge with other cronies. She barked orders at Grandfather, who acquiesced in intimidation. Grandfather was as timid as a wounded dog when it came to her demands. We all knew who wore the polyester pants in the family.

Grandfather walked bent over like the hunchback of Notre Dame. He couldn't look you in the eyes when he talked to you because the hunch was so severe. He wore plaid suspenders with polyester pants hiked up above his waist. His hair had nearly disappeared except for the cottony white tufts above his ears. His head reminded me of a shiny bowling ball, only hidden when he wore one of his expensive wool caps to cover it. He was quirky but likable compared to Imelda.

Julia often laughed and said she knew where I got my diva personality from. I didn't know what she was talking about. The nerve! I was not like Imelda.

"I just like things my way and only my way. Is that too much to ask?" I would retort to Julia. "If I ever end up like Imelda, just shoot me."

"Too late," she would reply.

So here I was, a college student, giving up my vacation and my birthday to help my ghastly grandmother and my meek grandfather sort, pack, and move their crap—I mean sentimental belongings—for the next five days. There were boxes of sappy collectibles, keepsakes, and junk that had accumulated in the house for forty years. I had to rummage through every single box of knick-knacks. I had to decide what knick to keep and which knack to toss. It would've gone a lot faster, but Imelda interceded each time I tried to pitch something. Not once. But. Every. Single. Time. I would be here until I was as old as her.

"We might need that plastic margarine tub for storing leftovers," she snapped, yanking it out of my hand. "Don't you throw my stuff away, Miss Sassy Pants."

At the end of the day, we had more stuff in the keep pile than the giveaway and trash piles combined. So Dad and I marked a box "special storage." That meant landfill. It was the only way to reduce the crap. I chuckled at the satisfaction that they were being tricked like children.

After the first night, I collapsed in bed exhausted. I had barely drifted off to sleep, and Grandfather was blowing a bullhorn that ripped me from Mr. Sandman. What on God's green Earth was that? What time was it? For Pete's sake! The bedside alarm clock read 5:30 a.m. In the morning!

"Rise and shine!" Grandfather bellowed outside my bedroom, blowing the horn one final time. "We've got work to do."

The audacity! This was outrageous. I put a pillow over my head to block out the morning.

"STOP THE MADNESS!" I screamed.

"Colette, get your lazy bones up. It's time to get moving," Imelda yelled, following behind Grandfather. The sun hadn't even risen, and Imelda was already barking orders. "The early bird catches the worm. We don't have all day to waste."

I crawled out of bed like a ferocious bear coming out of hibernation. I shuffled to Dad's room. I pleaded with him to let me sleep in longer. But Grandfather was blowing the bullhorn at him, too. He was waking up in the same confused stupor. By the time I made my case to go back to bed, I had lost the sleepiness to hibernate. The dreamy haze had vanished.

The process of sorting through junk continued for the rest of the week. The bullhorn sounded every morning at 5:30 a.m. I started going to bed at 7:00 at night like an old person because they woke me up so early. I was beginning to like my grandparents less and less if that was even possible. I would get even.

I decided to give them a little wake-up call of my own by blowing the bullhorn while they slept. So very early the following morning, I tiptoed down the hall with Grandfather's bullhorn in hand. I approached their bedroom and slowly pushed the door open, ready to blast the noise. And then I saw them. Oh, hot cross buns, did I see them in all their nakedness. I shrieked at the horror of witnessing my grandparents engaging in geriatric gymnastics with each other.

I dropped the bullhorn. It crashed to the ground and cracked. The crash jolted them out of their precarious position. They saw me see them. They reacted in shock and quickly pulled themselves apart. This revealed more of their vegetable garden—Grandfather's wilted cucumber and Imelda's withered prune. I didn't want to see this. This was a freak show.

I slammed their bedroom door shut and ran back to my room. I threw myself on my bed and cried in humiliation. I was now emotionally scarred. For life! This would require intensive therapy for post-traumatic stress disorder. That snapshot will be forever burned in my mind. Old people aren't supposed to have sex. It's just wrong. It's not natural. Weren't they done having sex by the time they were forty? They're too old for sex. Sex was for passionate young couples and for making babies. They didn't qualify for either.

I was mortified. I called Julia. I knew she would counsel me. She'd agree it was the freak show I knew it to be. She answered on the second ring. "Old people have sex?" I asked breathlessly.

"And lots of it," she said with conviction. Her laughter at my dismay filled the thousands of miles between us.

I slammed down the phone in disbelief at her ignorance. Sex between the elderly was no joking matter. She didn't know what she was talking about. Old people don't have sex.

•••••••••••

## JULIA, 23

I thought college had prepared me for the real world. Not even close. College was necessary to learn, but I was schooled for real today. Newly graduated, I interviewed for a job as an assistant administrator at a retirement community. I was interviewing to help run the assisted living facility. It was a coveted position, and Mama had pulled some strings to get me the interview. She had connections working at the community senior center. I also had graduated with top honors getting my degree in gerontology, so I was confident I would get the job.

The interviewer gave me a test before she even asked me any questions. "We want to give you a firsthand experience of a day in the life of a senior," she informed me. "This will help you understand how they feel, even for a brief time."

She shared it was important I complete the tasks appropriately to be considered for the job. I was nervous. Passing or failing this test apparently determined if I'd land the job. I guess graduating with top honors was useless. Instead, I had to go through an aging simulator experience in one of the living units.

The experiment started with the interviewer putting a pair of swim goggles with blurry lenses over my eyes. This was to mimic the effects of macular degeneration and cataracts. My eyesight instantly became that of a ninety-year-old. I could barely make out my hands inches from my face.

Next, the interviewer slipped a pair of rubber gloves onto my hands with corn kernels in the fingertips to simulate tactile numbness with peripheral neuropathy. In addition, she taped a couple of my fingers together to give me the sense of immobility caused by arthritis.

She placed a pair of headphones on my ears that pumped out extreme noises. I heard sirens, conversations, music, alarms, buzzing, laughing, and a dog barking. All at the same time. It was turmoil in my head. I couldn't make sense of any of the chaotic sounds.

"I can't even hear myself think," I yelled over the noise to the woman.

"It's what someone with dementia may experience," she explained. I think she was smiling. Or frowning. I couldn't tell through the blurred goggles.

With my hazy eyesight, semi-capable hands, and the confusing noises distracting me, I was required to accomplish various tasks. The tasks were to find white towels and fold them; wash the dishes in the sink; make the bed; sort blue socks from red socks; and cook oatmeal for breakfast. She repeated the list a second time of what I needed to do. This wouldn't be terrible. I could make oatmeal and do household chores.

"But you'll also need to do it all while in a wheelchair," she concluded. "I'm going to time you as well. Please try to accomplish everything within thirty minutes."

She left the room, and the countdown started. I quickly realized the vast discrepancy between what I thought I would do and what I could. My hands, covered by the corn-filled rubber gloves, wouldn't cooperate. I couldn't grasp the lid on the oatmeal container to open it, much less do all the necessary steps to prepare it. It was frustrating. After multiple attempts, I decided to move on to the next task. I abandoned the oatmeal.

I was already forgetting some of the items on the list, so I kept repeating the list to myself to remember them. But the noise was so infuriating. I felt myself getting irritable. I kept repeating the list over and over. But the never-ending sounds pelted at my brain like a hailstorm.

I wheeled around the bedroom, looking for socks to sort. Was I supposed to sort white socks or red towels? I couldn't retain the assignment in my head. It was slipping from my memory bank. I worked on the socks but couldn't tell the color difference anyway due to the foggy goggles. I struggled to decipher the colors.

I wheeled myself to the kitchenette. I knew there was something I needed to do besides cook oatmeal. I think it was to wash vegetables. I scrubbed the veggies in the basket on the counter. Yet I wasn't sure if it was fruit or veggies, based on what I could see. I had to handle each piece of produce to feel what it was.

I moved to the next task but lost focus on what I was asked to do. The sounds continued to scream in my head, and I couldn't stay on track. I couldn't function like this. As the minutes ticked away, I was unable to complete the list. I collapsed on the bed from mental exhaustion and started to cry. Like a baby. In a job interview. What was wrong with me? I wasn't going to pass this test. And I certainly would not get the job. I had failed miserably. I pulled myself off the bed, wiped my tears away with my corn fingers, and mentally prepared for rejection.

"How'd it go?" the interviewer asked, entering the room. She removed the headphones, goggles, and rubber gloves.

"Terrible," I said with complete honesty. I was humiliated that I wouldn't pass. And even worse, I cried. "I didn't finish the assignment. I couldn't remember what I was supposed to do, and the sounds from the headphones were making me crazy. I assume I failed and understand if you decide not to hire me."

"I'd like you to write about your experience," she said, ignoring my concession speech.

I wasn't sure why. This was only dragging out the inevitable. I wasn't going to get the job anyway, and now I had to provide an essay to prove it. She handed me paper and a pen and left me to write. I scribbled the following:

*I have a new sense of empathy for what frail people experience—people who have memory problems and can't see, walk, or use their hands. I never realized how bad it really is for them. I thought I had an understanding because I went to school for this. But in my naiveté, I was stupid to think I knew it just because I studied it. I learned the theory of aging. But I didn't understand what it meant to live it and to experience the difficulties for thirty minutes that old people experience every minute of every day of their lives. It gave me a new appreciation for the elderly and their ailments. I thought I could use what I learned in school, but I realize it also takes compassion, empathy, and patience to work with the elderly. I do have what it takes. I also have love and compassion, but I realize I failed the assignment. Thank you for giving me the opportunity to interview and for allowing me this learning experience, which I can take with me in my career somewhere else.*

The interviewer returned as I was writing away. I handed her my paper as tears welled up in my eyes. I had to come to terms with the fact that my new job was done before it even started. She read my paper, looked up, and handed it back to me.

"Julia, your response is exactly what we wanted to see," she said. "We want people willing to learn, to understand the struggles the elderly face. This makes you a better care provider because you can be empathetic to their needs. The test wasn't about completing it but your response to it."

"What are you saying?" I asked, perplexed.

"You're hired," she said. "You clearly have a heart for the aged, and we want you to be on our team to help care for them."

I had passed the first test in honoring the elderly.

• • • • • • • • • •

## COLETTE, 25

I was officially a college dropout. I nearly reached the end of my college career and decided there was far more value in beauty than in brains. I wanted a career that would allow me to make people pretty. So I had spent the last few years becoming a beauty expert.

After all the money my parents wasted on my education, they were unhappy with my decision, but I tried to convince them that my happiness was more important than theirs. The benefit was that I moved back home. What a perk for them! I wouldn't admit it to my parents, but I had actually enjoyed living in the attic after being forced to move there at thirteen. But I'd let them continue feeling guilty for my feigned miserable state of life.

I proudly finished cosmetology school with a license in hand and dreams in my heart. I was elated to open a small salon, even if it was tiny, with just two chair stations and a wash sink. I held a ribbon-cutting ceremony with one guest—me—to celebrate the grand opening. I popped a bottle of champagne and toasted myself.

To build business, I taped a homemade sign on the door promoting free haircuts today and that the first customer would win a year of free hair services. I imagined the winner as a sassy young woman who would be adventurous with new styles and colorings. It would be fun to have a young woman as a lifelong customer. We would become friends and gossip about heartthrobs and hair. Boyfriends and breakups. Fashion and friendship. All the drama twenty-somethings obsess about. I was stocking haircare products and lost in my thoughts when the door chimed. "I'll be right with you," I called cheerfully, my back to the patron.

*My first customer,* I silently shrieked. I felt the butterflies build in my stomach. This was it. I was so excited to begin the adventure of adulting.

"Thank you, dearie," the woman answered in a weak, rattling voice.

I turned around to be greeted by an elderly woman at the door. She was short and plump, shrunken and squished by the ill effects of time. She wore a bright red, wide-brimmed hat that covered most of her snowy white hair. My heart dropped at the realization that my year-long prize-winning customer was an old woman. So much for girl talk. Elderly women didn't talk about boyfriends, and they couldn't possibly have a desire for romance. Except for my crazy grandmother, whom I was still traumatized by.

I wouldn't be able to talk to this old customer about fashion. She certainly didn't have a sense of it with that hideous hat, frumpy floral house dress, and pudgy shoes. Where was my dream customer who was supposed to be dressed like a supermodel wearing stilettos, like me? I'd never wear those awful orthopedic shoes she was wearing. They looked like marshmallows. I'd wear high heels for the rest of my life. This granny and I were worlds apart in what we could share in conversation. I was disappointed. I wanted someone young and fresh to win the free hair services for a year. Maybe I just wouldn't tell her, and I could save the prize for someone else—someone more like me.

"Hello," I responded, faking a smile. I tried to mask my disappointment.

"I saw your sign for a free haircut today. May I get one?" the old woman asked, pulling the floppy hat off her head. It was made of red straw and had a cluster of feathers and bows with a plastic apple on one side. I wasn't sure why she needed a haircut since her hair was covered by this ghastly canopy anyway.

"Of course," I replied. "Have a seat. You can throw your hat over there." I pointed indifferently to the coat rack.

"I don't think so. I'll hold on to it."

She gripped it tighter as if it was worth a million bucks. She was exactly what I expected—a crazy old bat.

"What's your name?" I asked, loosely pinning a black cape around her wrinkled turkey neck.

"You can call me Granny Smith, as in the apple."

"That's a bit unusual," I replied with a laugh.

"My last name is Smith," she explained. "I make the best apple pie anyone's ever tasted. So when I became a grandma, way back when, I was nicknamed Granny Smith. I found it charming, and the name stuck."

She described the new hairstyle she wanted, and I began to cut away. I didn't know what to talk to an elderly woman about. So I asked the only thing I was the most curious to know.

"What's up with the hat?" I asked flippantly.

"It was a gift from my beloved husband," she answered softly.

"Oh."

An awkward silence followed. This was going nowhere. Maybe I'd have to improve my people skills as a hairdresser if I was going to have a myriad of customers and personalities to contend with. I'd also have to figure out how to converse with old people.

"Why do you wear it?" I ventured, less flippantly.

"I fondly remember my mother wore a hat just like it," Granny Smith said wistfully. "She passed away when I was just a little girl. She was buried in the hat. I only have one picture of her, and she's wearing it. I always wanted that red hat, and it made me sad thinking about it buried underground with her."

This is not where I thought the conversation was going to turn. Old people seemed to get all sappy and weepy when reminiscing about their past. I got uncomfortable with that. I wanted to bail out fast. But she didn't give me a chance to change the subject.

"My husband knew how much it meant to me," she continued. "He had a designer create an identical hat based on the picture I have of my mother. I added the green apple afterward because I'm fond of being known as Granny Smith."

She was stroking the green apple with her small, withered hands.

"Do you have the picture of her?" I asked. I wondered. Why did I care?

"Of course. It's all I have of her, so I carry it with me," she said, pulling the photo out of her old-fashioned handbag. The photo was very old and black and white. It had yellowed over time, and the corners were well-worn. Standing there was a young woman in her twenties, holding the hand of a small girl. There was no way of telling if the hat was red since the photo wasn't in color. Maybe it was gray or brown, and she didn't remember because of dementia.

"Are you sure it's red?" I snipped arrogantly as I snipped at her hair. The silver curls puddled onto the floor.

"Oh, yes. I remember it perfectly," she responded confidently. "It matched the color of her lipstick. She was so beautiful. That's me in the picture with her. She died just a few weeks after this was taken. I was so young. I don't remember much but her beauty and this red hat. This picture was taken more than seven decades ago."

She gazed at the photo and carefully slipped it back into her wallet.

"When did your husband have this hat designed for you?" I asked curiously.

"Five years ago. He gave it to me as a gift for my seventy-fifth birthday. I'm now eighty," she replied. "I've worn it every day since. People think I must be a little off my rocker, but I don't care at this age. The hat means so much to me. I stopped caring what people thought a long time ago. Now I do what pleases me. That's the advantage of getting old."

I laughed. "So, when you get old, you no longer give a hoot?"

"That's right. I wear this seemingly unfashionable hat for my enjoyment. I also gave up wearing high heels like yours because I cared more about my back than my beauty."

"I'll never give up wearing them," I said, admiring my hot pink heels.

"I know at your age you care what other people think. As you get older, you get thicker skin, and other people's opinions become irrelevant. Eventually, you stop caring because the opinions of others make no difference. And that's why I wear this gaudy hat."

"He must be a very kind husband to have made that for you," I said, eagerly wanting to hear more of the story.

"Yes, he was."

"Was?"

"He died two years ago. The hat means more to me than ever before. Now it represents both my mother and my husband."

I felt my throat tighten with sadness. I tried to fight back my emotions. It was ridiculous, the effect this old lady was having on me.

"Were you married a long time?" I asked.

"For fifty-five years. He was my best friend from the day I met him," she said.

"Wow, that's so beautiful."

"Are you married?" she inquired.

"No. Not yet. I've got time."

"Good girl. There's no reason to rush into it. You want to build your relationship as friends and then become lovers. I have a very handsome grandson I should introduce you to," she suggested. "You're a lovely girl, and you seem very nice. You two would get on very well."

I felt guilty that she thought I was nice. I had conjured up such awful judgments about her. I hadn't been kind, and I felt remorse for being so dismissive toward her. I didn't think we'd have anything to chat about, yet I found myself hanging on to her every word.

"Thanks, but that's not necessary," I replied. I wanted to close the door on the ridiculous idea of her playing matchmaker. She was silly to suggest such a thing. I dusted the fallen gray hairs off her neck and removed the cape. I took her red hat from her hands and placed it carefully back on her head. It was a gem, and I wanted to handle it like the priceless heirloom it was.

"We'll see. I might bring him in any way," she said, mischievously adjusting the brim.

We visited for over two hours. Time had flown by. I walked her to the door.

"So, it looks like I'm your first customer," she said, pinching my cheek.

"You are," I agreed, smiling. And then I said with sincerity, "As a result, you're the winner of a year's worth of free services."

"How wonderful!" She beamed. "I think there's lots of girl talk ahead."

• • • • • • • • • •

## JULIA, 26

After my beloved Abuela died, Abuelo lived in the studio apartment above our garage. It was hard to believe Abuela had been gone for three years already. Though the pain of missing her had diminished for me, it hadn't for Abuelo. He missed her more than ever. I wondered if he yearned for Heaven and longed for death the older he got.

I ensured he had plenty of companionship and would visit him in his small living space as often as possible. I believe that was the highlight of his life. His face would light up the moment I arrived. And then became forlorn when I left.

"Hi, Abuelo. How are you?" I asked, kissing him on his withered cheek when I walked into his humble living quarters.

"I'm on the right side of the dirt, so I must be okay," he joked. He hugged me as if he never wanted to let go. His loneliness was palpable.

He missed Abuela, and no matter how much he did to fill up his days, it wasn't enough to fill the empty hole in his heart where she once resided. I imagined that after fifty years of living with his wife, when he lost her, it was like losing a limb.

Visiting his apartment was always a treat and filled with treats. He stocked up on *pan dulce*—Mexican baked goods—as if it was a bakery. When I walked in the door, he'd jump up and pull out the pastries. It was his way of spoiling me. Even if I wasn't hungry, Abuelo wouldn't hear of me not eating and would still push the sweets my way. Long ago, I decided not to turn him down and risk hurting his feelings. So I'd indulge in his weekly treats. The calories I consumed were priceless.

After clearing our plates, he'd take a dusty vintage game off the bookshelf, and we'd play cribbage, Yahtzee, or backgammon for the rest of the evening. This entertainment allowed him to escape from the monotonous routine of TV, which so many seniors fell into because of boredom and lack of socialization.

"Julia, if you want more sweetbread, I cut a coupon out of the paper to save you twenty-five cents," he said. Abuelo was proud to be able to share everything with me—even coupons. I laughed at how seniors loved their discounts.

"Your Abuela loved sweet treats," Abuelo reminded me, sighing deeply as the memory flooded his mind. I remembered. It's what brought them together.

"Did I ever tell you how I fell in love with Abuela?" he asked.

Of course, he had. Abuelo had told me the story countless times. It was one of my favorites, and I enjoyed hearing about the legacy of how our family came to be.

"I knocked her off her feet. Literally," he went on. "I was coming out of the best bakery in town with my fiancée. I had a cinnamon cookie and café con leche in hand. My fiancée and I stopped at the corner bakery each week after church. It frustrated me that she wouldn't eat pastries. Life's too short not to indulge in a sweet treat. But we had a lot of incompatibility, much bigger than pan dulce.

"As we walked out of the café that fateful day, I stumbled into a gorgeous woman crossing before me. When we collided, I spilled my coffee onto her pure white blouse, and she fell backward onto the sidewalk. She was spitting mad and stunningly beautiful."

Abuelo's eyes twinkled as he lost himself in the memory of his own love story.

"She scraped her elbow. When I reached for her hand to help her back to her feet, I felt electricity between us, making my heart jump. I didn't know where this feeling came from but I knew I wanted to talk to her. I offered to walk her to the hospital, but she refused. She dusted herself off, making light of the pain. So I offered to walk her home. Of course, my fiancée wasn't thrilled about this. But I felt obligated to make sure she was okay. Men had more manners back in my day. We were chivalrous, which seems to be dead now.

"As the three of us walked together, I took my spot between them and locked my elbows with theirs. Here I was with my fiancée on one side and this stranger who made my heart beat uncontrollably on the other. My thoughts raced. I knew I was in trouble.

"We talked all the way to her home. Except for my fiancée. She didn't say a word. Maybe it was her instinct, and she sensed this beautiful stranger was on her turf. I didn't want to leave when we arrived at the woman's apartment. I asked for her phone number—to check up on her injuries, of course. She refused to give it to me. Oh, she was a stubborn one. She thanked us and walked into her apartment. It took an incredible amount of willpower to walk away. Yet I did.

"I figured I had to keep moving forward with my fiancée, but I was even more hesitant about our future. We had been courting for two years, and I was reluctant to marry her. I had lots of doubts, but nobody knew it. She pushed for the engagement, and I relented with a diamond ring. On the surface, we looked like a perfectly happy couple, but I had cold feet.

"A month had passed since I stumbled into the beautiful stranger, and I couldn't get her out of my thoughts. One day I found myself walking back to her apartment. I had no idea what I would do once I got there, but I was pulled by something bigger than me. When I got to the doorstep, I hesitated, immediately regretting my decision. What was I doing? I already had a wonderful gal who loved me and wanted to marry me. Yet I was drawn to this other woman I didn't even know.

"Weighing my options, I took a seat on the landing outside her apartment when the door opened, and she unexpectedly stepped out. I was stunned to see her. She was more beautiful than I remembered."

Abuelo paused, recalling the following lines of the story. They were always the same.

"She said, 'You're the guy who knocked me off my feet.' I was left speechless by her words and the softness of her voice. I jumped up to explain why I was there. But I had nothing. No words could express it.

"'Please let me buy you café con leche. I want to know your name. I want to know everything about you,' I begged. She hesitantly agreed. We walked to the same corner bakery where our worlds first collided and spent the afternoon talking and eating pan dulce. It was magical. She loved baked goods as much as me. It was then that I realized she was the person I wanted to spend the rest of my life with. After just an afternoon, I felt more at ease with her than I had ever felt with anyone. I didn't feel this way about my fiancée.

"I ended the engagement with my fiancée. I hurt her, and that still makes me sad. But she wasn't who I was supposed to marry. I courted your abuela.

She was sweet but feisty. She wasn't going to give herself over to me without a pursuit. That made me want her all the more. She wasn't a pushover. She made me work to win her heart. And she became the love of my life."

Abuelo's eyes glistened with tears. He was immersed in his own love story. I squeezed his hand to comfort the pain of love and loss he lived with.

"Julia, I want you to find that kind of love." Abuelo smiled, pulling himself back into the present. "Promise me you won't settle. The perfect man is out there waiting for you, but it's all about timing. You must be patient. Holding out for the one who makes your heart pitter-patter can be hard. When he comes, you'll know he's the one. That person comes crashing into your life, and you will never be the same."

I sighed deeply. The message for me was always the same. But he shared it repeatedly because he didn't want me to settle. It was sometimes hard to heed his promise because the loneliness of being single and longing for love could devour me. I wanted someone to love and to love me back, and it hadn't yet happened. I was in my late twenties. I feared my biological clock was ticking away, and I'd be an old maid forever.

"I could've settled, but I didn't. I don't want you to, either," Abuelo said. "This is the biggest decision of your life, so select carefully. Take your time in choosing. There's no need to rush into marriage, especially with someone not suited for you."

"I just don't know where my prince charming is," I said, my voice crackling with disappointment.

"It's better to wait for Mr. Right than settle with Mr. Right Now," he assured me. "Don't marry the wrong man. Even if it means staying single longer, you won't regret holding out. I promise."

I felt like I was failing the self-imposed timeline I invented for myself. So far, life wasn't going to plan. According to my version, I would've been married by now, with a couple of toddlers running around. My proverbial clock was ticking, and my ovaries were shriveling. I feared I'd be a washed-up woman at the age of seventy who didn't have a love story to share with any grandchildren.

But I clung to Abuelo's words. His love story gave me hope that I had a soulmate out there. He had found true love, and I prayed I would be as lucky.

"Abuelo, I promise you that when I get married, it will be to the love of my life," I committed, squeezing his hand tighter. "And when that day comes, you will be the one to give me away."

I kissed him on the forehead to seal the deal. I was making a promise to an old man who may not live to see that day. But I made the promise, nonetheless.

• • • • • • • • •

## Colette, 27

"Sorry, I'm closed," I called to the young man knocking on the salon door. I pointed to the sign that read, *Come Again Tomorrow.*

"But you're doing someone's hair now," he yelled through the glass.

He was right. I was washing Julia's hair. She was already experiencing premature graying in her twenties, and I convinced her to let me do a rinse to remove the silver streaks. I felt the gray hair added ten years to her age, and I didn't want her to look old unnecessarily.

"I need a haircut. Please," the man begged, smiling widely.

"All right," I said, letting him in. "It'll be a little bit before I finish her hair."

"That's fine. I'm willing to wait for you."

I glanced curiously at Julia in the mirror. Who was this stranger? Why was he so determined to have me cut his hair? He was nice-looking. I guessed he was close to my age—in his late twenties. He had sandy-brown hair with deep-set chocolate eyes. His white teeth sparkled when he smiled, and dimples appeared on both cheeks. He had a youthful, boy-next-door appearance. He was built like an athlete—strong and muscular. I was intrigued.

"I'm Gerrit," he said, introducing himself to Julia and me. His smile lit up his whole face. I liked him immediately. He was polite, and I sensed genuine warmth in him.

"I'm Colette," I replied. "Nice to meet you."

"I'm new around here. I just got settled in after returning from the military. I moved in with my grandma for a bit," he explained. "I was told to come here for a haircut because you're the best stylist in town."

I smiled and raised my eyebrows in curiosity. I had built up a large clientele in the last few years. I wondered which customer would've recommended me.

"Colette, don't worry about drying my hair," Julia suggested. "I can leave now so you can get to your other customer."

"Are you sure you don't want me to dry it?"

"No, this is more important," she said, winking at me.

She must've sensed something about the attraction between this stranger and me. She quickly grabbed her purse and walked out the door. I led Gerrit to the chair and put a cape around his neck. We enjoyed small talk. He was easy to chat with. The conversation flowed smoothly, and I caught myself not working on his hair as I got more steeped in talking. An hour later, I was still clipping away at a buzz cut that should've taken ten minutes.

"I better stop talking, or you'll never get out of here," I laughed flirtatiously.

"Maybe I don't want to get out of here," he said.

I saw him blush, which made me blush. We both awkwardly tried to hide the rising attraction.

"I'm enjoying getting to know you. Would you like to have dinner and keep talking?" he asked hopefully.

"When, right now?" I was taken aback. I felt a flutter in my heart.

"Unless you have somewhere else to be," he said.

"No," I said quickly. "I have to clean up here, though."

I felt butterflies. I hadn't felt this strongly for someone before. The chemistry was palpable. I wondered if he felt what I was feeling.

"Then, how about you clean up, and I'll pick up some food and bring it back here?" he asked.

"It's a date," I agreed. I hoped I wasn't too presumptuous.

"I insist I pay you for the haircut," he said. He handed me cash, his fingertips gently brushing against mine, sending a tingle through me.

"That makes two of us," I said, laughing. "I am worth every penny. However, I don't have proper change to pay you back."

"How about you pay me back when our date is over... maybe in fifty or sixty years?" he said with an air of confidence.

"I can do that," I consented. I couldn't believe I verbally agreed to this. I didn't even know him.

Was this love at first sight? It sure felt like it. Was it possible to feel like you've known someone your whole life, even if you just met him?

"Okay, let me pick up food and get back here so I can get to know you more," he said, hurrying out the door.

I swept up his fallen hair, then went into the bathroom to primp. I sprayed on extra perfume and touched up my makeup, dabbing on fresh lipstick. I lowered the lights in the salon to make it more romantic. Then I turned them back up. Maybe I was trying too hard.

While it seemed like an eternity, he returned thirty minutes later with bags of food in his hands. He set it up on the counter, and we dined in the salon.

"Can you turn the lights down at all? It's awfully bright in here," he commented with a laugh.

I nodded, giddy inside. We talked and laughed for hours. Sometime in the middle of the night, we wrapped up our date. I led him to the doors to escort him out so I could lock up. And there he kissed me. My skin prickled with excitement, and my heart fluttered. I looked deeply into his eyes, hoping to spend the rest of my life cutting his hair.

"By the way, who recommended you come to me for a haircut?" I asked, still curious as to who the mystery referral was.

"My grandma—Granny Smith. I think you know her."

• • • • • • • • •

## JULIA, 29

I jumped out of my skin from the sudden pounding on my office window. I looked up, startled to see Colette standing in the bushes.

"What in the Sam Hill are you doing?" I yelled, getting up from my desk and opening the window to scold her.

"I hate old fart homes, and I refuse to come inside," she said. "But I had to surprise you now. I couldn't wait until you were done working."

"Wow, this must be big news for you to scare the crap out of me like that."

"It is," she said.

She raised her left hand into the air, showing off a diamond engagement ring. We squealed in unison.

"Shriveled raisins, you're engaged to Gerrit!" I yelped. "Stay right there."

I ran out of my office and met her in the shrubs outside my window. I wrapped my arms around her in a celebratory hug.

"It's an antique ring. It belonged to Gerrit's grandma—Granny Smith. She brought us together through ringlets of hair and now a ring on my finger," I laughed.

Colette showed the diamond off proudly. It was a solitaire set in gold with diamond baguettes surrounding the center stone. I had to look at the ring a dozen times, admiring it from all angles and asking how he proposed. I needed every detail.

"Does she have any more grandsons? Because now I'm officially an old maid," I said. "I'm not married, engaged, or even dating anyone. At the age of twenty-nine, does that make me a spinster?"

"Well, Julia, working at an assisted living facility *is* an occupational hazard," Colette teased. "You're never going to meet anyone here. The youngest men you cross paths with are the residents, and they're like, what, one hundred years old?"

"No, they're only ninety-nine. Plenty young for me," I joked back. "I like them old. You know that. Ever since fantasizing about my college professor with the silver sideburns, I realized I like mature men."

"You're going to age much faster if you date them old," she said. "I'm just warning you. If you marry someone old, you'll play a nursemaid when you're young and in the prime of life. Do you want to do that to yourself—marry a man who will leave you a widow before you reach midlife?"

"Well, then set me up with a young stud if you think my knight in shining armor is already rusty," I challenged.

"Gerrit has many cute friends you can meet at the wedding," she promised. "I'll introduce you. There's no need to settle for an old man."

"I'm not settling for anyone," I answered defensively. "And I never said I wanted to date an old man. I just like them seasoned. And all the old men like to flirt with me around here."

I laughed as two male residents came speeding down the sidewalk on their scooters. One of them winked at Colette. She looked repulsed.

"Hey, sweet cheeks," I called out to him. "Don't make me jealous now by hitting on my best friend."

The men laughed and stopped their scooters, demanding I plant a kiss on their faces.

"Give me some sugar," one of the men said, tapping a finger on his cheek. Crawling out of the bushes, I obliged. Colette stayed put. It was all innocent fun. Both men whooped it up, beeping their horns. They zipped away laughing.

"Julia, you're a lost cause," Colette groaned, rolling her eyes. "You're too wrapped up in these old fogeys. You need a young man with stamina to keep up with you."

"I'm not dating these men," I protested. "Believe me. I like to date men that are mature, not old. There's a difference. But I like to flirt back with all of them. It makes them feel young at heart. They're still full of spunk, even at eighty, and they like to know someone cares."

Colette did not understand how lonely aging could be. If I could show the elderly a smidge of love and physical touch to make their day, then I've done my job. We, as a society, stop touching old people. They yearn to be touched, whether it's holding their hand, giving them a hug, or patting them on the shoulder. They lose the opportunities to be touched when they age. As their loved ones die, they don't have family to give them the physical connection they desire. I brought joy to their lives with a simple touch.

"Just giving them a hug or a peck on the cheek makes them feel alive," I explained. "The desire to be loved doesn't go away. Whether at thirty or seventy, they like the affection of a woman. It makes them feel like a man."

Colette remained in the bushes. "Nonsense. They're dirty old men. Old men are all the same," she insisted.

"Not true. If you've met one seventy-year-old, you've met one seventy-year-old. Just like if you've met one thirty-year-old, you've met one thirty-year-old," I argued. "You're overgeneralizing the population. I've met more snakes in their thirties than in their seventies. I call them dirty young men."

"Keep hitting on old geezers, and we'll see how far that gets you toward marriage and baby-making," she warned.

Colette's close-mindedness toward the elderly was a losing battle. But she'd figure it out someday. She would be struck with old age one day and learn on her own. Experience would be her wisdom in understanding the needs of old people.

"Let's get out of here," I said, changing the subject. "We'll celebrate your engagement and find me a dirty old man."

Colette climbed out of the bushes, pulling leaves out of her hair. She pinched my rear end and pretended to blame it on one of the scooter-driving men.

"Colette, act your age," I said, pinching her rear to get back at her.

"Not your shoe size," she teased in return.

# Tricenarians

## Ages 30 – 39

## C OLETTE, 30

Today I would promise Gerrit the rest of my life in holy matrimony. My fairytale wedding day had arrived as I entered into my thirties. It was a warm, sunny day, and May flowers were in full bloom, filling the fresh outdoor air with a sweet fragrance. It was the springtime wedding I had fantasized about as a little girl. I had embraced all the hopes and dreams every young bride looks forward to with her husband. Gerrit was the man I had dreamt about since I was young—the one I was promising my life to, who would be the father of my children, who would share in the joy of grandparenting, who would hold my hand until the last day when one of us would take our last breath.

As I slipped on my wedding dress and gazed in the full-length mirror, I was in awe of how beautifully I reflected. I was a bride who had met the man of her dreams. I would say "I do" to him forever.

But gnawing concerns crept into my mind. Forever was a long time. Would he still love me when my beauty faded, when my weight shifted, and I didn't have the svelte figure of my thirty-year-old self? When my appearance was of a shrunken old lady who no longer resembled the young woman I was today? Fifty years from now, when we celebrate our golden wedding anniversary, our picture will only have a mere similarity to who we were today. Who my husband is now is not who he will be when he's eighty. Nor will I be the same bride for him. I feared my beauty would dim both on the outside and the inside. Will the vibrant lady full of life inside me slowly reshape into something else? How much of the same person would he be? Will we appreciate the inevitable transformation in the other person? Is it possible to still love someone unfailingly for fifty, sixty, or seventy years? Can you make it through all the good times and the bad times and still stay in love? I could only hope our vows kept my husband bonded to me when I was no longer recognizable as the young, beautiful bride I was today.

Leading up to the wedding, I confided in Gerrit my fears and uncertainty, unsure if we had the stuff it took to make a marriage last forever. What did it take? I didn't know. He admitted he didn't know, either. But he was confident we'd learn together. He suggested we tap into the sage wisdom of our long-time married grandparents to have them share the secrets of success for marital bliss. I was reluctant because old people could be loose cannons. Who knew what would come spewing out of their mouths. He insisted it would be a nice touch to our wedding. I reluctantly agreed.

At the reception, the champagne was poured. Then Gerrit's maternal grandparents walked up to the head table and shared what had kept them together for so long.

"It's about compromise," Gerrit's grandpa started, lovingly holding his wife's frail hand. "For sixty years, I've given in to everything she wants."

"And when you admit you're wrong, I concur," she joked. "And I do let you get the last two words in: Yes, dear!"

"Ladies and gentlemen, you're witnessing a very special event today." Gerrit's grandpa continued with humor. "Not Gerrit and Colette's wedding, but the first and last time my wife will let me speak for both of us."

"Remember, love is blind. But marriage is an eye-opener," Gerrit's grandma interjected.

"Your love might run hot and cold as ours has," his grandpa quipped. "We make whoopie once in the summer and once in the winter."

The guests roared with laughter.

"Let me raise a toast to Gerrit," his grandpa concluded. "For when a man finds the perfect woman, he's set for life; but when a woman finds the perfect man, she'll spend her life trying to change him. So let's raise our champagne to Gerrit and take one final look. We're going to miss you, grandson."

The room reverberated with laughter and clinking glasses. I wanted to run and hide that these were the "words of wisdom" we were being subjected to. I had to admit, though, such wittiness at their age was spectacular. I didn't know old people could be so funny.

Gerrit's grandparents finished delivering their marital *roast* (it was definitely not a toast) and shuffled back to their seats. Then my paternal grandparents got up, and I felt myself become tense. I could only imagine what they would spout off about or how they would try to humiliate me. Imelda was good at that.

For the first time, she was not wearing a bright floral muumuu. I had never seen her dressed so nicely. I was surprised by her elegance. Her nails were even polished a shade of champagne to match her silk suit—no obnoxious orange.

"We are Colette's grandparents," Grandfather began. "We have—"

"Let me tell it, dear," Imelda interrupted, silencing him.

Why did this not surprise me? Even dressed in her finest silk, she was overbearing right down to her clanky old bones.

"We have been happily married for fifty years," Imelda continued, looping her arm in Grandfather's. "We'll celebrate our golden anniversary next month."

The guests applauded their milestone. "In our generation, divorce is taboo, compared to the whippersnappers who choose it so easily in today's generation. We were committed to building a foundation of mutual love and respect. There were many times we didn't like each other. But we always loved each other. Marriage is work and takes effort on both sides to make it successful. We worked hard to keep our marriage strong."

Imelda had to stop and regain her composure. She was getting choked up talking about their love. Or was it the work? Tears streamed down her face. I was worried about her makeup melting. Grandfather looked at her with total admiration. I guess if they could make it as a couple, anyone could.

I looked at Gerrit and saw tears welling up in his eyes. The tears were contagious. Even I couldn't help but feel joy for them, especially on my wedding day. I felt my heart swell with love as she finished their story.

"Colette and Gerrit, if I can offer any advice, it's not to keep score. Don't hold grudges or keep track of any wrongdoings. Resolve any problems before the sun goes down. And the best thing to do is remember this day and the love you have for each other. Reflect on what made you fall in love with one another. Celebrate your anniversaries with as much enthusiasm as you celebrate today's special day. Keep your eye on the prize of reaching your golden anniversary, and stay committed to your marriage. Love is all that lasts. So love each other until the last day."

Imelda raised her champagne and toasted our marriage. This was the most endearing I had ever seen her. She wasn't the crotchety old lady I always knew her to be. I saw her as a loving wife devoted to her husband, and she genuinely wanted to share her knowledge with me—the granddaughter she always tried to squash.

"We've toasted Gerrit. Now let's raise our glasses to Colette," Imelda proposed, her sincerity short-lived. "May Colette never show herself without makeup or with gray hair, so she always looks youthful and beautiful to Gerrit. That way, he won't trade her in for a younger version. And may your grandchildren never walk in on you making whoopee."

Again the room erupted in laughter. Imelda's sentiments obviously didn't extend as long as her marriage.

Unexpectedly, Granny Smith stood from her seat and walked over to grab the mic from Grandmother Imelda. "I, too, would like to offer some advice and toast the happy couple," she said. "While I may be widowed, I still know what it takes to have a successful marriage. There are plenty of times when you want to throw in the towel. The key is not to throw in the towel at the same time. Marriage is never a fifty-fifty proposition; it's always a hundred-hundred promise. The point is, together, you put in 100 percent all the time because you never know how much time you'll have together. Trust me. My marriage ended too quickly."

There wasn't a dry eye in the room after Granny Smith finished. Gerrit and I hugged her while everyone clapped and dabbed their eyes. I took the mic from Granny Smith.

"While she wants to toast us, it's more meaningful that we toast her. Without this wonderful woman, Gerrit and I would've never met. She's the reason we're all here today," I said. We all lifted our champagne glasses to honor Granny Smith.

The photographer asked the two married couples and Granny Smith, who shared their wisdom, to be photographed beside Gerrit and me. Around us was more than two hundred years of combined marital experience—the joy, sorrow, hope, healing, and love—all wrapped up in a single vow: "For better or for worse, for richer or for poorer, in sickness and in health, until death do us part."

As the photographer snapped away, I reflected on the advice of these sages: Marriage can be challenging, but if I wanted an enduring, loving relationship, I had to fight through the challenges, and, more importantly, I had to fight for the other person.

• • • • • • • • • •

## JULIA, 31

Colette and I had plans to go out dancing for our thirty-first birthdays. But she came down with the flu. Instead, I sat home and watched water boil for the tamales I was making. Being young and doing nothing on my birthday made me feel lonely. I called Mama and Papa and invited myself over to sit at their house. At least it was company.

Mama spent the evening ironing sheets before folding them and stacking them neatly in the linen closet. Papa sat at the table and worked a jigsaw puzzle. Neither spoke to each other. When Mama was done with the sheets, she pulled out her knitting basket and crocheted the beginning of another lopsided sweater. Or was it a scarf? Papa grew frustrated with the puzzle, cursing under his breath that there must be missing pieces. He always said this. There never were.

I watched my parents zone out into their own little worlds inside their heads. Is this what middle age looked like? Existing but not engaging? They seemed so checked out of life. After two hours of watching them, I decided watching water boil was more interesting. So I returned to my home. Spending my thirty-first birthday like this was like poking crochet hooks in my eyes. When had birthdays become so dull?

When Colette finally felt better, we decided we needed a girls' night out. It was Friday at 5:00 p.m., and I could sign off from work.

"Julia, your crazy girlfriend is sitting in her car, blasting her horn in the parking lot," my assistant buzzed my phone. "She's frightening the residents outside."

That was my cue to hurry up and meet Colette. I grabbed my purse and jacket and headed for the door. I didn't need any fatalities due to heart attacks because of Colette.

"You could come inside and get me," I said, climbing into her car.

"You know how I feel about nursing homes," she reminded me as she backed out of the parking space.

"You're being ridiculous," I told her. It was not the first time I said it to her and it wouldn't be the last.

"I'm never going inside a nursing home again," Colette vowed. "Those people scare me."

"What do you mean 'those' people?" I asked.

"All those geezers who live there. I'm afraid of them."

"Such rubbish," I replied, shaking my head in dismay.

"There is a real phobia of old people. It's called gerontophobia. And I have it," Colette insisted. "Besides, you're afraid of spiders. Talk about nonsense."

"It's hardly the same thing. A big, creepy arachnid compared to a loving human being," I said. "What's to be afraid of? Besides, you're not afraid of Granny Smith."

"That's because she's family. She's not like other old people," Colette said. "I find it ironic that we work in opposite industries. People flock to what I offer—beauty services. And people loathe what you offer—nursing care."

Colette had eloquently pointed this out to shift the focus away from her irrational phobia.

"You can't compare them," I argued. "I know 90 percent of the population would rather not move into a nursing home, but if we didn't have a place for them, the elder abuse rate would be higher."

"Right. Because kids would probably be in jail for killing their demented parents," Colette suggested. "It would drive me nuts. I had to watch my parents and Gram suffer through caring for Gramps before he was eventually put in a nursing home and died."

"So, there you have it. If it weren't for my work, crime would go up. However, according to you, I work in an industry that's not needed, compared to the beauty industry. I know how valuable your services are to ensure women don't go through life with unnecessary wrinkles. You are the true lifesaver," I concluded. My words were coated with sarcasm.

"Well, if I ever get old and senile, put me out of my misery before you put me into a nursing home," Colette said.

"Don't worry, I will," I joked. "I imagine you wouldn't be the easiest patient to care for."

"Now that's rubbish. I would be very pleasant. However, I demand satin sheets, a gold bedpan, and designer-label diapers. I don't expect anything less."

"You just proved my point," I said, rolling my eyes at the absurdity of her demands.

"And, of course, spa services. Please ensure my nails are always manicured," Colette continued, raising her snobby nose slightly higher. "I think there's a way to make your old farts' home sexy and sassy. Think of the business you could generate if your advertising targeted the adult children dumping their parents there."

"Excuse me. They're not *dumping* them. Families *place* their loved ones in assisted living or nursing homes for many reasons," I explained. "It's a loving thing to do when they can't provide care anymore. I've seen caregivers become ill after caring for a sick spouse or parent. In fact, studies show 60 percent of caregivers die before the person they're caring for because of the stress of caring for them. Nobody wants to die because of the heavy burden of caring for their loved one."

"Pinky promise me you'll never dump me into a nursing home, Julia," Colette said. "I'm serious. I don't ever, ever want to end up there."

"Colette, I won't pinky promise that," I replied. "I've seen many dedicated families promise their loved ones they won't be placed in nursing homes. Yet those people didn't realize how difficult it becomes."

"Well, I know Gerrit will love me enough not to ship me off to an old folks' home. But I can see you'll unload me the second I complain of a weak knee," Colette concluded. "If I have kids, they'll pinky promise on it. I'll make them do it before they turn eighteen, so they don't even know what they're promising."

"Let's finish this conversation in the restaurant," I said, pulling into the parking lot. "I find your ignorance so entertaining."

We arrived at our favorite Mexican restaurant and sat at the bar. The music was loud, and the place was jam-packed. We ordered two margaritas on the rocks with salt. The bartender took our orders and walked away without checking our IDs.

"Wait, don't you need to card us?" Colette yelled loudly to his back.

"No, you're all set," he replied. "You're plenty old. I don't need to see proof."

"That monster," Colette sneered, venom dripping from her mouth like a snake ready to devour its prey. "How dare he insult us like that?"

"He's not insulting us. We are plenty old to be drinking," I said, yelling above the noise of the music and crowd.

"Well, this is a first. I've never not been carded before. Apparently, he needs more training in spotting underage drinking because we definitely don't look old enough."

"Yeah, we do. We just turned thirty-one." I laughed.

"Maybe *you* look old enough, but *I* sure don't. I would've carded me if I was him," Colette decided. "He should lose his job for serving minors."

"Except for one important exception. We aren't minors," I argued. "We're not spring chicks anymore. We're thirty-one as of a week ago. Pretending to be younger than we are is pointless. You understand we're now facing forty as the next big milestone."

The bartender returned with two margaritas and a basket of chips and salsa as we argued back and forth.

"Do we look old to you?" Colette asked him.

"I am not answering," he wisely said. "This is not a safe conversation for any man to walk into."

"I'm feeling kinda old today, especially with not getting carded," Colette said.

"Well, then, can I see your ID?"

"Yeah, it's too late now," she chided.

"Correction noted," he said. "What's the occasion tonight that brings you two out?"

"We turned thirty-one last week. We're celebrating our belated birthdays together because I had the flu," Colette explained.

"Sorry to hear that, ma'am," he said.

"Really. Is that the best you got?" Colette snapped. "When did I become a ma'am? Ma'am is a title for old people. You're supposed to call me miss. Miss is for the young."

"Second correction noted. I think I better bow out now before I dig myself deeper." He walked away, avoiding any more traps.

"Good grief, this punk thinks we're old," Colette snarled. "Calling me ma'am is like putting margarita salt in the wound."

"The good news is we're not as old as we will be," I said. "But you've got to stop fighting against getting older."

"Well, I'm not going to surrender to it. I'll do whatever I need to do to stay forever young," she said.

"You're in denial if you think you won't get old. Or that you won't depend on your family," I said, resuming the earlier conversation. "But guess what? You will be. Right now, you think you'll never relinquish your independence. But I promise, as you get older, you will become more dependent upon others. It's a fact of life. But it's not a bad thing. We're always dependent on others, just in different ways throughout life."

I paused to lick the salt off the rim of my glass and to let her mull over my words. Colette stared at me, her eyes squinting in nervous thought.

"Do you think you'll ever have to put your parents in a nursing home?" Colette asked.

"I don't intend to. My Mexican heritage believes in caring for our loved ones at home," I explained. "But I've never had the talk with them. I need to before it's too late. I want to know what their wishes are."

"I'll be putting mine in a convalescent home. I'm not going to change their diapers and wipe their fannies," she answered. "There's no way I can care for them."

"So, it's safe to say your kids will put you in one," I joked.

"It won't be necessary. I expect to live a vibrant life until the day I die. And if I have children, they wouldn't do that to me."

"Ha! If that's what you think, you better treat them like royalty. Because someday they will be picking out your nursing home when they don't want to wipe *your* fanny," I said.

The bartender returned and handed us two shots of tequila.

"*Viva la vida*," he said. "This is to toast your belated birthdays."

"To the first third of our lives!" I toasted. "May the next two-thirds be just as wonderful."

We clinked our shot glasses and threw back the booze into our mouths. The tequila burned going down. The margaritas flowed easily the rest of the night. We found lots of things to toast.

"To being independent and always being able to wipe our own tushies," Colette toasted.

"To looking forever young like you do right now," the waiter chimed in, making up for his previous gaffes.

"To not living our parents' retirement with puzzles and knitting," I toasted.

The waiter returned with two more tequila slammers. We flung back the shots. He handed us sombreros. Colette grabbed hers and unexpectedly vomited on the inside of the crown.

"I think the flu has returned," Colette choked through tears of humiliation.

"I think you're too young to hold your liquor," the waiter suggested, squeezing his face in disgust.

"Finally, he recognizes your youthfulness, Colette," I teased as she lay miserably with her head slumped on the bar.

· · · · · · · · · ·

## COLETTE, 32

I sat nervously next to Gerrit in the doctor's office, holding his hand and waiting for the test results. I wanted to live in denial that I was pregnant. But my instincts knew. I waited in dread for the nurse to return and tell me I was going to be a mother. *Me* with a baby? I was too irresponsible to take on the care of another human being.

What was I thinking, getting pregnant? How reckless of me! I began to panic at the thought of becoming a mother—or worse, *my* mother. I jumped up from my chair and frantically paced the sterile exam room. My hands dripped with sweat. My cheeks flushed with anxiety. This was a big step in my life, and I wasn't ready for it.

Gerrit sat calmly, oblivious to my panic. He flipped through a parenting magazine without a care in the world. How could he be so at ease at a moment like this? My thoughts raced with fear. How did it happen that I had grown up and was facing parenthood? Wasn't I just fifteen, kissing my first boyfriend? Where did my youth go?

If I were pregnant, my stiletto-wearing, tequila-slamming days would be over. The sweat spread to the back of my neck. I continued to pace. Gerrit continued to read. I was terrified to be a parent. That meant I was one step closer to getting old. Grownups have babies. That meant I was a grownup. Mom always said parenting me caused her hair to turn gray prematurely. My mind raced to all the things I did that turned my mom's hair gray. Would that happen to me, too? I talked silently to the maybe-baby inside of me.

*I hope you're a better kid than me. I used to party with boys, drink booze, and smoke cigarettes. I hid it behind my parents' backs. I was a dumb kid back then. I know better now. But because I know what a troublemaker I was, I'll have to watch you like a hawk, smelling for booze and cigarettes on your breath. I'll listen in on your phone calls and won't let a boy come near you until I say so. That's what my mom did to me. Oh no, am I going to turn into my mother?*

*And please don't end up a teen parent. If you get pregnant, making me a grandmother before I'm old enough, I will ground you until your child is an adult. And please don't ask me if I ever did anything illegal. I don't want to lie to you. I just want to pretend to be a perfect parent so you can avoid my mistakes. I'm older—not old, missy—and wiser and know better. You'll think you're smarter than me as a kid, but you aren't. You'll think you know more than me as a teen, but you don't. You won't get smarter and wiser until you're a grownup. Growing up is what makes you more knowledgeable.*

"Colette, are you okay?" Gerrit asked, concern growing on his face. "You're mouthing words to yourself and pacing like a caged animal in heat."

"Is that supposed to make me feel better?" I snapped. "You're calling me a sweaty pig."

"That is not what I said."

"I think I'm having a panic attack," I gasped, trying to catch my breath. I had worked myself into a frenzy. My heart was pounding, and I couldn't breathe. I was nauseated. I felt like vomiting or passing out. Or both.

"Sit down and put your head between your legs," Gerrit urged. "If you're pregnant, this stress is not good for the baby."

I did as he said. I tried to calm my breathing. But the clock on the wall was ticking too loudly. It was like having someone drip water on my forehead in torture. The tick-tock overwhelmed my senses. I looked to see what time it was. I needed to get out of here. I bent back down and took slow, deep breaths. How much time had passed? I looked at the clock on the wall once again. Only seconds.

"Gerrit, I might be pregnant," I heaved, fighting the denial that the maybe-baby actually may be a baby.

"Of course, my dear, we wouldn't be here for any other reason," Gerrit smiled, squeezing my hand. He lifted it to his mouth and kissed it. He was more excited about this parenting thing than me.

The five-minute wait felt like five hours. The nurse finally walked in. I looked up from my bent-over position. She had a conspicuous smile on her face. Her happiness gave the conclusion away.

"Congratulations," she said, handing me the test results.

I didn't know whether to cry out of joy or fear.

"You're going to be a mother!" Gerrit squealed, wrapping me in an affectionate squeeze.

I cried. It wasn't joy. It was terror.

Nine months later, I held my newborn daughter, Valerie, in my arms and cried again. This time it really was joy. Becoming a mother was a beautiful thing. I wouldn't trade my house slippers for stilettos at this moment as I gazed upon the precious child that had my nose and lips. I had a mini-me. Growing up was fabulous if it meant having more mini-mes in the world. I looked at Mom and Granny Smith, who were eagerly waiting to hold Valerie. They now bestowed the titles of "Grandmother" and "Great-Grandmother." And I was crowned "Mother."

Less than two years later with the birth of my second daughter Nora, I would be crowned with that blessed title once again. Swapping stilettos for slippers was a privilege that I'd never take for granted.

• • • • • • • • • •

## JULIA, 34

Colette warned me that my career working for seniors in assisted living would hinder my opportunity to meet Mr. Right. But then I met Jack. He came into my office to get information on housing options for his mom.

I immediately took notice of his good looks. He had salt-and-pepper hair and a beard that was more salty than peppery, which I found attractive. It was a hallmark of distinguished charisma.

Naturally, I could hear Colette's voice preaching in my mind, "It's a double standard. Men get gray hair, and they're distinguished. Women get it, and they're extinguished."

I looked at Jack's hand to see if he was wearing a wedding band. He wasn't. That was a good sign.

"Are you familiar with the various levels of housing?" I asked, returning to the business at hand, which wasn't inspecting his.

"No, that's why I need *you*," he said, smiling seductively. (Okay, maybe not seductively, but there's nothing wrong with fantasizing).

"Let me show you around so you can see what we offer. Is your wife here to join us?" I slyly asked.

"No, I'm divorced. It's just me."

"Oh, good," I stumbled nervously on my words. "I mean, good that nobody will be missing out."

I grabbed my keys, feeling giddy inside like a schoolgirl. I closed the office door behind us and took him on a golf cart tour of the facility.

"We offer a continuum of care. It's called a Life Plan Community," I elaborated. "That means people can move from independent living up to the highest level of care in the nursing home all right here."

I drove Jack to the independent housing section.

"People who live in this part of the village don't receive any support services other than grounds work, house maintenance, and access to social activities," I said. "It's condo living, and yet residents can move into another setting easily when they need more care."

"Well, my mom is not qualified for this," he said. "She needs a lot of help."

"She might need assisted living, which offers increased help but still not nursing care," I explained. "Assisted living provides meals, housekeeping, chore duties, and personal assistance. But the residents aren't so frail that they need round-the-clock care. They can still maintain a fair amount of independence."

I drove him around longer to show him our radical alternative to nursing homes. I led him inside for a tour.

"Nursing level of care means someone gets all their needs met by us," I continued. "We provide extensive services like rehab and medication management. We bathe, feed, dress, and toilet them. If your mother has dementia, we offer memory care in a secured unit of the building so she can't wander off. We do specialized activities to keep their brains from atrophying."

I could tell Jack was trying to process all the information. It was daunting for families trying to discern what their loved ones needed. It could be agonizing to place someone in a nursing home. There was a lot of guilt that went along with the decision.

"I'm encouraged by what I see," he commented as we walked the halls. "It's not institutionalized like other nursing homes I've visited."

"It's designed to be like a neighborhood," I told him. "The hallways look like quaint streets with lampposts and painted murals of cityscapes. The windows are decorated with flower boxes outside each room so that it's not a sterile atmosphere."

"I never thought nursing homes were anything but long medical wards with people holed up in a shared room with one TV to fight over," he mused.

"Most nursing homes are that way," I admitted. "We still have long wards, but we provide something cozier so people can age in a dignified setting that doesn't look and feel like a prison. It's much more appealing."

We continued to walk and talk.

"Allow me to let you in on a secret," I confided. "I'm a little self-serving in wanting things done well. If I have to go into a nursing home someday, I want it to be like this."

"I'm very impressed with this place and with you," he said, smiling. I blushed. "And I'm overwhelmed at the same time. I'm not sure how to move forward making a decision."

"When you're ready, we can do an assessment to determine what level of care is best for your mom," I reassured him. "We'll make sure she gets placed appropriately."

"Thank you very much for showing me around. It was very nice talking to you. Very nice, in fact," Jack said as we returned to the front office. "I'll get back in touch very, very soon." That was a lot of verys. He seemed nervous suddenly. He shook my hand awkwardly and left. He was a good man. I liked him. I believed how a man treated his mom was a sign of how he'd treat his wife.

For the next two weeks, Jack constantly stopped by to discuss the most trivial things. While it would have been easier to call, he returned in person to ask about something silly—how many varieties of beans we served, the thread count on the bed sheets, and if there were clocks in all the rooms. I remembered Mr. Hendricks, my fifth-grade teacher, saying there was no such thing as a stupid question. And I thought of Abuela, in her infinite wisdom, who said there were plenty of stupid questions in this world. I think she won. The truth was, I didn't mind Jack's stupid questions. In fact, I noticed my heart would beat a little faster when he stopped in.

I shared Jack's stupid questions with Colette to get her take. And that he spoke nervously around me using lots of verys. I believed he was nervous about admitting his mom to our facility. She was certain it was because he liked me. She even bet me a hot fudge sundae. When she bet hot fudge sundaes, she was confident in her wagers.

The more I got to know his quirkiness, the more I liked Jack. Talking to him was as comfortable as wearing an old shoe. I looked forward to his visits but was perplexed by his off-beat questions. Today he stopped in because he wanted to taste the quality of our lettuce. I held back my laughter. I never had to deal with a more eccentric caregiver than Jack. But I was still giving him the benefit of the doubt for honoring his mother.

"Could I sample the food, specifically the salad bar?" he asked. "There is a salad bar, right? I want to make sure my mother will very much like the romaine here."

"Of course," I answered. "Our salad bar is the finest of any nursing home you'll visit. I can arrange for you to join the residents in the dining hall for a meal."

I was willing to do whatever it took to convince him his mother would be in good hands.

"And could you arrange to join me?" he asked. I saw him blush for the first time. Was Colette right that he liked me?

"Of course! It's a date," I answered playfully, which made his cheeks turn even redder. "Hopefully, I can answer your important questions about leafy greens."

I decided to have a little fun with this "date." We sat at a quiet table in the corner to give us privacy from the inquisitive residents. They knew I was single, and their curiosity got the best of them as they watched the mystery man with me.

"We do a lot of recreational activities here," I whispered slyly to Jack. "Sometimes we play poker. But it's not any old poker," I winked. "It's strip poker." I didn't want anyone to overhear me. I'd probably get fired for making this garbage up. But I was setting him up for the joke ahead.

"We also play beer pong," I continued whispering. "It's surprising how well the women can outlast the men. I think your mom will do great with our community games."

I paused to see Jack's reaction. There was none. He continued to chew his salad without the blink of an eye. So I stepped it up a notch.

"We also bring in tattoo artists so the residents can get inked. Of course, we don't force them, but they don't know what they're getting until after it's done. Last week, the banana on the woman's flabby derrière didn't go over well with her. Because of the flab, it looked like a melted yellow crayon. So it was fixed to be a big yellow school bus. We're good like that with our customer service."

I took a bite of salad and watched in anticipation of the expected horrific reaction Jack was sure to display. Instead, he laughed so hard salad toppings flew out of his mouth, splattering across the table.

"Okay, you got me," he said, recovering from his outburst of laughter. "I'll move my mom in this week. If you can invent a ridiculous story like that, it means you're not treating your residents poorly. If you did, you'd try and hide outrageous incidents, not make them up."

"You knew I was kidding?" I asked. I was more shocked than he was.

"Of course," he said. "Every nursing home I've visited used the same sales pitch. You made my decision very clear. Not to mention your patience with my ludicrous questions is astounding. I wanted to see how you'd treat someone who's being a nuisance, to know how you'd treat someone with dementia who can be even more taxing on your patience."

I laughed in surprise. "Wow, I was being tested and didn't even know it. I feel violated."

"Plus, my dumb questions were my excuse to come and see you," he smiled shyly, the flush in his cheeks returning. "You never lost patience with me. You're an exceptional woman to put up with all that."

"I thought you were just incredibly picky about your mother's care," I admitted, still chuckling.

"Well, I do want excellent care for my mom. I know she'll get it with you in charge. But I also want to keep getting to know you."

Jack suddenly took my hand from across the table and stared into my eyes. I was flustered now. I wasn't expecting this.

"Julia, I'd like to eat salad here with you and have residents staring at us again and again," he joked, looking around at the watchful eyes peering our way. "Can I take you on a date again to this very fine establishment that serves the very best romaine lettuce anywhere?"

"Yes. I'd love that," I answered, feeling butterflies tickle inside.

"Afterwards, we could spice it up with tattoos on our derrières, young lady," he laughed.

"Now you're talking, young man," I answered.

"You can say it—*old* man," he corrected, smiling. We both knew he wasn't a young man. "Have you noticed how much older I am than you?" He countered.

"I like them older," I flirted.

"I like them younger. It's a match made in a nursing home." He smiled, bringing my hand to his lips and tenderly kissing it. "I do need to ask you a very important and very serious question."

"Okay."

"What's your favorite kind of applesauce?"

"Chunky with cinnamon. Why?" I laughed again, assuming this was another of his ridiculous questions.

"Because when you're a little old lady with dentures, and you can't chew solids and need someone to feed you, I want to be by your side spooning applesauce into your mouth. I very, very, very much like you," he shared, eyes twinkling.

I very much liked his verys.

• • • • • • • • •

## COLETTE, 35

"Mom, you're stopping over again? You were just here," I said, rolling my eyes, exasperated that my mother was on my doorstep again. "Please don't ring the doorbell when you come. You're going to wake up the girls. What do you need?"

"I don't need anything. And I'm not here to see you. I'm here to see my precious grandchildren," Mom retorted. She entered without being invited in.

She dropped her coat on the couch and scanned the room for her grand-daughters.

"Mom, today's not a good day," I said. "Gerrit and I got into a huge fight before he left for work. The girls were ornery all morning. I just got them down for a nap. Plus, I started my period and have terrible PMS."

"Then I'm here to save you. It doesn't sound like you're managing very well. You need me to give you a helping hand," Mom chastised, judging the state of my life. "Look at this mess. You need more than a helping hand. You need a housekeeper. I'll clean until the girls wake up."

I knew I was a lousy homemaker and didn't need her to point it out. I juggled being a full-time stylist and a mom at the same time. I wasn't very good at balancing both roles. Why did it seem like other moms had their act together—home-cooked dinners made from scratch, children bathed every day, and houses that passed the white glove test? I failed miserably in all areas. I didn't need her reminding me.

I decided I would not be like her—constantly showing up unannounced to see her grandchildren and then criticizing the woman who gave her the grandchildren in the first place. I prayed I didn't turn into my overbearing mother.

"Mom, please, I'm asking you to leave."

With that, Mom started crying. I wasn't in the mood for this. She knew her tears would play on my sympathies. So I did what any daughter without boundaries would do. I let her stay. She immediately began complaining.

"Your father. He's driving me crazy. Ever since he retired last year, he's always in my space. I used to run the household my way, and now he's there all the time. Every minute of the day. He follows me around. He tries to undo my work. I've been managing the house for nearly forty years, and suddenly he wants to do things differently because he's home and bored."

Mom let her frustrations spill out for the next thirty minutes. She didn't even take a breath. Her hot mess of exasperation came to a boiling point and erupted all over me. I was the one who needed to explode today, and she stole my thunder. I led her to the kitchen and warmed up hot tea for both of us. I could've used a shot of whisky in mine, but it was only noon.

"Last week, he rearranged the kitchen cupboards and switched out the towels from one linen closet to another," Mom ranted. "He gave me pointers on how to use storage space more efficiently. He even alphabetized the spice rack. I had them arranged by common recipes. The nerve of him! He's acting like an intruder in my home."

"Why don't you suggest things to keep him busy—like golf?" I offered.

"He's already out on the course four times a week," Mom said.

"Well, be easy on him. Work has consumed his life for the last forty years. He's trying to fill a void now. He needs a little support from you to help him transition into retirement and figure out what to do with all this extra time on his hands."

"I'm trying," she said, "but I thought retirement would be different for us. I thought we'd travel more and do fun things together. He just wants to tinker around the house and rearrange cupboards. We keep bumping into each other in the same space. I didn't realize how much I loved my space when he was at work every day."

I pulled the whistling tea kettle off the stove and poured the boiling water into two cups. I handed her a teabag and sugar.

"I'm thinking of moving into the spare bedroom to sleep," she said, watching intently to see my reaction.

"Mom, you can't do that," I protested. "That doesn't sound good for your marriage."

"I need distance from him," she insisted. "Separate bedrooms is a great answer. Besides, sex with the same person gets boring after four decades of marriage. There's nothing new to explore."

"Mom, stop right there. I'm tuning you out," I said, covering my ears.

"Don't get me wrong, the sex is fine. But I don't need it every night like he does," she continued. "Even in his sixties, he still wants sex, sex, sex."

"Zip it, Mother. Too much information." I hummed to block out her words.

But covering my ears wasn't enough. Scars still existed from my grandparents' shenanigans. I didn't need to be triggered by my parents' extracurricular activities too. Some things in life just didn't need to be shared—my parents' sex life was one of them.

"It's not just the sex," she said, pulling my hands away from my ears. "It's also being able to sleep the way I like. He likes the room hot. I like it cold. He snores. I can't sleep when he starts that up. It's like a freight train going through our bedroom, and it's getting worse the older he gets."

"Have you talked to Dad about any of this?" I wondered. "Maybe if you told him you need a little more space during the day, you won't have to move out of the bedroom. You're feeling suffocated right now. But somehow, you've managed to sleep in a hot room with him snoring until now."

"I guess," she said, considering my perspective. "Do you realize he also reads the newspaper headlines to me each morning and steals the pleasure I get out of reading the paper? It's like telling me the spoilers of a great book."

"Mom, give it a rest. Talk to him and stop hyper-focusing on everything he's doing wrong in retirement. He doesn't even know he's doing this stuff to irritate you. You both need to adapt to this change."

"You don't understand. Change is harder the older you get," she said, her voice trailing. She sniffled back tears and stood up. I wondered when the role reversal occurred, and I started giving my mother advice. She began picking up all the scattered toys around the living room. She bent over gingerly. I could tell she was struggling with her arthritis.

"Mom, does it bother you?" I asked, taking the toy basket from her. The question was more about arthritis than life. I asked out of fear that I would end up with arthritis, too. But she was much more responsive to the question than what I meant it to be. She didn't usually open up about such deep topics; instead, she liked to complain. Grumbling about aches and pains, about my dad, and about how everyone was doing something wrong. That was more her style. But unexpectedly, she became self-reflective.

"No. Getting older doesn't bother me," she said. "Aging isn't an option. And I don't much care for the alternative. Aging isn't the enemy. It's the fear we live with about aging—that's the enemy."

"But you're slowing down in life. You complain all the time that your arthritis is getting worse. Don't you fear how much worse it's going to get? Doesn't that scare you?" I asked.

"No. Deep down, I'm grateful for my health, despite moving slower with arthritis. There's nothing to fear in getting older."

"I fear the things I'm going to lose. For example, I just found out I need glasses," I complained. "I'm only in my thirties, and already my eyesight is betraying me."

"Honey, even kids get glasses," Mom said. "So it's nothing to get worked up about. It doesn't mean you're getting old."

"My doctor said glasses are inevitable because our eyes are slowly dying. He told me that at some point, I may need bifocals. What's next to fail me? My hearing? My knees? My teeth?" I threw my hands in the air, adding drama to the conversation.

"Life is not easy no matter what age. It doesn't work out the way we thought it would," Mom reflected.

"Tell me about it. I couldn't wait to grow up. Now I can't figure out what the heck the rush was for," I joked.

"It is a wonderful journey, though," she added. "I wouldn't change anything. The sooner you recognize life doesn't go according to plan, the easier life becomes."

"Thank you, Mom," I said. "I do appreciate you, even if I don't always show it."

I recognized for the first time the equal relationship we now shared as mother and daughter. It had morphed into an adult relationship where we both gave each other advice. I wanted to honor my mom despite how she drove me nuts. Because someday, my girls would be in the same boat, rolling their eyes at me the way I rolled mine at my mom.

We visited and drank tea all afternoon. Inevitably, the conversation shifted back to Mom complaining about the difficulty of living with a retired husband and their sex life. The girls stirred in their rooms, waking from their afternoon naps. I could hear them chirping sweet little noises.

"Can I get them up?" Mom asked, beaming with excitement to see her grandchildren.

"Of course. I'll get dinner started while you tend to them," I said.

While dinner was cooking, I picked up around the house to make it presentable for Gerrit before he got home from work. Mom came downstairs with the girls. They were diapered, changed into fresh clothes, and had hair neatly tied up with bows. They were grinning ear-to-ear to be with their grandma. I did appreciate her help. I knew she didn't show up unexpectedly to drive me nuts. Rather, it was because she knew I'd never ask for help. I hoped to be as loving as her someday with my own grandkids. I definitely wouldn't be as domineering. My kids would accept my help the way I accepted my mom's, whether they liked it or not.

• • • • • • • • •

## JULIA, 36

I had been dating Jack for two years. I was ready to marry him but Jack did things slowly. He didn't rush into anything, especially marriage. I teased him, calling him "well-aged prime rib."

"Seasoned to perfection," he would retort. "Though I prefer to compare myself to a finely aged wine."

I was getting antsy with wanting to start a life with him. I wanted to marry him. And I wanted kids like Colette. Everywhere I went, I was reminded of being a spinster. The judgment seemed to flare up where babies were the focus—like baby showers and birthday parties. Today, it was at Nora's second birthday party. It made me miserable.

"When are you going to have a baby?" Colette's mom asked without reserve. "Your clock is ticking, you know."

"Mom, she's well aware," Colette scolded. "Don't worry, Julia, your eggs are not going to dry up, nor are your ovaries."

My eyes welled up with tears. "Yes, they are. My biological clock is running out of batteries. My fertility is going to expire. You've had two children already. It's not even on my radar," I cried. "I'm going to go to my grave, a childless old maid at the rate Jack is moving."

"Jack will marry you and make babies with you," Colette reassured. "He's just gotta get off his butt and do it."

As young kids, Colette and I dreamt we would both be married with children in our thirties. It worked out for Colette but not for me.

"You've got years ahead of you to push babies out," Colette said, trying to comfort me.

"But by the time I have kids, people will think they're my grandkids," I lamented. "People will say to you, 'You look so young to have a kid who's eighteen years old.' But they'll say to me, 'You look so old to have a kid who's eighteen *months*.'"

"That's true. I don't want to lie to you. I will look young, and you will look old," Colette agreed sarcastically.

The judgment of these conversations put me in a funk. I left the birthday party early to have my own pity party. I couldn't wait on Jack any longer. I needed to move on. I called him and ended our relationship. It was a quick call, and I hung up without letting him say a word. I cried myself to sleep. My heart was broken. Jack called incessantly. I refused to answer. I called in sick to work. For a week. I was depressed and needed a mental health break.

Eventually, my assistant called and told me something was happening at the facility and I'd better get there quickly. I threw on a pair of baggy sweats and a stained T-shirt. I didn't even do my hair or makeup. I would deal with the issue and return home to bed.

I sped to work worried. My imagination conjured up worst-case scenarios. I had no idea what I was facing, forcing me to rush in. When I pulled into my appointed parking spot, my assistant met me outside. She was holding a large gift box wrapped in white and silver paper with a shimmery crystal bow.

"What's this?" I asked, confused. "What's the crisis?

She ignored me, handed me the box, and said, "Open it."

I ripped the paper off and opened the box, which revealed a gorgeous crystal vase. I admired it as the sun sparkled through the glass, creating magnificent prisms.

"Come with me," she instructed. I was confused as to why she gave me this beautiful present. But she wouldn't say more. And then it hit me. I was being terminated and this was my farewell gift. I had never called into work sick before. And because I failed my perfect attendance record, I would be fired for it. But when I entered the building, white balloons were floating everywhere. There was a white runner on the carpet through the hallway. This didn't look like a severance.

"What is all this?" I asked, still trying to make sense of the decorations and unexpected gift. The residents were lined up and down the hall. Each of them was holding a white tulip—my favorite flower. The first resident, sitting in a wheelchair, waved me over and put her tulip in the vase. I bent down, hugged her warmly, and kissed her cheek. She smiled and patted my face warmly with her withered knobby hand. I continued to receive a tulip from every resident, hugging and thanking each of them as I walked along. I had no idea what was going on. I followed the white runner through the corridor, which led to the center courtyard. It was late spring, and the garden was warm. The flowers were in full bloom, bursting with vibrant colors and sweet aromas. The courtyard was decorated with more balloons.

As I walked outdoors, I saw him—Jack! He was dressed in a black tuxedo, beaming with joy. I put down the massive vase of tulips and ran to him. I wrapped my arms around him, grateful to be back in his presence. I had missed him. I kissed him tenderly before he could say anything. He gripped me in a tight hug.

"Julia, we have some unfinished business," Jack said.

"Do we?" I asked, intrigued.

He dropped to one knee, pulling a small black box out of his pocket. I squealed. I couldn't believe it. I welled up in tears now, realizing what this was all about. I wondered how long it had taken for him to pull this together and how the residents were able to keep it a secret from me. I was impressed with the extent of the planning.

"Julia, I adore you," Jack said earnestly. "I want to spend the rest of my life with you, where I can shower you with flowers. My heart was a barren desert before I met you. You've watered it with your love and allowed it to blossom in ways I never knew were possible. You put new life into me. I can't imagine you not blooming by my side forever."

I laughed at his mushy words. Cheesy was not his style. With that, he opened the box and pulled out a toy wristwatch.

"Will you stay by my side until the end of time?" he said, slipping the watch over my wrist. We both laughed hysterically at his practical joke. His quirkiness was still one of his best qualities.

"Of course!" I exclaimed, still laughing. "But I want the real deal."

"I thought you'd say that," he said, pulling another smaller black box out of his pocket. "Do you want to spend the rest of your life with me?"

"You know I do."

By now, I was crying fully. I croaked out a "Yes" as he took the sparkling diamond engagement band from the box and placed it on the sacred ring finger of my left hand. He got up from kneeling and lifted me off the ground, embracing me tightly in his arms.

"I can't wait to marry you and spend the rest of my life with you," I assured him. "I want to be with you until our last moment on Earth—feeding each other applesauce. But why didn't anyone tip me off that you were proposing to me? Look at me! I'm a hot mess with swollen bags under my eyes. I'm wearing filthy clothes. I haven't showered in days."

"I'm not just proposing to you, Julia," Jack said, now more soberly. "I'm marrying you."

"What are you talking about? I'm wearing sweats and a T-shirt. I haven't even combed my hair."

"Will you marry me today?" he asked.

"I would've married you two years ago," I answered.

"That's what I thought you'd say," he smiled. "So I have a bigger surprise for you. I had a selection of wedding dresses brought over for you to try on and pick out your favorite."

"But look at my face. I don't even have makeup on."

"I have someone here to do that for you, too," Jack said. "I have everything planned out if you want to do it here and now. Today."

"But I can't get married without Colette," I said. "She won't step foot in this place."

"Turn around," Jack instructed.

I did and there standing at the entrance of the room was Colette, wearing a gorgeous teal bridesmaid's dress. She rushed over to me and hugged me.

"I wouldn't miss your wedding for anything, even in a nursing home," she confessed. "C'mon, let's get you made up and dressed up so you can marry the love of your life."

With that, she took my hand and led me to my office, where a shimmering array of white dresses was displayed for my choosing.

Two hours later, my hair perfectly styled and my makeup flawlessly applied, I slipped into the most beautiful white silk wedding dress. It was straight-fitted with a scoop neck. It was simple and suited me perfectly. Jack also had shoes picked out for me—plain white satin flats. He knew me well. Wearing flats at my wedding—now that's wisdom.

I was ready to say "I do" in the nursing home where it all began for the two of us. Having a ceremony in a long-term care facility was unconventional, but it was incredibly meaningful for us, especially since Jack's mom already lived here.

I was also delighted to have my residents in attendance. It had been years since many of them had been to a wedding, and I knew mine would awaken memories of their own buried deep in their minds. Their faces glowed with happiness as invited guests.

Years ago, I promised Abeulo he would give me away. Jack even made sure I held true to that promise and invited my parents and Abeulo. I had the honor to push Abeulo down the aisle in his wheelchair so he could give me away. Abeulo kissed me and whispered in my ear, "I'm proud of you for not settling." He then took my hand and gave it to Jack.

Through our spontaneous vows, Jack and I promised we would love and honor each other through good days and bad, through health and sickness, until death separated us. I loved the extemporaneous vows we made to each other. Jack slipped a gorgeous wedding band on my finger, next to the engagement ring he had placed there only hours before. And then he kissed me—his bride.

As my maid of honor, Colette was brave enough to make the toast in this place she loathed so much. She honored Jack and me in front of the residents and our family. He and I held glasses of champagne while the residents toasted with sparkling grape juice (so the alcohol wouldn't interfere with their medications, of course).

"Julia and I once were little girls dreaming about our knights in shining armor," Colette's toast began. "We didn't know when they'd come, what they'd look like, or how we'd meet them. But we believed we'd know the feeling of love and want to be with that person for the rest of our lives. People who influenced our lives gave us the advice to marry someone who shares the same core values, is our best friend, and doesn't keep score of wrongdoings. I see Julia and Jack did just that. Thank you, Jack, for *finally* marrying my best friend so she wouldn't die an old maid."

Colette grabbed a spoon to clink against her glass. Jack bent me over for a passionate kiss as the guests cheered us on.

I couldn't have imagined a more spectacular wedding. I'm a simple girl, and Jack planned everything perfectly, knowing I wouldn't want an elaborate soiree or the stress of planning a million wedding details. I just wanted to marry Jack—the love of my life. My dream came true. I gave my heart to the man I adored, surrounded by friends and family. What I hadn't envisioned in my dream was being amongst a group of nursing home residents. But that's what made it even more special. I felt honored I could transport them to earlier times in their lives, so they could relive their own weddings in their minds. I allowed them to walk down memory lane to remember one of the most joyous times in a person's life—the day you stand by your lover's side, promising to grow old with him or her.

• • • ● • ● • • • •

## COLETTE, 37

Grandmother Imelda always said death occurred in threes. And she unknowingly predicted it for herself. Dad called me to break the news—both she and Grandfather had died within hours of each other. A home-care aide found them at their house in Punta Gorda. They had been married for more than seventy years and literally couldn't live apart. It was touching that they had such a deep love for each other, but it was sad they didn't radiate that same love towards others—especially me, their very lovable grandchild. It was perplexing, especially knowing how my mom and dad adored my kids.

My kids were fortunate their grandparents gave them the love and attention I craved from mine.

Dad was crying on the phone when he called. Did I have a cold soul that their deaths didn't make me cry? I wasn't broken up about it. They were old. It was their time. It was hard to feel sad when someone lived a long life.

And then Gerrit also called me crying. It wasn't often that Gerrit cried, so I knew it was serious. "Colette, Granny Smith died today," he sobbed into the phone. "She suffered a pulmonary embolism and died. She's dead."

The news hit me like a hammer. I felt like I had been punched in the stomach. I gripped the phone and sobbed with him. I couldn't cry moments earlier when I found out my grandparents had died, but I sure could for Gerrit's grandma. It's because she loved me. Her expired life would be a loss for me. When I regained my composure to talk, I dreaded telling Gerrit my news, too. Three grandparents dead in one day was a lot to absorb.

Grandfather and Imelda wanted no acknowledgment of their passing. In their style, they didn't want any fuss. Or, more likely, they didn't want to spend the money. They simply wanted to be cremated without a service or visitation.

Granny Smith's funeral was the exact opposite. She had pre-arranged and written out every detail of her funeral. Unlike my grandparents, she wanted hers to be a celebration of life. She didn't even want it called a funeral. She asked to be dressed in a formal gown and a rhinestone tiara, which had been stored at the funeral home. I was surprised she didn't want to be buried with her beloved red hat.

She expressed in her notes that if she was going to meet "the King of Kings," she better be dressed like royalty. She had become more spiritual at the end of her life, anticipating what her eternal future might look like.

In addition, she wanted a local band to perform music that was dynamic and booming. Not somber and depressing like most funerals. She requested they march her off to Heaven, "for the trumpet will sound, and the dead will be raised." Her last wish was to have us decorate her casket with messages of love in permanent marker.

The funeral director had shared Granny Smith's notes with us. She had written:

*If you're reading this, it's because I've cashed in my one-way ticket to go six feet under. I want my send-off to be loud and lively. I want a party to reflect my vibrant life. It's one last extravaganza before the final curtain goes down. I refuse to go into my grave prim and proper. I want to joyfully show everyone my life was a wild rollercoaster ride to the very end. What an adventure it has been.*

This was her legacy. Her vivacious, energetic personality shined through to the end, even at her celebration of life. I wanted to leave a legacy like hers: warm, loving, and passionate. I wanted to live like her.

A few weeks later, when the time came for the reading of the wills, we met with my grandparents' attorney first. He flew up to meet with us to save the trip to Florida.

We gathered in my parents' living room. Mom, Dad, Gerrit, and I sat in a semi-circle across from the attorney. We held our breaths, anticipating what was bequeathed to us. I knew my grandparents were very wealthy. I was nervous and excited to find out how much we could inherit. Gerrit clutched my hand. He, too, was anticipating a windfall. We could buy a new house, save for the girls' college education, or build a nest egg for retirement—so many possibilities.

The attorney read Grandfather and Imelda's statement aloud:

*"While we were so generous with all of you in so many ways during our life—with our time, love, and money—we felt it wasn't necessary to spoil you any further now that we're gone. We want to share what we have with others so they may enjoy the same riches you enjoyed from us. Therefore, we are giving away our entire estate, valued at approximately five million dollars, to a children's hospital. This last will and testament expresses our wishes without undue influence or duress."*

It was a simple statement, but it was earth-shattering. The attorney finished reading the legalities and placed the paper on the coffee table. Nobody moved. I was angry on so many levels. The fallacies in all of this were tough to stomach. They gave us *nothing* in their lives. And now they were giving it all to a children's hospital? They didn't even like children. I wanted to be sick. I looked at my parents. Dad's face had drained of all color. These were his parents, and they gave him nothing. He sat pale and void of emotion. He had done so much for them. He had always been there for them and wasn't getting one cent of their fortune. I was devastated for him at the discovery he was written out of their will.

"Well, that's it then. I'll walk you all out," Dad said tensely. He abruptly stood up and threw their will into the garbage. He then escorted Gerrit, me, and the attorney to the door without saying another word. He slammed the door behind us.

Gerrit and I remained silent in the car on the way to the reading of his grandmother's will. We were both in shock. No new house. No college education for Valerie and Nora. No retirement savings. Nothing.

When we met up with Gerrit's family at Granny Smith's attorney's office, the mood was completely different. Gerrit's family was lighthearted and happy. They knew there wasn't much in Granny Smith's estate, but they also knew she would leave them with something meaningful.

"She doesn't have much to give away, but we're excited to see what her final wishes are," Gerrit's mom told me, hugging me as we greeted everyone. Gerrit's family was nestled into the attorney's office in anticipation.

"Good afternoon, everyone," the attorney began. "I'm sorry that this has to be the reason we meet. But let me get started. Granny Smith was an exceptional woman and wouldn't want you to be sad today." He read her will:

*"My Dearest Family,*

*I didn't acquire much in life. I lived simply and humbly but with great love. I shared what I had with you in the best way I could—with stops for ice cream, visits over coffee, darling outfits for my precious great-grandchildren, and little handouts of cash to buy whatever you liked. It wasn't much by society's standards, but I gave away all I had. It gave me great joy to do this. We can't take our money and belongings to heaven, so I decided it was better to give my possessions and money away while I was still alive. That way, I could enjoy the process of people receiving these gifts. I have written each of you a love letter so you know how much you mean to me. In the letters, I identify the personal belongings that I want each of you to have to remember me by. I hope what*

*you're given holds the same sentimental value for you that it held for me. I love
you all so dearly.*

*Granny Smith"*

There wasn't a dry eye in the room. Granny Smith was such a beautiful
woman, and she lived her life doing good for others. The attorney handed
out the labeled envelopes to each of us to read individually. I opened my
letter. It was written in her curvy handwriting. There was so much I would
miss about her. Even her handwriting.

*My Dearest Colette,*

*You were a whippersnapper the first day I met you. I know you judged me as a
silly old woman with a strange name and a flamboyant hat. You saw only my
old age and peculiarities and wanted to run and hide. But we instantly became
friends. I was enthralled with your beauty (I never had beautiful features like
yours) and knew your spirited personality would blend nicely with my family.
I couldn't wait for Gerrit to meet you because I knew you two were perfect for
each other. I'm so blessed you said yes to Gerrit when he proposed to you with my
engagement ring. It meant so much that you received it and him. In addition,
I want you to have my wide-brimmed red hat. I know you first thought it was
hideous, but I also know you will cherish it forever because of how it bonded
us and what it represents. It brought you and Gerrit together. And from that
union came two great-granddaughters. Thank you for making me a "great"
great-grandmother. I will be watching over you. I am much closer than you
think, for we never leave our loved ones.*

*All my love, Granny Smith*

The tears poured down my cheeks. I had been given a simple hat as my inheritance, and it meant more to me than any of the millions my grandparents
could've shared. I couldn't help but think that losing two sets of grandparents simultaneously allowed me to see the differences in their legacies and
therefore choose mine.

Grandfather and Imelda's legacy was that of being cold, stingy, and selfish
with their family. They had millions, and yet they gave us nothing. Gerrit's
grandmother's legacy was love. She devoted her life to her family. She gave

all that she had and poured herself into caring for those around her. Imelda's and Granny Smith's characters were worlds apart. Their legacies were extreme opposites.

What was my legacy going to be? I had to choose how I was going to be remembered. I decided I wanted my legacy to be love, like Granny Smith's.

• • • • • • • • • •

## JULIA, 38

Trying to have a baby at my age was not easy. Jack and I struggled after our wedding to get pregnant. We didn't struggle with the sex part—that was fabulous. We struggled with the his-and-her elements coming together to make the baby part. My doctors informed me fertility started to decline at the age of thirty and then dropped off more sharply after thirty-five. So the prediction that my ovaries would dry up was somewhat accurate.

After wasting more money than I dared to count buying pregnancy tests, only a single red line showed up each time, becoming my monthly curse. I was thirty-eight when the stick finally tested positive.

"Two red lines!" I shrieked in the bathroom at my office. I would finally move from being an old maid to a milkmaid.

When I learned I was pregnant, I stopped coloring my hair. Cold turkey. Colette had been doing hair colorings for me since I was in my twenties when I developed silver streaks. I hadn't seen my natural color since then. It would be interesting to see how much gray I had after all these years, with it hidden beneath the artificial coloring. But I was ready to ditch the dye. What did I care anyway? Would anyone really judge me for the color of my hair? It took time to grow out, and when I started the process, a blunt line of new gray growth was a stark contrast to the dark brown that had been my fake color for years. Colette offered to blend the transition, but I refused. I was going to love the skin I was in.

"You look like a skunk," Colette told me. She never minced words.

By the time my daughter Carolann was born, I had a full head of gray hair. People far too often assumed I was Carolann's grandma. It was a case of mistaken identity.

"How old is your granddaughter?" an unknowing stranger inquired. I was out shopping for diapers, and the young female cashier had asked. Carolann was one month old and sleeping, strapped in the carrier locked onto the cart.

"She's my daughter," I retorted.

"Oh, my apologies. I just thought you looked too old to have a baby," she said. "You must hear that a lot."

I said nothing. I wouldn't waste my breath on this young person's ignorance. I snatched the diapers from her and charged out of the store. I buckled Carolann back in the car. Coincidentally, she began to cry. It's what I wanted to do, too. I had gotten my first taste of being judged for my gray hair. I could return to Colette and have her dye my hair back to brown. But I told myself I had thicker skin than that. So instead, I wrote affirmations like *Gray hair is grayt* and *You're aging grayce-fully* on my shopping list—right under the line item for diapers. Clearly, I wasn't old if I had a newborn. I had to stop letting ignorant critics get under my skin.

My next stop was to the library to check out parenting books. As a new mom, parenting wasn't as easy as I expected. I didn't want to get it wrong. This was my most significant assignment in life, and I had to do it perfectly. I wanted to get a *Proud Parent of an Honor Roll Student* bumper sticker, so I had better start now making sure Carolann got straight As like me. But that depended on me giving her a good head start in life.

"Where are your parenting books?" I asked the librarian. She led me to the non-fiction section and pointed them out.

"If you also need books on grandparenting, they're the next aisle over," she said.

"Then I'll be sure to let my *mother* know since she'd be the one to check those out," I snapped at the woman.

"Oh, I just assumed..." her voice trailed off in embarrassment. She turned around and hurried off. I filled my book bag with a dozen books on good parenting skills.

My final stop was to tour a daycare facility where I considered placing Carolann when I returned to work after maternity leave.

I assured myself they wouldn't get me confused, towing Carolann in the carrier. They must see mothers in all shapes and sizes, all ages, and all hair colors.

"Will Carolann's mother be joining you as well?" the man at the front desk asked as he checked me in.

"Who do you think I am?" I replied.

"The grandma."

"Nope," I said. And in a moment of postpartum hormonal insanity, I unbuttoned my blouse, pulled out my engorged milk-filled boobs, and lifted Carolann to suck from my breast. "Who do you think I am now?"

"Wow. Okay. I can see you're not the grandma," he said.

"Bingo. I'm her mom. Just because I have gray hair doesn't mean I'm the grandma," I argued. "That's a terrible way to stereotype someone."

I stood there with both breasts hanging out while Carolann suckled on one of them. I wanted there to be no misunderstanding that I provided meals on heels. The moms who were dropping off their kids watched the spectacle as I exposed myself. They all began to applaud me for my brazenness. I had lost my mind for a brief second. I began to regret my impulsivity. I was too prim and proper to be so reckless. But by becoming a mother, I now had superhuman powers. I made milk, and I was going to fight ageism for my daughter's sake. I wanted Carolann to grow up in a world without judgment on her external appearance.

I tucked my girls—my boobs and Carolann—back into their bra and car seat, respectively, and hurried out of the daycare. I jumped into my car and cried in humiliation. I could never show my face there again.

From that day forward, I wouldn't cry over spilled milk or gray hair.

# Quadragenrians
## Ages 40 – 49

**J**ULIA, 40

I tossed and turned back and forth. Sheet pulled on. Sheet kicked off. I stared at the ceiling, then forced my eyes shut. Only to start the sleepless dance again. I looked at the clock. Again. And again. Another thirty minutes passed. I squeezed my eyes tighter, forcing myself to relax.

"I need to sleep," I groaned into my pillow.

For years Mama complained about not sleeping well. It got worse the older she got. Was this the beginning of age-related insomnia now that I had reached forty? I wasn't expecting it to happen so soon. I was still much too young for menopause symptoms to creep in.

After playing various sheep-jumping games in my head, I finally nodded off when the phone rang and jolted me out of my much-needed slumber. I clumsily picked up the hand receiver in the dark, knocking over something on my nightstand. I couldn't see a thing or get my bearings. The red numbers on the clock glowed 1:03 a.m. I had only just fallen asleep.

"Hello," I whispered. I didn't want to wake Jack sleeping peacefully beside me.

"Julia, something has happened!" Colette breathed heavily into the phone.

"Oh, dear God. What is it?" I panicked, propelling myself up. This was not the kind of phone call you wanted in the middle of the night. I tried to comprehend what it could be—a fatal car accident, house fire, or other tragic event—that warranted an unexpected wake-up call in the wee hours of the night. The news could be devastating. I held my breath.

"I found a gray hair," Colette shrieked. "I have gray hair, Julia. It's the beginning. This is the beginning of the end."

"A gray hair?" I hissed into the phone. "That's all?

"No, that's not all. I also have pimpkles."

"What the heck are pimpkles?" I asked.

"Pimples and wrinkles occurring at the same time," she explained. "It's bad enough that I still get acne like a teenager, and I'm developing wrinkles, but now I have a gray hair popping up. My body has officially gone insane."

"You scared the crap out of me. I've had gray hair for years. Who cares? It's a gray hair on your head," I dismissed. Jack was stirring. I hoped he wouldn't wake up over this nonsense. A gray hair was not mid-dle-of-the-night phone call worthy. This was preposterous.

"No, not on my head. Down there," she explained.

"Down where?"

"Down *there*."

I started laughing. Jack stirred again, so I stuffed my head under the pillow to talk quieter.

"Why are you laughing? I didn't know gray hairs grew *there*," Colette said.

"Welcome to midlife. Now go to sleep before you stress yourself out and grow more in other worse places," I chided.

"There are worse places than that?" Colette asked. "Where?"

"Never mind. Go to bed. You need your beauty sleep since we're forty when we wake up. Heaven knows you need it."

"Oh, no. I'm not turning forty," she declared.

"That's funny."

"I'm serious. I decided I'm not forty. I'm not ready yet. I'm waiting until next year."

"You can't do that," I said. "You can't not turn forty because you don't want to."

"Of course, I can. I can do whatever I want when I'm forty," she argued.

"But wait, you're supposedly not yet forty," I countered. "So you can't do whatever you want. It'll have to wait until you're of age."

"You're talking in circles. Anyway, have a great time celebrating your birthday. I'm sorry I won't be there with you," she said, ignoring my logic.

"You can't leave me to celebrate our biggest milestone birthday alone," I protested.

"It's my birthday, and I'll lie if I want to, lie if I want to, lie if I want to," Colette sang into the phone, changing the lyrics on the classic tune.

"You're not going to celebrate this birthday with me?" I asked.

"No. And you don't have to, either."

"I'm not going to deny my age."

"Well then, when I turn forty next year, we can celebrate again."

"You really don't plan to turn forty today?" I asked her. The question was ridiculous even to ask.

"No, not until next year," she said.

"And you're not going to celebrate with me?"

"Not today. But I will in a year," she said. "I'll let you go over the hill first, and I'll watch in fear to see what happens."

"The idea of over the hill doesn't mean you go downhill declining. It means you're gaining momentum going down the other side," I said. "This speed leads us to another hill to ascend when we're fifty. The journey keeps going, Colette. It's not a bell curve where over the hill leads down to our demise."

"Whatever you say. But let's face it. You're over the hill, and I won't be there for another twelve months," Colette said.

"I wouldn't change my age for anything," I replied. "I'm sorry you'll miss out today because, at forty, the view from the top of the peak is amazing."

After hanging up with Colette, I lay staring at the ceiling the rest of the night, unable to fall back to sleep. The next day I celebrated without Colette. I didn't care that it was the big four-oh. I embraced it. Turning forty was great. It was even better than turning thirty.

•••••••••

## COLETTE, 42 (OR 40 THE SECOND TIME AROUND)

Not one but two years later, I finally decided to turn forty. I pushed it back a second year because I still wasn't ready. It felt right this time—two years after the fact. Not that I was completely ready now, but I wasn't in the mood then to reach my peak where midlife began. I wanted to get on with the momentum everyone talked about. But it was a hard pill to swallow that I was now living in the Middle Ages.

Since deciding to turn forty, I wanted to have a birthday party in the peak of summer when it's hot and sunny. If I were inventing the year I turned forty, I would also make up the day. I wanted a summer birthday to celebrate at the beach on a Lake Michigan coastal town, with sand between my toes and sun on my highly sun-screened face. I still hadn't tanned my face since college. I wasn't going to take any risks with sunspots at this age.

"I'm going to throw myself a surprise party," I told Julia. We were at the park together with our girls.

The nonsense of my suggestion made her laugh.

"Where's the surprise if you know about it?" she asked. "I don't know what's funnier, the fact that you're throwing yourself a fortieth *surprise* party or doing it at forty-two."

"I fail to see any humor in it. I'll invite everyone I know and ask them not to RSVP. The surprise will be seeing who shows up," I answered.

"So, you want a no-surprise surprise party for a fortieth birthday that doesn't happen to be your fortieth nor on your actual birth date?" Julia asked. I could tell she was processing the ridiculousness of it.

"Yes. And I'll have you rent out a beach bar and the caterer and manage all the decorations. I'll give you a blank check to make it happen."

"While I certainly have no problem spending other people's money, I won't do it," Julia said.

"What do you mean you won't do it?" I demanded.

"I'm not going to feed into this madness. It's fake—all of it. I refuse to support this hoax of yours, lying about your age," Julia explained.

"It's meant to be fun. A joke," I argued.

"Sorry, it's the principle of it," Julia said. "I'm not going to stand by and watch this charade. I won't pretend it's okay for you to lie about your age and have all others buy into it. I have more integrity than that."

"Are you serious? You won't humor me and my guests by pulling this off?"

"No," she insisted. "It's not a message I want to pass down to my daughter. Do you feel good about modeling this for your girls?"

"Why do you always have to be so pragmatic and rigid?" I yelled. "Can't you just relax and have some fun occasionally?" My tone was loud and sharp. Others in the park took notice.

"This isn't about me. This is about our daughters and helping them accept and embrace who they are," Julia growled. "It's also about you buying into all the propaganda that turning forty is something bad. I don't want to be a part of it."

A fierce argument ensued in the park that day. Julia stood her ground, and I stood mine. We both dug in our high heels. We couldn't see eye to eye on aging. We walked away that day, angry at each other, and stopped talking. I moved forward with my own party plans without Julia.

I summoned Gerrit to help me. He did it, though not enthusiastically. I invited a hundred friends and family and asked them not to RSVP. The invitations were black with white lettering that read, *A surprise party with a twist. I know you're coming, just don't tell me.* It must've seemed I lost my marbles when people read it. My age had finally done me in—put me over the edge.

The invitation required everyone to dress as zombies. Likely a decision resulting from too much wine when I was planning. I did it to imitate *Día de los Muertos*—Day of the Dead, the Mexican tradition that mocks death. Having a zombie costume party was like punching death in the face. If Julia's Mexican family can laugh at death, I would start a movement to get middle-agers to laugh at aging on their birthdays. One zombie at a time.

For the party, I dressed in a ripped-up, black gothic dress. I layered white makeup on my face and black makeup around my eyes. I looked so bad; I looked good.

Gerrit rented out a beach bar for the party. He stuck cardboard gravestones in the sand and littered the tables with over the hill decorations. The over-sized banner that hung above the bar read, *Lordy, Lordy! Look Who's Forty!* At some point during the party, someone crossed out the forty and scribbled in forty-two. Ha! I wondered who knew the truth.

With all the guests dressed as zombies, too, the party atmosphere was a great attempt to make a mockery of turning forty. The DJ pumped music, the liquor flowed freely, and laughter filled the air. Nearly everyone danced until well after midnight. We all dripped with sweat from the Michigan summer heat, and as the zombie makeup melted off our faces, we looked even more grotesque than before.

I received gag gifts like Depends undergarments, a walking cane, Preparation H, denture cream, and orthopedic compression socks. It was all very humorous. I laughed hard, knowing I'd never need them. I wasn't going to fall prey to these enemies.

I had the time of my life, except I was sad Julia wasn't there. Despite our fight, I sent her an invitation, but she didn't show up to celebrate.

Having a fake second fortieth birthday helped me step into midlife easier. This time I embraced it, and it felt better to do so. Maybe it's more rewarding to go back and celebrate a milestone birthday the second time when you're already older and can more fully appreciate the younger age. Or maybe I was delusional.

"Forty is fabulous!" I shouted into the DJ's microphone.

"Don't you mean forty-two?" someone yelled back. I ignored the bully.

The next morning all the optimism about feeling fabulous was replaced with feeling ill from a bad hangover. It was a harsh reminder that recovering from a night of drinking took days when you reached middle age. The hangover proved I wasn't a spring chick anymore.

• • • • • • • • •

## JULIA, 43

"Fred in the bed" was the scandal that marred my career. It was disastrous after working so tediously never to make a blunder. I prided myself on my excellent work ethic.

The crisis erupted at the nursing home while I was executive director. For years I coasted in my job, running the facility tightly as if it was a cruise ship full of retirees. But then all sex broke loose. The controversy erupted when Fred and Harriet, two ninety-year-old residents with dementia, had sex with each other. Apparently, Fred wandered to Harriet's room in the middle of the night, and they got frisky. The problem wasn't they had sex. The problem was they were both married to other people.

A nurse panicked after discovering the rendezvous during a routine morning med pass. As she spread the news, the place went up in flames of chaos about how to manage this crisis.

This was the taboo of taboos—nursing home sex! And it fired up a range of emotions with the staff. Working with the elderly meant there was never a dull moment. Whoever said the elderly were boring never had the delight of working with them. I called an emergency team meeting.

"The craving for human touch doesn't diminish with age," I explained to the staff. "The desire for intimacy lingers in our hearts and bodies until the day we die."

"But she's got dementia. She couldn't have consented to this," one of the nurse aides argued.

"He's got dementia, too. He couldn't have consented, either," another piped up.

"Do patients with dementia have the ability to consent?" another asked.

"Making the decision about wanting sex requires minimal capacity. It's an intuitive desire," I explained. "If they're content in each other's arms, then I would assume this was consensual, even if it occurs beyond a cognitive level. I'm not going to raise an issue with it. Who are we to police this basic human need?"

"Does that mean it's okay they did this when they've got spouses who don't know what's going on?" a nurse aide asked.

"Should we be telling the spouses?" another nurse aide asked.

I wasn't sure how to answer these questions. We were in uncharted territory, and the ethics of this conversation weren't going to be solved easily. So I brushed it under the rug. I asked the staff to let the situation go. I instructed them to keep an eye on the couple and redirect them if they started to cross the fine line.

Now, anyone who cares for the elderly knows to remove rugs because they're tripping hazards. I should've pulled the proverbial rug I swept the crisis under, for it tripped me up.

Mostly, Fred and Harriet would hold each other's hands. But the escapade fueled the debate on appropriate touching and consensual sex between patients with dementia. We needed to start having more constructive conversations about geriatric sexuality. In the end, I decided not to tell their spouses.

Maybe that was the wrong decision, but I felt it would hurt more than it would help.

And then it happened again, this time with dire consequences. Instead of one of the nurses walking in on the two lovebirds, it was Harriet's husband. He began yelling, demanding to know why his wife was in bed with another man.

I tried to calm him from creating a spectacle. He didn't understand it wasn't the wife he knew who was making these decisions, but only a shell of her. Dementia had erased nearly all her memories, except for the desire to be with a man. She even called Fred by her husband's name. Deep in the reservoirs of her mind, she thought she was making love to her husband. She didn't know the difference. Should she be punished for living out her instinctual need to connect with another human being?

I surmised that Harriet and Fred were filling a need greater than the conscious mind can communicate. They were genuinely finding happiness through touch and connecting beyond a cerebral level. I knew Harriet's husband couldn't understand this. He was the coherent spouse. It was intensely painful for him to see his wife lose all memory of him, including her fidelity commitment. The bond established decades ago had unraveled like a loose thread, and Harriet's husband wanted to knit it back together to its original shape. But dementia made it impossible to do. The fabric had frayed apart and would only continue to unravel as time passed.

Harriet's husband was irate from the incident and refused to look at it from a different vantage point. Instead, he filed a grievance against me, bringing in an ombudsman to investigate.

"I suspect these shenanigans won't happen in a place where the staff cares enough to ensure their residents aren't being taken advantage of," he said as he angrily filled out the discharge papers. He was moving her out to place her in another nursing home.

"Sir, I can assure you it wasn't because of my staff. Your wife lost in their own mind, found comfort through touch. She thought she was with you," I defended. "She lives in her own reality."

"It's your job to keep them in *our* reality."

"Their reality is nothing we can control. It's the destruction of dementia that changes reality for them," I explained.

He wouldn't listen to my explanation. I understood he was deeply hurt. He failed to see the disease for what it was and how it destroyed the mind. I watched with sadness as he wheeled Harriet out of our nursing home—her home, the place she had recognized as her source of security. It broke my heart that her life, comforts, and safety net would be ripped out from beneath her because her husband misunderstood dementia.

I wondered if she had stayed in our nursing home—if she hadn't been forced to disconnect from the source that brought her joy—if she would've lived longer. I feared she wouldn't easily transition to a new facility. My fears were warranted when she died a month later.

I struggled immensely. Maybe I wasn't cut out for this work any longer if I couldn't keep residents and their families protected. I needed Colette's advice, but we still weren't talking. I had reached out with an olive branch, but she was still too hurt that I didn't support her fake birthday. My calls went unanswered.

I had to navigate this personal crisis without the advice of my best friend. My staff criticized how I handled it. The polarizing views over the issue brought out emotional responses in everyone. I had many sleepless nights and workless days fighting against the questions and regrets in my mind.

When is sex in a nursing home okay? What if it's between people who have dementia? When do we, as professionals, intervene or turn a blind eye to the actions of adults under our care?

There were days in my career I marveled that I got paid to do what I loved. Then there were days when I couldn't get paid enough to do the work. This controversy, and the ethics surrounding it, were one of those times. Sex in nursing homes wasn't a subject approached in tidy conversations. It's not coffee talk. "Let's chat about the elderly having sex," said nobody. Ever.

After this scandal, I became disillusioned with my job. No amount of money could make up for witnessing the pain that dementia brought to families, along with people's emotional responses to senior citizen sex. I was pressured from all angles to address it the way that pleased everyone, and it was impossible to do.

I was being pushed out. I wouldn't let the board of directors fire me, which was impending, so I quit before it happened. Somebody else would have to be the trailblazer of sex in the oldest old. It wouldn't be me. I was a coward and a quitter. Everything unfolds at the right time, and this wasn't the time to pioneer the ethics of elder sexuality. It would remain a taboo subject for now.

• • • • • • • • • •

## COLETTE, 44

"I'm the bologna in the middle," I growled at Gerrit under my breath as I dished partially frozen lasagna onto four dinner plates. I was irritable after a long hard day, and he was my punching bag.

"What do you mean?" Gerrit asked noncommittally, not looking up from reading his newspaper.

"I'm a sandwich caregiver. I'm sandwiched between taking care of our daughters and my parents. I'm the bologna," I explained.

"I'd say you're more like the turkey," he quipped, getting up to walk out.

"Thanks for your support!" I snapped. I was stressed, and he was ignoring my suffering.

"Let's talk. What's going on?" he asked, sitting back down to listen to my ranting. "What problem can I solve for you?"

I set everyone's dinner plates roughly down on the table. They were lucky to even have a meal after the day I had.

"I'm exhausted," I sighed. "I packed lunches, got the girls off to school, washed two loads of laundry, and joined the rat race at work. On break, I checked on Mom, recovering from her knee replacement. Dad was dizzy and disoriented because he switched to a new medication. I called the doctor to get a different prescription. I then had to drive Mom to physical therapy. I picked up Dad's pills at the pharmacy." I felt hot tears form as I rattled off my day. "My boss yelled at me for missing a meeting. After work, I grabbed this lousy frozen lasagna at the store, and here I am, still on my feet, serving you all."

Gerrit looked at me as the tears flooded down my cheeks. I felt sorry for myself, describing my terrible, no-good, very bad day as a caregiver.

"Is that all?" he asked.

"No. That was just today. I can go into what I did yesterday and what I've got tomorrow. I'm overwhelmed trying to take care of everyone and everything."

"If there's anything I can do to help, just let me know," he said, returning to his paper.

I stared at him incredulously. He had to ask *if* there was anything he could do to help? Couldn't he see on his own how he could help? I stormed out of the kitchen.

I crawled into my bed numb and pulled the blankets over my head. I was exhausted. The responsibilities of caring for my aging parents were taking their toll. As an only child, I managed everything alone.

Plus, I didn't like this role reversal. My parents were supposed to take care of me since I was their kid. It didn't feel natural for kids to take care of their parents. *It's time they went into an old folks' home,* I thought. I'd tell them tomorrow. For now, I went to sleep—too tired and upset.

The following day I returned to my parent's house, where they had lived since I was a baby. I dreaded the conversation. I wanted Julia to do this for me. She was the expert and could convince them. But I hadn't talked to her since our fight about my fake fortieth-birthday party over two years ago. Maybe it was time to let my grudge go. It seemed so trivial now.

I couldn't do this on my own. I needed Julia's help. Even more, I needed Julia. Maybe this crisis would reconnect us. I dialed her and said it was an emergency. To me, this was an emergency. She agreed to meet.

Waiting for Julia, I passed the time making coffee and toast with jam for myself. Mom asked if I was making some for them, too. Was I supposed to? Geesh, I thought doing nearly everything for them already was enough. But I relented. I delivered coffee and toast to the dining room and placed them on the crocheted doily in the center of the table.

"We need to talk," I began impatiently. I couldn't wait any longer for Julia.

"What is it, dear? Are you pregnant?" Mom joked. Her voice was weak and raspy. The strength of her vocal cords had faded with age.

"Mom, at my age, I'm not knocked up."

"Oh no, my granddaughters are?" she assumed, filling in the blanks of my announcement.

"No, not them, either," I said, bracing myself for what came next. "Remember when you moved me into the attic? It's kinda like that. It's time for you to move into an old folks' home. I'm moving you tomorrow."

"What are you talking about? We don't need to move into a place for old people. We're not like them," Mom huffed.

I couldn't believe her denial. Had they not looked in the mirror in the last decade to see how old they were?

"I disagree. And Julia's coming over here to tell you, too," I said. "Look how feeble you both are. A home for the aged is the best place for you."

"We are not moving out of this house, missy," Dad protested, slamming his fist on the table.

"Nor are we aged," Mom argued.

"Why are you trying to force us to leave our home?" Dad yelled.

I had stirred up a ruckus like a fox stirs up a henhouse. They squawked and screeched and made quite a commotion. Mom waved her cane at me in anger. Dad paced back and forth across the room, throwing his hands up in the air. This was not going well. Maybe I should've waited for Julia. The argument continued. Then Julia arrived.

"Julia, thank goodness you're here!" Mom, Dad, and I yelped in unison when she finally walked in. I gave her a long-overdue hug.

"What's going on?" Julia asked, concern on her face.

Mom and I stumbled on each other's sentences trying to make our point, while Dad argued with no one in particular. Our voices rose higher in an attempt to override each other.

"ENOUGH!" Julia shouted. "Colette said it was an emergency."

"It is," Mom and I belted simultaneously.

"Colette is trying to kidnap us!" Dad yelled.

"And dump us in a convalescent home," Mom continued. "Julia, you've got to save us."

"She's going to imprison us," Dad added.

"I'm not trying to kidnap you. I simply said I'm moving you into a nursing home," I corrected.

"What?" Julia asked, perplexed. "Why?"

"It's true," Dad said. "Just before you walked in, she threatened to put us away. If you hadn't come, we might have ended up in another state."

"It was only a suggestion," I defended myself. "I wanted to discuss it with you and see what your thoughts were. I guess I know your thoughts now."

"It was a threat, not a suggestion," Mom said, wrapping her arm around Julia's to side against me.

"Let's talk this out rationally," Julia said. "Colette, why on God's green Earth do you think your parents should be forced out of their home?"

"Because I can't care for them anymore," I insisted. "I'm managing so many of their medical issues. Mom needs therapy and walks with a cane. Dad's on a bazillion prescriptions. They're so needy, and I thought it was time."

"Those concerns don't warrant your parents going to assisted living. And certainly not a nursing home," Julia soothed.

"But they need help, and I can't do it all," I cried. The stress of caring for them was backed up like a dam, and the floodgates opened with a vengeance.

"I understand. But they don't qualify for a nursing home. Contrary to your fake medical background in deciding these things, they're not sick or frail enough," she laughed.

"Really? You mean they have to get worse than this?" I was dumbfounded.

"Colette, they're not as bad as you think. While they're still of sound mind and body, they can make their own decisions. You can't just move them against their wishes. You don't have guardianship over them."

"It's not like I was holding them hostage. It was a mere suggestion," I lied. "So, if not a nursing home, how about assisted living?"

"Assisted living is expensive. It ranges from forty to fifty thousand dollars a year. They'll burn through their savings in no time if it's not needed. And guess what happens when they run out of money?"

"The government will take care of them?" I countered.

"Ha! Not even close. Assisted living facilities are for-profit businesses. When the money runs out, they'll run your parents out. Your parents get evicted, and guess who they'll move in with?" Julia pointed at me. "Then they won't have a dime left. Assisted living is not like nursing care. They can push you out if you run out of money."

"There's no way I'll spend my hard-earned dollars on an overpriced rest home," Dad interjected. "I can rest here for free."

Julia was so knowledgeable about the aging process. I sat in awe as I listened to her list off dollars and cents on housing options.

"This is a good time to discuss long-term care planning," Julia advised. "The conversation should've happened long before now to avoid all this. But it's not too late. No damage has been done." She winked at Mom and Dad.

Mom smiled at Julia, then sneered at me. She had become more cantankerous with age. I sure hoped I didn't end up like that.

"Whatever happened to 'Honor your mother and father'?" Dad asked. "Now kids dump their parents when they think they've become a burden."

"That's not what I was trying to do," I fibbed, but hell if I'd admit it out loud.

"Let's bring everyone's emotions down and finish the conversation like mature adults," Julia suggested.

"Fine. Let me get more coffee for everyone," I said, getting up from the table.

"I'll take a fresh cup and new toast, please," Mom said, pushing her plate of food away. "Who knows if you were trying to poison us, too? I'm not eating what you served earlier."

As I busied myself in the kitchen making non-poisonous toast, I listened carefully to Julia's empathetic conversation with my parents.

"The reality is, 70 percent of couples are going to need some kind of long-term care," Julia was explaining. "If you don't have this conversation early, then everyone's at risk. It's important to talk about your wishes with Colette and understand her limitations as a caregiver. She's caring for you and your granddaughters, trying to be a good wife, and managing a career. It's a lot for one person. She's burned out. So be easy on her, too."

The four of us worked to put a care plan together. The agreement outlined their wishes and what they could afford for homecare, assisted living, or a nursing home if the time came.

"Don't dismiss independent living. People who move in wish they would've done it sooner," Julia explained. "And you aren't likely to need other long-term facilities. Only about 2.5 percent of older adults go into assisted living, and 4.5 percent go into skilled nursing. It's a tiny percentage of the population. The vast majority age at home, whether it's their own home or independent living."

"For now, let's get homecare aides in to help with basic necessities. It will give Colette a break and ensure you get the care you need."

After "the talk" was over, Julia and I walked out together. I wrapped my arms around her in a tight embrace.

"I don't know what I'd do without you. Thank you for coming to our rescue. If it wasn't for you, I might've shipped them to another country," I joked, sniffling back tears.

"This was one way to get us talking again." Julia laughed. "It shouldn't have to come down to herding your parents off like cattle because their daughter is a drama queen."

"It sucks to grow old," I said. "Some people don't do it very well. Whoever said you can age gracefully is full of it—ALL of it."

"Ahh, don't be so hard on your parents," Julia said.

"I wasn't talking about them," I sighed. "I was talking about me."

Without saying a word about our two-year-old fight, this was our reconciliation.

•••••••••

## JULIA, 46

My daughter Carolann had begged me to go to the mall for back-to-school shopping. It was still peak summer, but already school clothes were out. Why did stores bring out seasonal merchandise so early, long before the season began? It frustrated me that society hurried everything along and made us move faster through life. I tried to keep Carolann grounded and not grow up too quickly. I remember I couldn't wait to grow up. I wanted to help Carolann enjoy the moment instead of rushing into the next season—whether it was clothes or the next phase of life. Unfortunately, it's just part of being a kid—you want to hurry up and grow up.

Carolann was a tween, sandwiched between being a child and a teen. There were still many apron strings tying her to me. Slowly, over the next few years, as she journeyed through, the strings would be cut one by one. Soon enough, she would be out on her own living independent of me, and the apron strings would be severed. It pained me to think about it. I wanted to hold back time.

We walked through the mall, and I reminisced about when Colette and I hung out here as kids. It was nostalgic that I had a child the same age Colette and I were when we would shop together. I expected this time with Carolann would be as fun as my time with Colette. The difference now, though, was that I was the parent.

The mall became a battlefield over age-appropriate fashions. What she said was stylish, I said was trashy. What I found perfect, she found dull. There was no agreement on anything.

"Carolann, let's go into this store. This is your favorite," I said as we approached a kids' clothing shop.

"I hate that store," she said, puckering up her face.

"No, you don't."

"Yes, I do."

"Since when?"

"Since they started carrying baby clothes."

"Well then, where do you want to go?"

"There," she said, pointing to a teen clothing store. By the looks of the mannequins, the outfits showed more flesh than fabric.

"That's too grown-up for you."

"No, it's not. You're old-fashioned. That's what everyone wears," she said, striding into the store. I reluctantly followed.

Everything she picked out was too short, too tight, too low. The outfits showed too much cleavage, too much waist, too much leg, and altogether too much skin. We argued over what was permissible for her age. She walked out with two items we mutually agreed on—headbands. This was going to be a long day of shopping.

"Mom, I think I could use a bra," she said sheepishly.

I gulped on the words. We headed to the lingerie section of the department store.

"I like this," she said, holding up a hot pink leopard lace bra with extra padding.

"Um, no. That's too risqué for a young girl your age," I said. "That's something I would wear."

"Mom, you're too old to wear that," she laughed.

"No, I'm not," I snapped, grabbing it from her hands. I pulled the matching thong to go with it.

"Yes, you are," she said. "You need these."

She held up a girdle. It was a granny panty. It was huge and unflattering.

"Excuse me, I don't appreciate that," I said, chuckling. "I can wear leopard print if I want to, no matter my age."

"Whatever you say, Mom," Carolann quipped.

After much arguing, we found more modest training bras appropriate for her.

We took a handful of bras into the dressing room and the sexy leopard set and girdle for me. As we undressed, I compared my body to hers in the mirror. I could see that my age was causing my weight to shift. I carried more of it in my waist like a tire. Belly fat developed around my midsection, where the visceral fat settled. This wasn't the shape I used to be. I knew this weight shift was inevitable due to estrogen levels changing in my body. I knew about the effects of age and weight gain and saw it with the residents I worked with. I just wasn't paying attention to when it happened to me. Senescence is a slow process. But I didn't feel bad about it. Nature was doing its job.

I moved my eyes down the mirror and inspected my thighs. They had grown thicker, creating more of a pear shape. Dimples of cellulite puckered my skin. I made a mental note to start exercising more. I had to be careful, so I didn't gain too much weight from aging. I also needed to be more careful with my eating habits as my metabolism slowed down with age. It would be harder to drop pounds the older I got.

I tried on the leopard-print bra and underwear. Bulges of underarm fat spilled over the elastic sides. And yet my breasts barely filled the cup. They had lost all volume after breastfeeding, and now they were just withered sacks of skin that hung too low. The thong dug sharply between my cheeks. I had a good laugh at how ridiculous I looked. Carolann was in hysterics. Maybe I was getting too old for sexy lingerie. I tried on the granny panty. It fit perfectly. Go figure!

I wondered about miniskirts and low-cut shirts, and other seductive apparel. Was there an age when provocative became prohibited? When should women stop dressing sexy? Should old ladies wear miniskirts at eighty? I barely wore miniskirts at forty-six anymore. I doubted I'd even wear a skirt above the knee at sixty.

Carolann and I shopped through the rest of the department store. We passed the cosmetics counter, and she begged me to let the cosmetic girl put some makeup on her.

"You need to wait to wear makeup," I said. "Remember, I didn't even get to wear makeup until I was fifteen at my quinceañera. You're too young right now."

"No, I'm not."

"Yes, you are," I said. "When you get to high school, then you can start wearing it."

"Why do I have to wait so long?"

"You don't need to look like you're twenty when you're not"

"Makeup isn't about making you look older. It's about making you look beautiful," the cosmetic girl interjected. I ignored her.

"You're beautiful without makeup. Even more so," I said. "Plus, you shouldn't feel the need to change your appearance. I don't wear much makeup for that reason."

"It's not about changing your appearance; it's about enhancing it," the cosmetic girl added. I scowled at her this time as if I needed this twenty-something know-it-all to give me parenting advice. She backed away and pretended to be busy. Smart girl.

"Please, Mom, can she put on a little blush and lip gloss on me?" Carolann begged.

I caved. "Fine."

The cosmetic girl scurried back, hoping for a sale. This was not the mountain I was going to die on. When Carolann became a teenager, there would be bigger dragons to slay than this one. Abuelo's best advice to me was to pick my battles. Times were changing anyway. The rules of growing up were evolving with my daughter and her generation.

This was one of those times I didn't want Carolann growing up too fast. If I could do anything for her, it would be to help her hold on to her youth and not rush life. There was plenty of time to be a grownup.

The cosmetic girl brushed rouge onto Carolann's cheeks and dabbed tinted gloss on her lips. She added a little eye color for effect. Carolann looked beautiful.

"Thanks, Mom," Carolann said, studying her face in the mirror. She was smiling from ear to ear. She jumped off the stool and kissed me on the cheek, leaving a lip gloss stain behind.

"You're welcome. It's times like this we'll always remember," I said, grinning.

I reminded myself it was okay to let her be who she was. She was a typical adolescent—excited for her future and the next stage of life.

Why didn't adults have that same enthusiasm for reaching the next stage of life? What if adults looked forward to growing older and viewed it as the most exciting period in life? What if we tried to hurry up time to reach our elderly years, the same way kids did to grow up? What a transformed society we would live in if old age were revered as the most marvelous time of our lives. Age discrimination, ageism, and the fears about growing old would vanish. Being a senior citizen would be celebrated as winning the race. And you'd receive a trophy for being old.

• • • • • • • • •

## COLETTE, 47

I was exhausted after another long work week at the salon. I was ready to unwind with quiet time. It was a rare occasion that I was home without Gerrit or the girls, and I welcomed the serenity. I poured myself a glass of wine and kicked off my leopard print shoes. My feet and lower back ached for days after standing in high heels all day. I used to wear heels every day and not flinch. Now I could barely wear them two days in a row. But I wasn't ready to trade them in. I'll ditch them when I'm ninety, but not yet. I turned on soft jazz and sipped my wine, allowing myself to relax.

The phone rang and jarred me from the serenity. It was most likely Julia. She was the only one who called me on a Friday night.

"Hello," I answered.

"I just poured myself a glass of Merlot," Julia said.

"I just poured myself Chardonnay," I mirrored.

"I think I need glasses," Julia suggested.

"You know you can drink wine right out of the bottle. You don't need glasses for wine," I joked.

"Silly, I mean bifocals. At forty-seven, my eyesight is finally giving out," Julia said.

"Well, I've had glasses now for a while. They're not so bad."

"But you wear contacts. Not glasses."

"Close enough. They're adaptive eyeballs for the visually impaired."

"So, it's a Friday night, and we're couch potatoes. Do you remember when we wouldn't be caught dead on a Friday night doing nothing?"

"Yes. And our weekend nights wouldn't even start until 10:00 p.m.?" Julia replied.

"Those were the days," I said, taking a sip of wine. "Before you know it, we'll be having dinner at 4:30 p.m. and retiring to bed by 7:00 p.m."

Julia laughed. "That time might come sooner than we think. I'm already there. I haven't even had dinner yet, and I'm in my pajamas, looking forward to bedtime."

"It's the rat race of life. Working. Raising kids. Playing the good wife," I listed off the responsibilities that led to Friday fatigue. "Seriously, when does life slow down? When will we ever enjoy a little peace?"

"When we're dead," Julia said. "That's why gravestones are marked, *Rest in peace*. You won't get it until then."

"That's disheartening."

"So, what grand plans do you have tonight?" Julia asked.

"I'm lathering my face in a clay mask. And I brought home hair coloring from the salon, so I'm gonna wash the gray right outta my hair," I sang to the tune of the Clairol commercial.

"Where are Gerrit and the girls?"

"The girls have a sleepover with friends. Gerrit's working late, as usual," I answered. "He's wrapped up in a special project for work. He's been gone a lot lately, come to think of it."

"Hmmm."

"What's that 'hmmm' for?" I asked, sipping more wine.

"Nothing. I'm not saying a word," Julia said. "It just sounds suspicious."

"Really? You think so?"

"I don't know. Enjoy your evening with your hair kit. I'll be watching a movie with Carolann and Jack and will likely fall asleep before it starts." She laughed again.

"Sounds thrilling," I said. "We lead such dull lives at this age."

"And good luck with your hair. Promise me you won't call me in sheer panic because you left it on too long, and your hair turns blue," Julia cautioned.

I was happy to skip a meal with no one to cook dinner for. Fasting was probably good for anti-aging. I grabbed the box of hair rinse and the facial mask and headed for the bathroom. I examined my face in the mirror. What reflected was not what I felt on the inside. I felt much younger than I looked. I smeared the mask onto my face, avoiding the areas around my eyes. The green, sticky paste made me glow like an alien.

I wrapped myself in a robe, snapped rubber gloves onto my hands, and squirted the hair coloring from the plastic bottle onto my gray roots. The crème rinse made my hair stand on end. It was like brown glue.

"I'm a real beauty queen." I laughed aloud at my hideous image in the mirror. "What we women go through to stay beautiful for our husbands."

I reclined on the couch, putting a towel under my head to prevent the dye from bleeding on the fabric. I had thirty minutes to rest while the coloring did its job. I felt myself dozing off to sleep when I heard Gerrit enter the house. He was home unexpectedly early.

"Colette?" he called from the back hallway.

"In the living room," I answered, hearing his footsteps on the wood floor.

I listened for him to approach. I uncovered the cucumbers from my eyes when the footsteps stopped. I sat up to face him. I imagined I must be a dream girl with all the grime on me.

"Colette, I need to talk to you," Gerrit said. His eyes were filled with dread.

"What is it?" I asked. The panic rose in my chest.

"I'm moving out," he said without hesitation.

"What?" I asked, confused. This was all so abrupt.

"I want a divorce."

"What are you talking about?"

"I want a divorce."

"Are you out of your mind?"

"No. I want a divorce."

"I heard you the first time. I'm not deaf. Why?" The anger peaked in my voice and became a high-pitched screeching sound.

"It's complicated."

"WHY?" I screamed.

"I met someone."

"You met someone?"

"Yes, someone who makes me feel alive inside."

"Oh, this is good. Who is she?" I sneered. Rage was building inside of me.

"The assistant in my office," he answered under his breath.

"How old is she?" I demanded, venom saturating my voice. "This young bimbo of yours."

"It doesn't matter how old she is."

"How old is she?" I yelled, getting off the couch to stand in his face.

"Twenty-eight."

"Are you kidding me? You're despicable. She's young enough to be your daughter."

"No, not really."

"You are not trading me in for a trophy wife. Do you understand that? You do not have permission to do this to me."

"This is exactly why I'm divorcing you because you're so controlling. And you're not nice. It's gotten worse as you've gotten older. For the record, I'm not trading you in for a trophy wife."

"What about our vows? For better or for worse? Have you forgotten you promised to be with me through it all? Until death?"

"People change. I'm not the same person I was when we got married. Neither are you. You can't expect people to stay in love forever."

"Yes, I can. That's what marriage is. Staying together forever."

"Maybe for some. But I don't like who we've become in midlife. We're just too different now than we were in our younger years."

"Based on what? On what I look like?" I remembered my ghastly appearance as the timer buzzed to wash out the dye. I slumped back down on the couch. I knew I looked hideous at this moment. This was what forty-eight looked like. No wonder my husband was leaving me for a young broad.

"It's because of your lousy attitude toward me," he said. "You don't put anyone first but yourself. I've had it."

"Is it about the way I look? Is it not okay to look almost forty?"

"Um, Colette, you're almost fifty."

"Screw you," I yelled. If he was trading me in for a trophy wife, I had no other reason to believe it wasn't based on appearance.

"Colette, we've been nothing but roommates for a long time. I'm looking for a real partner. Someone who respects me wants to be with me, and doesn't put my needs at the bottom of the list. You put the kids, Julia, your parents, everyone ahead of me."

"That is not true."

"Of course, it is, and you know it."

"I'm not letting you do this to me and the girls," I cried, grabbing a pillow off the couch and throwing it at him. I wanted to throw something harder. I grabbed a book and hurled it at him. It hit his forehead, leaving a big red welt.

"Get control of yourself," he said. "You have no choice. I've already filed. Here are the papers." He tossed a thick envelope onto the coffee table.

"You're really leaving me for a young tramp?" I screamed. My throat burned from the intensity. I was in shock. I wanted to throw something else.

"Don't you dare call her that."

"That's what she is. A bimbo. A tramp. You're trading me in for a younger version as if I'm a used car and you're looking to upgrade to a newer model. She'll grow old, too, you know?"

"Whatever. This isn't about her age. This is about how she treats me. Just sign the papers," he yelled.

"I'll never forgive you for this, Gerrit," I seethed. "Never. You don't deserve my forgiveness. And you don't deserve the ring back, either—even if it did belong to your grandma."

He stormed out of the house. The door banged behind him. I grabbed our crystal wedding frame, which sat on the fireplace mantel, and slammed it to the floor. It shattered into a thousand pieces, as had my marriage. I sat in stunned silence, too shell-shocked to move. The hair dye dripped down my face and onto the towel around my shoulders. It could stay on forever and ruin my hair. I didn't give a fig if my hair did turn blue.

Two hours later, I dragged myself into the shower and washed my hair. The gray was gone. And so was Gerrit. I sobbed as the dirty water mixed with my acid tears. What was the point of working hard to keep my youthful appearance if my husband rejected me? He didn't want me old. He didn't want me even as I tried to stay young. He wanted a trade-in model.

Is this what happens when you get old? People reject you and dismiss you and toss you aside? I vowed to do whatever was required to look youthful for the rest of my life. Apparently, that's what would've kept my husband by my side—a young-looking wife.

· · · · · · · · · ·

## JULIA, 48

Long before the big five-oh, the Association of Mature American Citizens started mailing me membership solicitations. I waited for the next solicitation every few weeks, weighing which freebie would be the best. Did I pull the trigger on the lunch cooler, tote bag, or car gadget flashlight? It was like gambling to decide which prize to cash my chips in for. After the fourth solicitation arrived, I hit the jackpot—a picnic basket. Plus, I bought the lifetime membership option. That way, I had peace of mind knowing I would never miss out.

I would get Colette a subscription, too. However, I'd subscribe her for just a year. She'd need to take baby steps to acclimate to being a member. I wanted to give this to her as a pick-me-up after her divorce. On the weekends that Gerrit had the girls for parenting time, she spent the time at my house moping. She was entitled to her pity party after what Gerrit did. But I hated seeing her so sad. I wanted to do something to cheer her up.

"I got a gift for you," I told Colette. I flashed the red-white-and-blue plastic card in front of her.

"That's my surprise? A membership to a senior citizen's discount club? And you think that's going to make me feel better?"

I handed it to her. She wouldn't take it. She kept her arms crossed, lying sad and depressed on my couch.

"The discounts are great," I offered, smiling cheerfully.

Colette scowled. "Girl, you forget I'm willing to *pay* money to be younger," she retorted. "I'm not about to join a retirees club to save a few bucks. What AMAC needs to do is offer a discount on cosmetic surgery. Maybe I'd pay for an AMAC membership if it could save me some money for a little nip here and a little tuck there."

"There are lots of perks," I said, trying to convince her.

"The only perk I want when I turn fifty is perky boobs."

"Sorry, sweetie, when your boobs hang as low as yours, you better settle for three-dollar pancakes," I joked. It fell flat. She didn't laugh.

"Julia, is this as good as life gets?" Colette groaned. She was sullen, and her dark attitude reflected in the dark circles under her eyes. I knew she wasn't coping well with her divorce.

"If this is the peak as we approach fifty, then what the heck will old age bring when we go over the hill?" Colette sighed.

"If I can offer you some reassurance, Colette, I was reading an article in the magazine that proves life gets better as we get older."

"I don't buy it. Besides, women even peak sexually in their forties. Now my sex appeal is going to waste!" Colette cried.

"Well, the bell curve of life is a misnomer. We don't peak in midlife, and nobody can scientifically define when midlife begins or ends. The study reports that the bell curve is actually flipped upside down. Experts call it the U-curve of happiness." I pulled out the article and read it to her.

*"Happiness and life satisfaction are high in your twenties. They hit rock bottom around fifty and then rise again, surpassing the happiness you experienced in your twenties. The research is uncontested—life only gets better the older you get."*

Colette grabbed the magazine out of my hands. Her tears slowed as she absorbed the optimistic data. She continued to read it out loud.

*"The mounting evidence proves satisfaction with life increases from their early fifties into their sixties and seventies and even beyond. The emotional peak of life may not occur until well into your seventies."*

She threw the magazine back at me. "But what about sex?" she paused to ask. "I'm missing the best sex of my life."

"If it's any consolation, you won't even know what you're missing if you're not getting any," I joked—still no laughter from her.

We were at the lowest point of life based on the U-curve. Someday we'd be experiencing the best years of life and the best sex ever when we reached the incline on the happiness curve. That was good and bad news—it was still decades away.

"I want sex in my seventies."

"You used to say old people don't have sex," I said.

"We aren't old when we're seventy. Old is when we're ninety."

"I'll be sure to ask you what age old is when we're ninety. The answer might surprise you," I said. "Just because you won't keep the magazine doesn't mean AMAC won't track you down," I teased her. "Your membership card is already on its way. They will find you."

"Then I'll change my address to yours," she said. "Or better yet, I'll move to a deserted island."

"They'll still find you."

She laughed. Finally. It was good to see her smile for a change. I hoped the U-curve of happiness was true—for both our sakes.

• • • • • • • • • •

## COLETTE, 49

I sat uncomfortably on the exam table. The stiff paper "gown" barely covered me below the waist. I loathed my annual lady checkup. I refused to call it a pap smear, which sounded too vulgar. I flipped through an outdated *Journal of Gerontology* publication. Why didn't doctors' offices have better magazines?

The doctor finally walked in. He wasn't my usual doctor. This man was a heartthrob, a beautiful specimen of a creature. Tall, dark, and gorgeous. He looked like he had stepped off the cover of *GQ Magazine*.

*C'mon! Why did I have to get the young, good-looking doctor for this appointment?* I thought. I would've sprayed the land down under with perfume. Maybe I should've tried a Brazilian for once in my life.

"Hello, Colette. I'm Dr. Kwiatkowski," he said, shaking my hand briefly. "I'm a partner in this practice. Your regular doctor retired, so I'll be taking over his patients. We're doing a pap test today, correct? Is there a chance you could be pregnant?"

"Only by immaculate conception," I joked.

He smiled, flashing pearly white teeth. My goodness, it was getting hot in here. I broke out in a sweat.

"Go ahead and lie down. Move to the end of the exam table and put your feet into the stirrups."

I did what I was told. I stared at the ceiling and tried to think about anything but his gorgeous face examining my nether region.

"You'll feel a little pressure," he said, inserting the metal speculum. Why was it always so cold?

"Doctor, is something vibrating?" I asked.

He laughed. "That would be your cellphone."

"I can't exactly reach it. Could you hand it to me?"

He obliged. I answered it.

"Colette, it's your mother. I've got to talk to you right now. Where are you?"

"I'm at the gynecologist's office for my lady appointment."

"That's wonderful. Good for you," Mom chirped. I wasn't sure she heard me correctly. "You know, I should talk to your doctor about this problem your father has. Put me on speaker so I can ask him a question."

"Mother, that's a terrible idea."

"If you don't, *you'll* have to give your father an enema."

"Here's the doctor," I said, quickly putting the phone on speaker.

I would do anything to avoid giving my dad an enema. I covered the mouthpiece of the phone and whispered to the doctor. "Is it all right if you talk to my mom? She has a medical question."

He nodded. I could tell he was amused by this unconventional exam.

"Hello, doctor. Colette's father has terrible constipation, just like Colette suffers from. How do we fix his plumbing?"

"You've got to be kidding me?" I said. My cheeks turned red from embarrassment. It was bad enough having a young, handsome doctor do my lady checkup. Now my dad's bowel habits worsened the humiliation.

"Well, you could try prune juice. Lots of water. Metamucil fiber is good. If that doesn't work, then Colette may have to give him an enema."

"Thank you, doctor. And will these treatments help Colette? She also suffers from constipation."

"Yes, ma'am, they'll help her, too," Dr. Kwiatkowski said, smirking at me. I was ready to drown in a sea of humiliation.

"My bowels work just fine, Mother," I argued.

"Doctor, how is Colette doing down there? Is everything okay?" Mom asked, destroying my remaining dignity.

And then I was saved by the bell—another call ringing on my cellphone. "Mom, I've got to go. I've got a call coming in." It was Julia.

"You saved my life," I told her.

"What's up?"

"Well, my legs are for my gynecologist."

"Dang, woman, are you getting some action?" Julia pried.

"You could say that," I said. "Maybe after this, I'll get a boob-o-gram. Talk about action."

I winced as Doctor Kwiatkowski swiped inside my cervix with a swab. This must be how a pumpkin felt getting carved into a jack-o-lantern.

"The joys of reaching middle-age milestones," I lamented.

Julia laughed. "At least you don't have to cough like a man while the doctor checks the family jewels."

"I think I'd rather have the doctor man-handle my man sac than this," I said.

Realizing what I blurted out, I told the doctor, "I don't really have a scrotum."

"Yes, I can see that," he said, pulling what felt like a sixty-foot metal rod out of my six-inch lady tunnel. He looked at me like I was an idiot. He snapped the latex gloves off his hands, throwing them into the biohazard bin as if my V-J was a toxic dump.

"You can sit up," he said. "It'll take a couple of days to get results back. No news is good news, so everything is normal if you don't hear back. I want to give you some information about menopause before you leave."

"Colette, put me on speaker," Julia requested. "I want to hear what he has to say. I have a question for him."

Oh no! Not another one.

"Doctor, I'm noticing vaginal dryness. Is that normal for my age of forty-nine?" Julia asked.

"Yes, it's normal," Dr. Kwiatkowski replied. "It's perimenopause. You've probably been premenopausal for a while."

"Colette, do you suffer from dryness, too?" Julia asked inquisitively.

"I hope you're only asking about my hands," I squirmed, wanting to crawl further into the hole I was already deep within. "Why are you calling anyway?"

"I don't remember. I guess I'm having a senior moment," Julia said. "Doctor, does this mean I've got Alzheimer's?"

"Not at all. Absentmindedness is a normal part of menopause," he reassured. "Do either of you suffer from hot flashes, trouble sleeping, or mood swings yet? They're also normal symptoms of menopause."

*There's nothing normal about menopause,* I thought. As if periods, pregnancy, labor, and delivery weren't enough punishment for women. Now we get to deal with dried-out V-Js, sweating, sleeplessness, and irritability, too?

"When does the torture of menopause end?" I asked Doctor Kwiatkowski.

"On average, four years from the time the symptoms start in the perimenopausal stage until they subside postmenopause. But it varies among women," he answered. "If the irritability, hot flashes, and sleeplessness are too uncomfortable, we can try hormone therapy. But I'd rather wait and see how you do before we mess with hormones."

"What about sex?" Julia asked. "Colette isn't getting any. She's divorced. I'm married and getting plenty of good sex, but I'm worried about my libido and if sex will still feel good after menopause."

*Was she still having good sex this many years into marriage?* I wondered. I was envious.

"Vaginal dryness is very common, as well as a drop in testosterone, which affects your libido. A vaginal cream can help with dryness and make sex less painful. If your libido decreases, it can be fixed with supplements."

My mind wandered to when I got the menstrual talk from my mom—back when I started my period as a twelve-year-old, and she hugged me over the toilet and cried. She'd gushed with emotion that I had become a woman.

It was awkward—the bloody mess and her sappiness. It seemed like yesterday that we talked about this change. Yet here I was, already approaching menopause—the next change.

Nothing felt different emotionally when my period began. There was no big mental transition to make me feel like a woman. But I felt like this current one was huge. After forty years of having a menstrual cycle, it was winding down. My eggs were shriveling up, and my hormones were shutting off.

If my mom had "the talk" with me today, what would she say? "You're an old woman now"?

How come moms don't have a menopause talk with us? This was a significant change, too. I was at the end of my fertility. I felt melancholy that my reproductive years were ending. Menopause needed a handbook. And a "talk."

I suddenly started crying. It came out of nowhere and surprised me. Five minutes ago, I was laughing. It was like the flip of a switch. I felt crazy. I cried from the grief that my fertility was dying. My identity as a fertile, life-producing woman was coming to an end. This was a major life transition that I wasn't prepared for. What was my purpose if I no longer had life-bearing femininity, which was part of my existence for the last forty years? I was losing my fertility, and it would lead to changes in my sexuality. I would no longer bear children and was no longer a wife. I feared I'd feel less of a woman.

The doctor looked at me sympathetically as I cried. Julia kept asking over the phone if I was okay. I couldn't answer. I wasn't sure.

"I'll note in your chart that your symptoms are already underway. Mood swings are normal," Dr. Kwiatkowski said. "I promise when you come out of menopause, you'll be filled with a renewed vigor."

"I was prepared to handle the hot flashes and night sweats," I whimpered. "But I wasn't prepared for this emotional instability and the funeral of my fertility."

"I recommend you talk to a counselor," Dr. Kwiatkowski said. "Menopause involves mourning a loss, which no one talks about. It's a real thing you're feeling. And yet this transition is never addressed from a psychological perspective. Doctors approach it from a biological standpoint. But it's also a grieving process."

I wanted to go home and cry for the next four years until I was fully in menopause.

"Look at the upside, Colette," Julia offered cheerfully. "We'll never have another visit from Aunt Flo again for the rest of our lives! What if menopause is a metamorphosis, like coming out of our cocoons as beautiful butterflies? We're only plain caterpillars now. The molting of a caterpillar is like us shedding our uterine lining to be transformed into something greater."

"Julia, what the Sam Hill are you talking about?" I asked.

"I have no idea," she said, laughing. "I'm just giving you a pep talk to not feel so bad about menopause. It scares the crap out of me, too. I'm trying to make it less scary by inventing philosophical gibberish."

"Colette, I agree with your friend," Dr. Kwiatkowski interjected. "It's important to feel the pain of this loss and mourn the fertility you're leaving behind. But remember, all of life is a transition. Every step of the way, we're metamorphosing into something beautiful. You are young and beautiful, Colette, and you'll mature into someone even more beautiful on the other side of this change."

Dr. Kwiatkowski winked at me. My new doctor had just become my new best friend.

# Quinquagenarians

## Ages 50 – 59

## JULIA, 50

It was a monumental birthday. I was fifty! I loved being pampered on my birthday. Jack delivered me breakfast in bed—scrambled eggs, bacon, sliced melon, and a glass of fresh-squeezed mimosa. On the bed tray alongside the plate of food, he placed a single red rose and a new book to read. He jumped back into bed and ate with me.

After we picked up the food, we started to get frisky, only to be interrupted by the doorbell. Jack answered it and returned a few minutes later, bounding up the stairs. He had a delivery in hand. It was a gift box and a bouquet of pink tulips with a greeting card tucked in it. I tore the envelope open to read the birthday wishes.

*Dear Julia,*
*Nifty, nifty! Look who's fifty!*
*Let's remove fine lines with Botox to appear as quite the hot fox.*
*Botulism will be your new pal. Microderm will make you firm, gal.*
*Primping ladies at the day spa. Men will whistle ohh la la la la.*
*Enough of the rhyme. It's your time. Let's go to the spa on my dime!*
*Love, Colette*

I laughed with delight. I tore the wrapping paper off the box and pulled out a black T-shirt decorated on the front with rhinestones that spelled out *Sexy Senior*.

The phone rang. It was Colette on the other end. "Do you love your flowers?" she asked. "And your T-shirt?"

"I do love them. Thank you."

"And here's the best surprise. I'm treating you to Botox to celebrate *your* birthday," she said.

"Why do I get the feeling it's more of a gift for you?" I asked. "And don't forget it's also *your* fiftieth birthday."

"If you recall, I'm still a couple of years younger than you," Colette said. "Remember my fortieth birthday came after yours?"

"Only because you planned your party two years later. It doesn't mean you're two years younger," I protested, laughing.

"You can try to argue with me all you want, but I had a hundred people at that shindig. They'll vouch it was my fortieth birthday," she argued back.

"I've known you for fifty years, sweetie pie, and we still share the same birthday," I retorted. "When will you reset the clock to the correct year?"

"Never. Anyway, get Botox with me," she said, changing the subject. "This is for you too. I want you to be beautiful."

"I am beautiful," I argued. "I don't need Botox to prove it."

"Of course, but a little botulism can enhance your beauty. Don't you want the frown lines on your forehead and around your eyes to disappear and give your face a fuller, more radiant effect?"

"You've been reading too many advertisements for cosmetic procedures," I said.

"Okay, not my words," Colette admitted, "but I want us to drink from the fountain of youth. Let me treat you to a day at the spa. You can have done whatever you want to look beautiful for Jack."

"Jack already says I'm beautiful. He tells me that all the time."

"He's your husband. He's supposed to say that," Colette said. "Come get Botox with me. Everyone's doing it. It'll be our first time. It's like we're virgins."

"We're definitely not virgins." I laughed. "We have children to prove it. And loose vaginas."

"Please?" Colette begged.

"You sound like a teenager trying to peer pressure me."

"Maybe a little."

"I'm not interested. It goes against everything I believe in."

"Look, I'll be honest. This is all about me," she said.

"No kidding."

"You know I'm terrified of needles. With Botox, they stab you over and over with needles in your face. I need you by my side to get this done."

"You don't have to do it, you know. Plus, you don't need me."

"I do. I need your emotional support."

"Well, I can't. I have a mammogram scheduled today."

"You scheduled a boob smasher on your fiftieth birthday? What would compel you to do that?"

"Because we're supposed to start getting them when we turn fifty," I said.

"You don't need to start right on your fiftieth birthday."

"It's important to be prompt," I argued.

"Why am I not surprised you'd be so quick to get it done?"

"Well, it's an easy way to remember every two years to get a mammogram."

"On your birthday? Every two years, on your birthday, you'll have a boob-o-gram?" She asked. I could hear her roll her eyes over the phone.

"Of course. At least until I'm seventy-four, when they're no longer recommended," I said.

"Julia, you're something else. Your uptightness never ceases to amaze me."

"I'll take that as a compliment."

"So, back to Botox. Come with me. Please, please, please," she begged.

I imagined her puppy dog eyes trying to win me over as she pleaded. It was a pathetic display for a grown woman.

"I'll think about it," I said.

"So, you'll get it done with me?" she squealed.

"I said I'll think about it," I repeated.

"I'll be at the spa at noon," she said, excitedly finishing the phone call. "I better see you there. Oh, and wear your new T-shirt. I'll be wearing mine that reads *Sexy Junior*."

"Of course yours would say that because you have the world fooled that you're not a senior." I laughed and ended the call.

I showered and shaved. If I was raising my arms for a mammogram, I didn't want any armpit hairs poking out. I slipped on the *Sexy Senior* T-shirt and walked out the door, feeling proud to wear it.

After the squeezing, prodding, and pinching of the mammogram, I reluctantly drove to the day spa. I knew this was a bad idea. Colette could be very convincing, and I knew she'd try and persuade me to alter my appearance with Botox.

I parked outside the building. Colette's car was already there. She had arrived early, eager to get a taste of the fountain of youth. But I sat in my car and wrestled with the decision of whether to get Botox or not. It was five minutes to noon. I still had five minutes to weigh my fate. I knew it was a slippery slope, and I had always been determined to age naturally and with dignity. I had promised myself that and touted it all the time. I didn't necessarily want to inject poison into my skin to eliminate wrinkles for a few months.

I looked in the rearview mirror and pulled the frown lines taut to smooth out my forehead. I was curious about what my face could look like again with a youthful appearance. It felt like an angel was on one shoulder, and the devil was on the other, battling over Botox. It was a mind game. Spiritual warfare over beauty. I imagined it playing out in my head.

*Devil: "Wouldn't it be great to see your face freshened up? You'll capture a taste of youth again and remove the wrinkles that stare back at you. Just this once. To see what all the hype is about. Colette wants to treat you to this. It's an expensive birthday gift from her. It won't cost you a thing. Take advantage of it. It's a chance to look young like Colette. You will look luminous."*

*Angel: "But the treatment doesn't last, and chasing after a fleeting glimpse of youth gets expensive. And do you want to look frozen? People won't be able to tell if you're smiling or frowning. And it is poison. Why would you willingly inject poison into your body for a glance at your face without frown lines? And you'd be a hypocrite if you gave in to this. How can you encourage others to age naturally if you don't do it? Aren't you leading the charge to embrace your age? Besides, you already look luminous."*

I sat paralyzed in my car—as paralyzed as my facial muscles would be if I got the injectables. I dropped my head on the steering wheel and gripped it with my hands. I struggled with what to do. I agonized over the polarizing options. I didn't want to be a sellout, but I was curious. I could go in and allow my best friend to pamper me, or I could drive away and keep my integrity and belief system intact.

My watch chimed noon. My decision was made.

• • • • • • • • •

## COLETTE, 51

Raising teenagers was the most difficult job in the world. The trials of my daughters exerting their independence and autonomy and wanting to be adults were stressful to our relationship. Maybe that was the natural order of separation for my daughters and me to have clashed in the last couple of years. Then it would be easier to cut the apron strings when it was time for them to move to college.

It was bittersweet when Valerie, my firstborn, flew the coop and left for college. She was strong-willed. I didn't know where she got it from. I couldn't wait for her to leave home so our relationship wouldn't deteriorate in the storm of teenage drama. But then it was heart-wrenching when she did move out. She left a big hole in my home that only she could fill.

Fortunately, the loss was temporarily cushioned while I still had my younger daughter Nora at home. But then it was her turn to fly away. I never expected it would be so hard the day Nora moved to college. It was excruciating packing her up. I wanted to be stoic and handle this with a stiff upper lip. But I was a mess. I was a drama queen once again.

We emptied her room box-by-box as we loaded the car. Slowly, the life she lived in my home was fading. The only traces of her existence were dusty nightstands, bookshelves cluttered with anything but books, and a stripped-down bed. With her life packed up in the back of my car, the time came to drive her to her new life. I stood and gazed at her nearly empty room. She sat on the edge of her bed, and I saw a glimpse of her as a little girl. It broke my heart.

"Are you ready?" she asked me.

"No," I said, breaking down in tears. How can you ever be ready to let your child go? Of course, you have to, but there's no preparation for this. I wasn't ready. I would never be ready. But it was time.

Summer was winding down when we drove two hours to her new home on campus. We shared stories. We laughed and cried, reminiscing over the past. Out of the blue, with pure heartfelt emotion, she said, "I love you, Mom." They were the most beautiful four words that could ever touch my ears from my child's lips. She was feeling sentimental and wanted me to know she loved me. Despite all my faults and failures as a parent, she loved me. I couldn't have asked for a better gift in life than to hear my daughter say this with such conviction.

My sweet baby girl was all grown up now. She was beginning a new chapter and had matured into a beautiful young lady. She was starting her life as her own person, without the interception of me making decisions for her. She was free to live as she chose. As a parent, I wanted to continue protecting her from all the bad things in the world. But I knew it was no longer possible. She was paving her way and would experience all the joys and sorrows that life offered. I couldn't wait to watch her soar.

After a busy and distracting day of unpacking and setting up her dorm room, the inevitable came—the time to say goodbye. I knew it wasn't death's permanent goodbye, but it was goodbye to the life we had shared for eighteen years. The life we lived together was ending. We were physically detaching from each other. It felt like death.

When she was in kindergarten, I remember her clinging to my leg, crying because she didn't want to let go of me to start school. Today, I was the one clinging to her. Age changed our vantage point so dramatically in life. There was so much I wanted to say to her.

"If I had to do it all over again, I wouldn't make you eat zucchini and asparagus when you were eight," I said, laughing through tears as we embraced in a hug outside her dorm.

"You were just trying to be a good mom," she replied.

"Why didn't I just give you carrots, which you preferred, instead of the greens you hated? I wanted you to grow up to be healthy. I wanted the very best for you."

She smiled. "Mom, you did give me the best."

She walked me back to my car. We gripped each other in one last tender hug, tears pouring down our cheeks. She stepped away from the car, and I reluctantly drove away. I watched her wave through my rearview mirror.

I began the long drive home alone. The passenger seat, where Nora had sat a few hours earlier, was now empty. I had dropped my baby girl off to college. It was heart-wrenching to drive home without her.

Julia called me on my way back to check on my emotional state. She knew I wouldn't be holding up well.

"Be thankful. She's just two hours away," she encouraged. I sniffled back the tears, listening to her attempts to cheer me up.

"It doesn't matter whether she's two hours away or two-hundred hours away," I said. "The hole in my home and heart is the same. Neither daughter is going to be there to fill it."

The tears came pouring out. Nora wouldn't be sleeping in her bed any longer for me to watch over her. I would never be able to kiss my little girl goodnight, share stories over dinner, or watch TV reruns together. There would be a gaping hole that the short distance of "just two hours" couldn't fill.

When I got home, I grabbed a piece of paper and a pen and wrote Nora a letter. I wanted to tell her again how much I loved her, how proud she made me, and how beautiful she was. I hoped I had told her this enough in her lifetime. How do we know if we've done enough for our kids?

*Dear Nora,*

*You are so dear to me. As expected, the tears overwhelmed me on the drive home as I left you behind. I thought about all the ways I was a good parent, and naturally, I thought of the ways I missed the mark. I'm sorry for all the ways I failed you. There wasn't a custom handbook on parenting you. I promise I did the best I could with the resources and knowledge I had at the time. I wish I could turn back the clock and start over. I'd savor the time with you more and be fully present for you.*

*I wish I had done things differently when you were a child. I would've given you more hugs and kisses before bedtime, even when you were a teenager. I would've spoiled you with more trips for ice cream, painting your nails, and feeding you your favorite cereal for dinner. I would've given you an extra fifteen*

*minutes to stay up at bedtime "just because." Maybe that's what grandparent-*
*ing is for—spoiling our grandkids silly and a chance to redo parenting with*
*only love and without discipline. I can't believe you're in college already. I feel*
*like it was just my turn. I don't know where the time went. It goes so fast. I wish*
*I could hold on to you longer and slow down life. But I can't. I can only hope to*
*do as my old school principal once told me—it sounded so stupid then—to "stop*
*and smell the roses." Nora, take time to smell the roses.*

*I love you, Mom*

I sat on Nora's bed and sobbed. I said goodbye and good luck to my second
child. I was a true empty-nester now. My life and house sat empty. My mind
drifted to the things I said I couldn't wait to do once my daughters were
grown and out of the house. Suddenly this list seemed less important. I had
done my job as a parent. I had successfully raised my kids not to be criminals,
or other deplorable things whispered about in social circles. They would be
happy, healthy, functioning members of society, despite my flaws as a human
being in raising them.

I looked around my small, quaint home. It now felt big and cold without
my girls to fill it. The silence was deafening. I yearned to hear the sounds of
their laughter or even their arguments with each other.

I had raised them, and my role as a mother was waning. I was transitioning
into a new type of parenting role. Yet my life would be filled with new
opportunities. Wasn't that the benefit of being an empty-nester—to live life
the way I wanted, without the restrictions of caring for children? I knew this
was what people looked forward to in middle age—their kids flying the coop,
so everyone gained freedom—but sitting in an empty nest as the mother hen
felt like I had lost my purpose. What was my purpose now that my children
were raised? For the past two decades, that's what I had come to master. I was
no longer the domestic manager of their lives. I had been laid off from the
job.

It had been eighteen years since I first held Nora and twenty since I first
held Valerie when they were newborn babies. They were adults living their
own lives now. My little girls were all grown up, which meant I, too, had
moved just as quickly along the timeline of life from young parent to midlif-
er.

As a middle-aged, divorced woman, I had to figure out what would come next in this stage of life. The parenting chapter had closed. What chapter followed? I tried to imagine what was ahead, and my future was clouded with fear, sadness, hope, and anticipation. It was a mixed brew of emotions. Who was I now? What was next for me? I had no idea.

Struggling with the uncertainty of what my new purpose and role would be, I cried myself to sleep on Nora's bed. I was lost on this new path of life. What shoes would I fill?

* • • • • • • • • •

### Julia, 54

"My husband is going through a midlife crisis," I lamented to Colette. "And I'm not sure where Jack's going to land after he's arrived."

She had met me for a glass of wine during happy hour at a local winery. I needed to talk through my concerns with her.

"What's going on?" Colette asked.

"Jack came home with a wild new haircut last month," I explained. "Then he grew a beard. He let the hair grow more each day until the gray wires filled his face. I told him I refused to kiss him until he shaved it off."

"What was his response?"

"He said it was a fair trade."

"He was joking, right?" Colette asked.

"Of course," I said. "But then he went shopping and bought himself a new wardrobe, including new boxers."

"Oh boy! When your spouse starts buying new underwear, they're having an affair," Colette said.

"Today, he pulled into the driveway with a brand-new sports car. A convertible, mind you," I went on.

"What color?" Colette asked.

"Why does it matter?"

"It's very telling."

"Candy-apple red," I said. She cringed at the answer.

"Julia, you're in trouble," Colette warned. "If he's looking to shack up, this certainly would be a way to attract younger, more attractive women. Trust me, I know from my cheating ex-dog."

"My husband's not cheating on me," I defended.

"Julia, he started buying new underwear," she said, raising an eyebrow. "That's suspect."

"I refuse to believe he's cheating on me. That's not Jack. You're just jaded because of Gerrit."

"Maybe. But, Julia, you need to take control of your marriage before he ends up on that path. Marriage can grow stagnant in midlife. You need to fight back," Colette urged.

"By purchasing more expensive jewelry for myself and showing him up?"

"No, I don't mean fight *him*. I mean, take control of his affections," Colette suggested. "Don't fight fire with fire. Become the fire. You need to sizzle."

The wine was obviously affecting her.

"How?" I asked.

"You aren't going to like what I have to say," she said.

"You're still my best friend after fifty-four years," I reminded her. "You can tell me anything."

"Julia, you've let yourself go," Colette said carefully. "You aren't the eye candy he wants. Men are visual creatures. They want a woman who looks young and fresh and cares for her appearance."

"But I...I..." I stammered.

Colette talked over me, drowning out what I had to say. "You don't wear makeup. You don't color your hair to cover up the gray."

"So what? What's wrong with natural?" I said defensively, my voice starting to rise.

"Well, why don't you ask your wandering husband?" Colette answered.

"He's *not* having an affair," I insisted. "He wouldn't do that to me just because I don't look like the version of myself he married years ago."

"It's not just about appearances, Julia. You need to dig deeper to decide if you're presenting yourself in the most beautiful way on the inside too. Marriage gets dry and boring when you've been with the same person for years like you've been with Jack. You need to spice things up."

"By sprinkling some cinnamon on my buns?" I joked, trying to lighten the mood. I knew this could turn into an argument, and Colette wasn't the one this battle was with.

"I've got a better idea," she said. "You know that shiny new convertible he just bought?"

"Yes."

"You need to use it to your advantage."

"How?"

"Have a photo shoot with it," she said.

"I need to take pictures of his new car?" I asked, perplexed.

"No, silly, you need to be *in* the pictures—naked on that shiny new car," she clarified. "A *boudoir* photo shoot."

I laughed so hard at the suggestion that wine sprayed out of my mouth. It was the most ridiculous idea I'd ever heard. "Colette, I'm fifty-four years old. I'm too old to do nudie photos."

"That's exactly what I'm talking about, Julia. You act too old to have fun. Jack probably feels it, too, so he's looking for fun elsewhere. You can still have fun in your fifties, you know?"

"But I'm too old for *that*."

"For Pete's sake, you sound like your mother!" she exclaimed. "You're only as old as you want to tell yourself. It would be freeing to let your inner sexuality explode out of you. You've been the prim-and-proper girl your whole life. Your sexy body is buried underneath those frumpy beige clothes."

I looked at my outfit. She was right. They were frumpy. And they were beige.

"You've got to revolutionize yourself. Fifty is the new thirty, sweetie," she continued.

"I'm willing to bet no thirty-year-old would agree. Thirty-somethings wouldn't hesitate to say we're not in their age bracket," I disputed.

"My point is, my inner age says I'm thirty," she said. "What's your inner age say? How old do you feel on the inside? Not the age the calendar says you are."

"Then my inner age is also fifty-four."

"It doesn't have to be. You can feel younger if you don't act your age."

"Not your shoe size?" I bantered.

Colette ignored my attempt at humor. "Age is just a silly number on some chronological timeframe. And studies show if you perceive yourself as old, you may age worse."

"How would you know that?" I asked. I had read the research data but was shocked she would know this.

"I read it in a journal on aging at my last doctor's appointment," she said. "Take my word for it. Negative thoughts on aging lead to growing older faster."

"You sound like me. Except I've never had negative thoughts about aging. That's your department," I reminded her.

"Well, maybe I'm getting wiser with age."

"So, if Jack is cheating on me, is it because I'm too old?" I asked.

"You're not too old for him. Remember, he's fifteen years your senior. Your wrinkles, gray hair, and old attitude are the problem for him."

"That's nonsense. He loves me for who I am."

"He'll love you more if you live to the full potential of who you could be," Colette explained. "Do the photos. Be a heartthrob, and make his heart skip a beat."

"If I do them, they're for his eyes only. I won't let you see them."

"Honey, we've got the same girl parts," she chided. "I've got what you've got, except less cellulite."

Two weeks later, a professional photographer set up a makeshift studio in our garage to take photos of me with Jack's red sports car.

Colette did my hair and makeup, per her demand. I was trembling like a virgin schoolgirl like the first time a boy tried getting to second base with me. I felt so unprepared. I had no idea what I was supposed to do. I wasn't sure if this photographer would go farther than I wanted with the poses. If he did, I'd slap his hand away like the boy who tried getting to third base with me back in the day.

I drank a glass of wine while Colette finished up. And then I made her leave. Terrified, I clutched my robe, hugging it tightly around my naked body as I walked out into the garage. What was I so afraid of—my inner beauty or the embarrassment that the pictures would show how awful I looked at fifty-four?

"Julia, I'm ready for you," the photographer said, making final adjustments to his camera lens.

"I think I need another glass of wine to relax," I said. I took a deep breath, feeling myself break out in a hot flash. I ran back into the house and poured another glass of wine. I drank it in one endless swig, then returned to the mock studio.

"Drop your robe, Julia," the photographer commanded.

I did as he said. I stood bare naked, except for the sleazy stilettos laced up my ankles. They were the tallest shoes I'd ever worn. I hobbled to walk in them. I felt dizzy. I wasn't sure if it was the heels, my nerves, or the wine. Eventually, a warm, relaxed feeling overtook my body from the effects of the alcohol. I had become at ease and comfortable with the discreetness of the session. The photographer kept it completely professional and helped me pose for the camera.

After the shoot, he uploaded the images onto a computer to show me the results. I was shocked and ecstatic with how beautiful the photos came out. I didn't know I could look so seductive sprawled out wearing candy-apple red lipstick the same color as the car. I didn't know I had it in me at this age to be hot and steamy. The photos were racy. But I don't kiss and tell. They're for my eyes only. And Jack's

"We can edit the photos if you like, to remove any imperfections," the photographer offered. "I can do some trick photography with a little nip here and tuck there."

I looked closer at the imperfections he referred to—my "cottage cheese" thighs, the dimples in my rear end, and the scar across my belly from a C-section. It's not often we get a full view of our own naked body other than a glance in the mirror. The photos perfectly captured my imperfect sensuality. I couldn't believe that I still had this in me. Sometimes I felt so much older than I looked. Colette was right. I had aged myself with my attitude. Through these photos, I saw that I still had sex appeal.

"We can make all those wrinkles and signs of an aging body vanish with a few touch-ups," the photographer said.

"Not a chance," I declared. "Mid-fifty is fab. This is what fifty-four looks like, and I'm not going to hide it."

I had one of the photos printed in a huge size and framed for Jack's birthday.

Jack suggested we order takeout and stay home for his birthday. That would be perfect. I couldn't exactly bring his birthday gift to a restaurant. I'd get arrested for indecent exposure.

After we ate, I needed reassurance that he wasn't cheating before I gave him his gift.

"My darling Julia, I bought the underwear and improved my appearance for you so that you wouldn't grow tired of me," he said, kissing away all my insecurities. "I bought the car for us to have fun in life."

I shouldn't have let Colette put doubts in my head. I felt ashamed for even questioning Jack's love for me. It gave me the confidence to provide him with his risqué present. I pulled out the gift-wrapped box tied with a giant red bow. My hands were shaking. Why was I so nervous to give it to my husband? It's not like he hadn't seen me naked over the last two decades of our marriage.

"How about we eat dessert before I unwrap presents?" he suggested.

"Sure, but this gift *is* dessert," I countered.

"All right, let me eat up then." He laughed, pulling me onto his lap and covering my neck in tender kisses.

Jack slowly unwrapped the package. When he saw my naked body spread out seductively across the hood of his sports car, he gripped his chest.

"Julia, call an ambulance," he said.

"Does my naked body really have that kind of effect on you?" I asked in surprise. He was certainly doing a good job acting enthusiastically in response to my nudity.

"No, I think—I'm having—a heart attack." Jack gulped, gasping for air.

He wasn't kidding. I grabbed the phone and called 911. I guess my nude photo really did cause his heart to skip a beat.

• • • • • • • • •

## COLETTE, 55

I pulled an all-nighter, which meant I hadn't gotten up once in the night to pee. But I woke abruptly in a puddle of liquid and panicked. Had I wet the bed? It couldn't be pee. The moisture drenched me from head to toe. I examined my nightgown and the sheets. It was perspiration. Night sweats gave new meaning to sleeping in a water bed. Being unclean repulsed me. After decades of bleeding, I was now subjected to this? *Will I ever feel fresh in life?* I wondered. I showered to rinse the slimy dew from my skin, then washed the soggy sheets.

During perimenopause, the sweat dripped out of my pores. Calling them hot flashes was a joke. Why weren't they named perpetual flames? Nobody warned me what a hot flash really was. But this was not just hot. This was as scorching as the Sahara Desert. It could be frigid outside, and I would still shed layers trying to regulate my broken internal thermometer.

To keep cool and prevent hyperthermia from invading my body, I stripped off my clothes at home and walked around the house naked. I pressed my bare body against the cold sliding glass door to cool down. I welcomed the relief. But my neighbors across the yard shut their curtains. I guess they didn't enjoy the relief as much as I did.

I was a middle-aged divorcee with extended menopause. It was a trifecta for needing some kind of therapy. Maybe retail therapy. I could buy a new pair of shoes. Or I could start marital counseling. Clearly, I didn't have a husband, but the counselor could advise me on how to find one. I was a lonely woman with no one to electrify with these thermal power surges. I opted to shop for both shoes and men. I would start dating men that were younger than me. I was still hot, even if it was just from the hot flashes. I could sizzle things up with my heat alone.

I called my gynecologist, Dr. Kwiatkowski, and asked him out. He was thirty-five and knew his way around a woman's body. He was a gynecologist, after all. I was fifty-five, but the age difference wasn't nearly as big a stretch as my stretch marks. He would have to squint hard not to see the age difference or my wrinkles.

I justified that a twenty-year gap was no big deal. But he might disagree. So I didn't call it a date. I asked him if he could meet for coffee. He suggested the hospital cafeteria. I told him I had some questions about hormonal changes. I tried to flirt, but it fell flat. He gave me pamphlets on battling the symptoms of menopause. Was I losing my touch with men because of my age?

I kept asking him out for conversation over coffee. He kept bringing me brochures—literature on colonoscopies and hysterectomies. I wanted to give him one on lobotomies. Didn't his brain recognize that I was attracted to him? I enjoyed being a cougar, except he didn't even go to first base with me. I would have to continue being the prowess, enjoying the hunt to snag a buck twenty years younger.

"I'm going out with Dr. K again," I told Julia.

"Does he have a first name?"

"I'm sure he does. But I like to refer to him as a doctor."

"Does he ever ask you out, or are you doing all the lifting?" Julia asked.

"I think he knows I'm a modern woman, and he's happy to have me plan the meetup."

"Meetup? So, it's not a date?"

"Not officially. I think he's slow to get in the sack," I explained.

"Colette, I'm not sure he's dating you," Julia said.

"Preposterous. How could he not date a forty-something sex-kitten like me?"

"Because you're not forty-something," she said. "Plus, he's never asked you out or kissed you. He gives you brochures on medical treatments."

"That's all speculation," I said.

"Where do you meet for coffee?"

"In the hospital cafeteria."

"Colette, you're a lost cause. You're not his sex-kitten. You're his patient."

I improved my game each time Dr. K and I had a meetup. I wore miniskirts that hiked farther up. And shirts that fell farther down. But he didn't catch the bait I was casting. I was afraid my sex appeal wasn't so appealing. It made me want to try harder.

My daughter Valerie started dating a man while I was meet-upping with Dr. K. She was twenty-five, and he was ten years older. So we had some common ground on age-gap dating. I felt like a schoolgirl when we compared our relationships. Whether in your twenties or fifties, dating still creates the same captivating electricity. I loved feeling the magnetic pull of having a man desire me. Valerie said the same. Love is universal and doesn't discriminate based on age.

After a few weeks, Valerie wanted me to meet her beau. Things were getting serious. We made plans to have dinner so I could meet her knight in shining armor. She had been tight-lipped on sharing too much information. She wanted to know things were serious before she started telling her family about him.

"I think I'm falling in love," Valerie gushed. "He's perfect, and I can't wait to introduce you."

"I'm so happy for you," I said, smiling at my beautiful daughter. "But I think it's about time we have the sex talk."

"Mother, I'm twenty-five years old. It's a bit late to pull out the birds-and-bees manual," she said. "Besides, I think we should be having a raw conversation about you dating a much younger man."

*When did my daughter get old enough to start parenting me?* I wondered.

"He's young enough to be your kid," Valerie said.

"How dare you insult me?" I shrieked in feigned dismay. "I'm not *that* old."

"Don't you think it's outrageous to be dating a guy twenty years your junior? He's so young I could be dating him."

"If he ever asks, I plan to tell him I'm forty," I said.

"Isn't he your doctor? He knows your real age."

I ignored her assumption. We spent the next hour talking like love-struck teenagers, waiting for her dream date to arrive.

"Here he comes," Valerie said excitedly, jumping from her chair.

I turned to meet Valerie's dream man. He just happened to be mine, too.

"Dr. Kwiatkowski!" both of us exclaimed in unison. I lost out to a younger woman once again.

• • • • • • • • • •

## JULIA, 56

Colette once warned me that by marrying a much older man, I would play a nursemaid to him someday. I didn't care at the time. It didn't matter. I hadn't understood what that meant—what it *really* meant. But now I understood. I had been caring for Jack for two years since his heart attack, followed shortly by a stroke. From that day on, he constantly battled with health problems, filling my calendar with appointments and therapies. He lost the use of his right arm and right leg. They were paralyzed as a result of the stroke.

Due to the demands of his continuous needs, I became a full-time caregiver to Jack. It was a journey that catapulted me into depression. Two years after that fateful day, I felt the heavy weight of stress and burden in my role.

In all my years working in long-term care, I saw the stress families experienced caring for their loved ones. I had even counseled Colette. I didn't know it would feel so suffocating. Now that I was a caregiver, I had greater empathy for anyone caring for a loved one. It's a hard job, and I felt so ill-equipped, even with all my professional development.

I was slowly losing my own identity in caring for his well-being. I took on the role of a pharmacist dispensing meds, a chauffeur driving him to appointments, a physical therapist exercising his limbs, and many other functions and duties. The depression overwhelmed me at times. I hated this new reality. I spent my days counting pills, scheduling doctor's appointments, and doing a hundred other tasks to keep him alive and well. Then I felt guilty for feeling resentful. I loved him dearly, but secretly and selfishly, there were moments I wished he would pass. The guilt for even thinking such a horrific thing ate me up inside. What kind of a wretched wife was I for wanting him to die? I sobbed so loudly in the quiet of the night; my body convulsed with exhaustion from my life as a caregiver and the horrendous guilt I felt in being honest.

I did things I never would've imagined doing for my husband. I had to cut foods into baby bite-sized pieces so he wouldn't choke. Eventually, I pureed every meal. I helped him to the bathroom with the aid of his walker. I lowered him to squat on the toilet seat and stepped out to give him privacy and keep his pride intact. Eventually, I changed a catheter daily. He lost all dignity when I wiped him after he used the toilet. I saw humiliation reflect in his eyes.

When he was ready for bed, I undressed him. I methodically lifted his shirt over his head, slipped one arm out at a time, removed his pants, pulled off his socks, and fitted him into his adult diaper. In the morning, the routine repeated itself. It was a daunting job. It was tiring and never-ending. I didn't want his life to be over. I just wanted his humiliating suffering and the bone-tiring duties to be over. I had to face the reality that he wouldn't improve but would continue declining.

It was terrible watching the light burn out in Jack as he moved closer to death. Then the day came when I called in hospice. I knew hospice care didn't always mean the end. Instead, it meant a higher quality of life for what life remained. It wasn't a service for when nothing more could be done. Rather, it provided relief and support for the family and peace and comfort for the patient during the dying process.

Isn't that what life was, after all? A slow, dying process. From the day we are born, we're one step closer to our dying day. It's a mistake to think that death and dying begin somewhere late in life. It begins on day one of life.

With each day that passed, Jack's life energy dimmed. I saw him fade before my eyes. And as he faded, my strength and resolve wilted, too. I felt like I was dying along with him. It was so hard. And so sad. I hated myself for pitying my circumstances. My emotions competed between love and turmoil.

"Would you get me some applesauce?" Jack asked one day, his voice weak and his words slurred.

I smiled tenderly at him. "Of course," I said.

In an act of love, I poured applesauce into a glass bowl and began feeding him small spoonfuls. He couldn't open his mouth completely, so drips of applesauce spilled onto his chin. I leaned over and gave him a soft kiss on his lips. In moments like this, the hardship of caregiving vanished and was replaced with sacrificial love. This is what the vows of marriage consisted of devotion, commitment, and serving. This is what it meant to grow old with someone—to spoon-feed them applesauce when they were incapacitated.

"Will you show me your birthday picture again?" He mumbled. A faint sparkle appeared in his eyes.

"Oh dear, it gave you a heart attack once before. I don't want that to happen again," I teased.

"That will only put you out of your misery," he said sadly.

"I'm here for the duration, as promised on our wedding day." I took his frail hand in mine and kissed it. "Till death do us part, and not a moment sooner."

"I was supposed to be feeding *you* applesauce," he said wistfully. "I promised when you became an old lady and needed someone to feed you applesauce that I would be the one spooning it into your mouth."

"Well, then, here's your chance," I said.

I placed the spoon in Jack's hand and guided it into the applesauce. With a trembling hand, he scooped a spoonful of it, then lifted it to my mouth to feed me the applesauce. He had kept his promise from twenty years ago.

I adored this man. It crushed my heart to think we wouldn't grow old together. We cried together, our salty tears blending into one stream.

That was the first and last time we spoon-fed each other applesauce. Jack died a week later. I realized all the agony of caring for him had been worth every minute in exchange for the blessing of being able to love someone so unconditionally. It was the saddest day of my life when he left me. And I would have given anything—even the most brutal days of caregiving—to get him back so we could spoon-feed each other applesauce again.

In the grief of Jack's death, I forgot the suffering of caregiving. It was replaced with a deep sense of honor that I had been able to care for him. It's the greatest act of love—to serve one another.

· · · · · · · · · ·

## COLETTE, 57

"You're going to be a grandma," Valerie squealed, handing me a pregnancy test with double pink lines.

"But you're not even married."

"Oh, Mom, don't be so old-fashioned. You don't have to be married to have a baby."

She and Dr. K still hadn't tied the knot, though he had proposed with an obnoxiously large diamond ring. I quickly overcame the humiliation of having a crush on her boyfriend and embraced him like a son.

I was overflowing with joy at Valerie's news. It was greater than joy. To say I was enthusiastic was an understatement. There were important things to do to prepare for the baby's arrival, like deciding on my nickname. I refused to be called Grandma. I could get on board with Mimi. It was French for "cute and adorable." Then I discovered it was Biblical for "sea of bitterness or sorrow." That was depressing. So I landed on Nana, which meant "grace" in Hebrew. Perfect for me!

Then I had to plan a shower. I wanted to celebrate with everyone I knew and boast about my soon-to-be grandchild. Isn't that what all grandparents do—brag?

"You've got to be kidding me!" Valerie exclaimed as she came storming into my house. My party plans didn't go over so well with her.

"Hello to you, too," I said. "You shouldn't get so worked up, for the baby's sake."

"Mom, you can't throw *yourself* a baby shower for *my* baby," she declared.

"But I'm not. I'm throwing myself a *grandbaby* shower. There's a difference."

"You need to cancel this. It's ridiculous."

"I can't. The invitations have already gone out in the mail."

"No kidding," she said. "How do you think I learned about it? I got my invitation today. I'm not coming to this hogwash of a party." She threw the invitation in the garbage.

"Oh, honey, you're hormonal from the pregnancy," I soothed. "You have to be there. Besides, this is all about you."

"No, it's about you."

"Maybe a little," I admitted. "But can I help it? I'm going to be a Nana. I want to celebrate."

"Then celebrate at *my* baby shower."

"I'll do that, too," I assured her.

"You're still going ahead with this ridiculous grandbaby shower?"

"I have to. I've already registered," I said.

"You registered yourself for baby gifts?" Valerie huffed in exasperation.

"I want to make sure I've got everything I need to be the best Nana to this little bundle of love," I said, rubbing her protruding belly. "I want the baby to know I'm the best grandparent in the world."

*Gerrit doesn't deserve to be the favored grandparent,* I thought sourly.

"Do you understand how obnoxious this is?" Valerie asked.

"Of course," I said. "But there's nothing ordinary about being a first-time grandmother. It's the most exciting event in the world. You don't understand now, but you will when you become a grandma."

"You can't throw yourself a baby shower," she demanded again.

"I'm not. I'm throwing a grandbaby shower." She still didn't seem to understand the difference.

"You're hopeless," Valerie said.

"That is true," I conceded. "Will you be there?"

"Do I have a choice? You're throwing yourself a baby shower for my baby."

I planned an over-the-top celebration, and as promised, Valerie was there. How could she not be? We always got over our disputes and carried on. She was a lot like me. It was what allowed our family's dysfunction to function so well.

The party went off beautifully. And other grandmas-to-be decided to hold grandbaby showers, too. They loved the idea. I was an influencer. We had done our time as parents. Now it was time to relish in the joy as grandparents.

My friends spoiled me with gifts. They outdid themselves by buying a crib for all the sleepovers at my house, a baby monitor to watch the baby sleep, and even bubble wrap to tape around the furniture. That was supposed to be a gag gift. I thought it was a brilliant idea.

I wanted a security system for my home to ensure no one would break in and kidnap my grandchild. But I didn't get that. The baby superstore didn't sell a home security system. I found it a missed opportunity for the retailer to cash in on the over-protectiveness and paranoia of first-time grandparents. I was an obsessed Nana, and the precious little bundle hadn't yet arrived. But my house was bubble-wrapped and ready.

At the end of Valerie's pregnancy, when she called to tell me she was in labor at the hospital, I became frantic. It was 3:00 in the morning, but I was going to the hospital to wait no matter what time it was. I hurried to put on my *World's Best Nana* T-shirt over my nightgown. Realizing I had procrastinated putting cautionary signs on my car, I raced to the garage. I scurried to screw my new license plate cover sign—*Let Me Tell You About My Grandchildren*—on the front. Then I stuck four window decals that read, *Baby on Board. Back Off* on each side of my car.

I drove like a mad woman to the hospital. Only when I reached the OB department did I realize my shirt was on backward and inside out, and I had forgotten to change out of my slippers. I was too pumped with adrenaline to care.

I paced the halls for the next six hours in my fluffy pink slippers. I wanted to be wide awake when Dr. K came to get me. Finally, at dawn, he showed up in the family waiting room.

"It's a girl!" he exclaimed, giving me a huge hug.

I broke down crying. I was overcome with a profound sense of happiness. I entered Valerie's room and heard my newborn grandbaby's feeble cry. She was precious. I was smitten. It was love at first sight.

"Mom, meet Taylor, your granddaughter," Valerie said. I took Taylor in my arms and marveled.

"This is the most exhilarating thing I've ever experienced," I said, inspecting her tiny toes and fingers.

Holding my first grandchild was a heavenly experience. The overwhelming love I felt for her radiated out of my heart and poured into her. It was better than I had ever dreamt.

"Even better than holding me the first time?" Valerie asked.

"It's a different type of love. It's pure magic having this grandchild to adore," I answered. "I feel like my whole life has been leading up to this moment. I hope you'll be rewarded with the title of grandmother someday. It's a love you won't want to miss. And it's a love you won't understand until you become a grandparent."

My outlook on life went from good to grand with the birth of this baby. That's why the word grandparenting exists. I didn't think life could get any better than it was at this moment. The unconditional love for a grandchild was beyond explanation.

I had now been inaugurated into the grandparents' club. It's an exclusive group you can only join when you become a grandparent because you suddenly realize the elite status you hold as a grandparent.

Two days later, Valerie and Taylor were ready to go home. I insisted on driving them. I would be a watchdog, a security guard, a militant to protect and serve my granddaughter.

"Tell Dr. K I'll be driving you both home," I said.

"He's my husband," Valerie replied. "First, he has a name. Secondly, he can drive us."

"I insist."

"Mom, we can drive ourselves home," Valerie argued. "We have it under control."

"But the roads aren't safe out there. There are lots of crazy drivers."

"Yes, from what I hear, you're one of them."

"Nonsense. Everything you heard about the incident at the ice cream parlor is based on urban legend. Besides, it was Julia who crashed the car, not me. I won't take no for an answer. There's precious cargo on board. My car is bigger and safer."

"Mom, that's ridiculous."

"Nothing is ridiculous when it comes to the ultimate safety of my grandchild," I declared. "Just meet me in front of the hospital, and I'll get you both securely home. I will not let you win this argument."

"Fine, Mom," Valerie said, giving up the fight.

I made the valet attendant snap at least forty pictures from every angle: putting the baby in the car seat, strapping her into the car, closing the door, and waving through the window. I wouldn't let a single moment of this precious child's life go undocumented.

I drove the slowest I'd ever driven in my life. I wasn't taking any chances.

Cars honked around me. I flipped them off. I was not going to drive the speed limit and endanger my granddaughter—the most extraordinary angel the world had ever known.

"Can't you read the signs on the car, you ass? I have a baby on board!" I yelled out the window. "Going thirty-five miles an hour is too dangerous for a newborn, you know?"

"Language, Mom, the baby can hear you," Valerie reminded.

"Of course. I'm so sorry. I'll never swear again. Never, dammit."

I drove home with the sense that I was floating on clouds. I already loved everything about being Nana. My daughter wouldn't have to lift a finger with me always nearby, closely watching over her shoulders, giving her countless pieces of advice on parenting. Oh, how she was going to love my involvement. But at least I wasn't overbearing like my mom was.

It was the most marvelous day of my life. Too bad we couldn't become grandmothers in our twenties.

• • • • • • • • •

**JULIA, 59**

I had my annual routine checkup with my geriatrician. Geriatricians are very specialized in the field of aging, but there's a shortage of them, and they're not easy to find. When mine opened his new practice, I jumped quickly to be one of his first patients. I was well beyond menopause. Yet I felt I had a laundry list of issues affecting me. I brought my checklist of concerns:

- *Urine leaking when I laughed or coughed*

- *Thinning hair*

- *Yellowing teeth*

- *Hemorrhoids*

The geriatrician recommended:

- *Kegel exercises*

- *Collagen*

- *Baking soda toothpaste*

- *Preparation H*

"Let's talk about scheduling a colonoscopy," he suggested. "You're overdue for one. Once you've had your first, assuming it's normal, you won't need to do it again for another ten years."

It bothered me that I was late to get it. I wasn't late for anything. How did I miss this?

"But I don't have a history of colorectal cancer in my family," I said, trying to reassure myself.

"Eighty-five percent of people who develop colorectal cancer also don't have it in their family history," he explained. "It's important to get a colonoscopy. The risk of developing this type of cancer increases with age."

"Well, I do want to be alive to watch my granddaughter Ayden grow up, so I should get it done," I agreed.

Carolann and her husband had just had a precious daughter. I'd finally joined the grandparents' club with Colette and wanted to stay healthy for my new grandchild. I'd do everything necessary to have a long life with my family.

"It requires a bit of...well, let's just say, *prep* work," my doctor said. "I'm going to refer you to a gastroenterologist. He's better prepared to help you get through the, uh, bathroom experience."

*What did he mean by bathroom experience?* I wondered.

I met with the gastroenterologist, who warned me the prep might be uncomfortable. He gave me two bottles of liquids to drink and a pamphlet to review. The people modeling on the brochure were smiling. One couple was riding a tandem bike together. Another was playing tennis. They all looked happy, so whatever the bathroom experience was, they certainly weren't affected by it. It didn't look so terrible based on how active they were.

I started my prep to cleanse my colon the day before the scheduled procedure. I drank the first liter of magnesium citrate, which could only be described as Colon Drano. It was a clear liquid that pushed out any food I ate back in the fourth grade in about thirty seconds. The package cautioned, *May cause loose, watery stools.* I found the word stools to be misleading. Instead, the box should've read, *May cause loose water.* I could've used a life jacket while on the toilet.

As for the brochure cautioning it might be uncomfortable. Giving birth without an epidural was uncomfortable. This, on the other hand, was like being hung upside down by a coat hanger from my colon, dangling five feet from the pits of hell.

The pamphlet also merely suggested to wear loose-fitting clothing and stay near the bathroom. I didn't believe it until I filled my pants the first time. Why didn't they *warn* me to wear loose-fitting clothing and stay near the bathroom? The pamphlet made it seem optional. After the accident, I stayed in the bathroom the rest of the day. And, just when I thought I was done with the cleanse, I had to drink another gallon of Colon Drano.

Mama offered to stay with me, but I refused her help. I thought she was fussing for nothing. But now, I could've used her help. She could've wiped my burning bottom with moisturizing baby wipes and coated it with baby powder like when I was an infant.

I swallowed another gallon of the bowel poison and a shot of vodka to chase it down. It was clear, after all. The doctor said I had to avoid beverages that had red or blue dye. He didn't say anything about clear vodka. Besides, I found it helpful to numb the flames combusting from my derrière.

I was allowed to consume clear liquids, like broth, but I was terrified that anything I put in my mouth would come back out in more liquid form than it went in. I collapsed in bed, exhausted from the intestinal aerobic workout of losing fifteen pounds in a single day.

The next day Mama drove me to the procedure. I hoped any residual loose water wouldn't accidentally spill from me. I had already thrown one set of unsalvageable clothes away. I didn't want to blow out another.

My nerves were wrecked going into the procedure. I knew it would be invasive when a tube the length of the Great Wall of China got inserted into my pipes. The reward for this kind of preventative healthcare was I got knocked out. The sedation put me to sleep, and I enjoyed a midday nap. I recovered the next day.

"How'd it go?" Colette asked after the procedure. "You know I'm scheduled, and if you say it was bad, it might deter me."

Colette had tried calling to check on me during the prep phase, but I didn't answer. I was too distracted by the bombs detonating in my intestines to give heed to her trivial conversation. Nor did I want her to witness the live bathroom concert.

"Let's just say you wouldn't wish this upon your worst enemy—even Gerrit," I joked.

Colette groaned. "That bad?"

After working through the emotional trauma of pooping my pants as an adult, I'm happy to report that my plumbing came back clean as a hog's casing used for bratwurst. I was proud of my intestines for representing me well. The clean bill of health meant I wouldn't undergo this war again for another ten years.

Funny how the markers of life during this phase of life changed to be preventative medical procedures. It was odd to think the next time I'd get my reminder postcard in the mail for a colonoscopy, I'd be a decade older. Time flies when you're busy keeping yourself alive.

# Sexagenarians

## Ages 60 – 69

## COLETTE, 60

I had quit working as a stylist after my divorce from Gerrit. For the past fifteen years, I had been pounding the pavement in stilettos as a regional sales manager for an anti-aging skincare company. Being an empty nester allowed me to pour myself into my career. I had turned sixty a few days ago and didn't plan to retire anytime soon. Work gave me purpose.

My boss invited me to the corporate office for a meeting. I had a hunch my success was paying off, and I'd be promoted to the vacant position of vice president. I was a shoo-in. He didn't call it an interview. He didn't have to. I was a smart cookie.

In my excitement, I bought a new, sharp-looking, hot-pink suit and a pair of pink and purple striped heels to match. I looked amazing and was at the top of my game.

The drive to the headquarters was a breeze. I spent the two-hour drive in my convertible with the top down singing. With the wind blowing through my hair, I practiced my acceptance speech. *Wow, I'm good*, I thought.

I got to the office, and everyone was so friendly. Likely, they were tipped off that I'd be their boss. They didn't want to get off on the wrong foot with me. I waited in the lobby and picked up an outdated AARP magazine. I flipped to an article about the detrimental effects of retirement. The research said people declined the fastest when they stopped working. Retirement was bad for the brain. It increased the risk of dementia, doubled the chances of cognitive decline, and worsened physical health. The evidence was compelling—working rather than retiring would keep me young. I decided I'd work until I was hauled away in a hearse.

My boss called me into his office. I took a seat opposite his desk. The butterflies in my stomach fluttered. He folded his hands confidently and placed them on the wooden surface of his desk—such a stance of authority. I would have to use that as VP.

"Colette, you've been a valuable employee for the last fifteen years. Your efforts contributed to your success and to the success of this company," he began. I felt my anticipation rise. "We value all you've done. And we need people who have their best work ahead of them, not behind them."

I held my breath tightly, waiting to exhale and accept his congratulations and the lucrative offer.

"With that said," he hesitated, lowering his voice to diffuse his next words. "We are taking the company in a different direction. There's no easy way to say this, but we're letting you go. We need someone to sell our anti-aging products who's less, well, seasoned."

"Younger?!" I demanded. I choked on the word, anger rising in my chest. This felt like the trauma of Gerrit dumping me for a younger wife.

"Fresher," he corrected. "If we want to be successful, we need faces that better tell the story of our products."

"I'm sorry. Can you repeat what you just said?" I stammered, locking my hands into a death grip. "Am I being fired for being too old?"

"Not fired. We're restructuring. We just don't have a job for you," he answered. "You've done nothing wrong."

"But I did. I got old," I said. He ignored the comment. "How am I too old to work if I'm too young to collect social security?" I asked.

"As a goodwill gesture, you'll receive a severance package and your pension. You'll be taken care of," he explained. "You can also stay two more weeks to finish the work we need completed. Plus, to recognize your many years of service, we'll throw you a retirement party."

"But I'm not retiring. Why would you throw me a retirement party?" Was this his cheap attempt to make me feel better or to make him feel better?

His words were like a mudslide sloshing in my head. I closed my eyes, trying to make sense of this meeting. When I looked at him again, I could see his lips moving, but I couldn't comprehend his words. They sounded distorted like a movie reel running too slow.

It was a crushing blow. An explosion of my ego. The company I had devoted myself to was ruining my career because I was too old for its anti-aging products. I wanted to whack my boss with a book like I did to Gerrit, but I couldn't risk losing my buyout.

Shocked and angered, I charged from his office and ran out of the building. In the chaos, I tripped and fell in the parking lot. One of my brand-new stilettos had wedged in a crack in the pavement, and the heel broke off. I was defeated. Ruining my most expensive pair of shoes exasperated my anguish.

I pulled myself up, yanked the broken heel out of the asphalt, hobbled lopsided to my car, got in, and slammed the door. I pounded my fists on the steering wheel, teardrops splattering onto my new suit. A massive meltdown was underway as makeup ran down my face. I looked in the mirror to see rivers of black mascara. I was a horror show.

The breeze that had felt so exhilarating earlier now annoyed me as my hair blew into my eyes and mouth. I knew I looked like a crazed woman with my hair flying and makeup smeared. But what did I care? Who did I have to impress?

I called Julia. She was my red wine and could calm me. When she answered, I was a blubbering mess. My wrath poured out in a string of rambling sentences.

"It's flat-out age discrimination! The way I see it, I was at the top of the pay scale, and now I will be replaced by someone they can pay less. Don't they know the idiom 'you get what you pay for?' I was very loyal and committed to this company. I was with them for fifteen years. I have a lot of historical knowledge that some young upstart can't bring to the table. They said they'd give me a severance package with a retirement party. What a joke. I'm the one out on my ass at sixty years old. What's to celebrate?"

I took a short breath—so quick Julia couldn't get in a word—and continued rambling.

"How am I going to find another job? I know my age will be a deterrent from other companies that cling to age bias. That's what I'm facing now—age discrimination. I'd sue them, but it's hard to prove. I haven't worried about my age in my career until now. I mistakenly clung to the belief that my age was an asset. I bring the wisdom, knowledge, and experience that a newcomer lacks. But I guess they don't want seasoned."

Another quick breath.

"I'm not ready to retire. I'll die early if I retire, according to an article I read. Where am I going to work? What am I going to do? Someone decided for me that I was going to retire. Is that because, at sixty years old, I *appear* as if I'm going to retire? Did they let me go based on how many wrinkles I have or how much of my hair is gray?"

And then I stopped blubbering. I had run out of fuel for venting.

"Are you finished?" Julia asked sympathetically on the other end of the phone.

"Yes."

"Well then, there's only one thing to do."

"What's that?" I asked.

"Egg your boss's house like we did as kids when someone picked on us."

I laughed through my crying. Maybe it was hysteria. If only our adult problems could be handled as easily as when we were kids and life was simple. Oh, to be young again. Why did life have to be so difficult?

I cried for the next two weeks until my final day, which ended with a tacky retirement party. Colleagues in my age bracket looked worried. *What if it happens to me?* I could see them fearfully asking themselves.

I was given a gold-and-diamond pin, a bottle of wine, and a houseplant. I'd pawn the pin, slam the wine, and kill the plant. But I fed into the lie that it was a lovely party and they were lovely gifts. Didn't they recognize the irony in how they had just ousted me, and now they were throwing a party in my honor?

The woman from HR, who took my security badge and office keys, attempted to keep the conversation light. "Colette, what do you want to do when you grow up?"

"I'm already grown up." I was confused by the question.

"That's not what I mean," she said. "You have all kinds of opportunities now. What do you want to do now that you get to decide?"

*As if it was for me to decide*, I bitterly thought. But my fake smile hid the bitterness well.

"You're not bound by a paycheck and held captive to this job anymore," she continued. "What would you like to do now that no one is telling you what to do? What's on your bucket list? How will you reimagine life?"

"I have no idea," I said. That was the most profound response I could muster. I hadn't given any thought to those questions. I'd been dealing with the trauma of being tossed overboard. I focused on the awful idea of *who* would want me at my age instead of asking *what* I wanted at my age.

"There are so many possibilities to take life in a new direction," she offered. "You can take control of your life and steer your own ship."

"How do I even know what to do?" I asked rhetorically.

"It's for you to discover. Use this moment to decide what's next," she continued reassuringly. "You have opportunities now you didn't have when you worked."

More opportunities? I hadn't looked at it that way. I felt I had lost my chance for success. When had society led people to believe we were washed up at sixty or whatever age discrimination starts? She claimed I had more opportunities than ever. Yet I felt the world was closing in because of my age.

"Embrace a new mindset in the power of being an older worker," she continued. "Recognize your value. Discover your passion and find your purpose. Reinvent yourself."

This was all so radically different from what I believed. I hadn't given any weight to reinventing my life. I knew I didn't want to retire sitting in a rocking chair, settling into the sunset. But I wasn't expecting a forced retirement. I assumed I'd work until I decided I was done, not when a company decided.

"Here's a new way to think about it," she said. "We all know the legend of Marie Antoinette. To the people of France, who were without bread on the eve of the French Revolution, she infamously said, 'Let them eat cake.'"

She handed me a piece of my retirement cake. "This is your cake moment, Colette. You're on the verge of a revolution. You have no bread, so go and eat cake. Enjoy more than just breadcrumbs."

"Then I shall eat cake," I replied, stuffing a large piece into my mouth. I wasn't entirely convinced, but I'd take whatever encouragement she was dishing out.

Maybe this was the start of my cake story. My retirement was beginning with the sweetness of the dessert.

· · · · · · · · · ·

## JULIA, 61

There comes a time when life begins to slow down. So much of living was managing a hectic pace, trying to get it all done, checking it off the list, and then moving to the next thing.

But now I felt peace settle in me, and I yearned to slow down. It was not about doing less; it was about doing more with purpose.

I also stopped worrying about what others thought of me. I was consumed with other people's opinions in my twenties and thirties. What I wore or didn't wear; said or didn't say. Then in my forties, something shifted in my mindset, and I became less focused on others' judgment. In my fifties, I was comfortable in my skin for the first time. Now that I was sixty, I turned inward and was more reflective.

I chose to celebrate my sixty-first birthday in a meaningful way. I booked a women's retreat weekend to find the deeper meaning in life and be more intentional with the next twenty or thirty years I hoped to be blessed with. I invited Colette to join me. It was my gift to her.

I didn't give her much detail. This would be a retreat weekend to discover our inner beauty. She wasn't one to be too contemplative. She'd be all for the relaxation, with less reflection.

I packed one overnight bag. She packed two suitcases. For a three-day trip!

"You brought half your closet," I chided.

"Oh, sweetheart, don't insult my wardrobe. It might be half of yours, but it's only a fraction of mine," she quipped, loading her suitcases into my car. "Where are we going anyway? I packed for all options."

"We're taking a journey inward. To discover our hearts' happiness and purpose in life," I answered cryptically.

"It doesn't sound like my cup of wine." She laughed, but the roll of her eyes spoke volumes of her uncertainty. "Will I be singing kumbaya? And calling my ex-lovers to apologize for breaking their hearts?"

"If the shoe fits. Can you even remember all the lovers you've scorned?" I teased. "It's about finding your purpose. What dreams did we leave on the side of the road? We're going to pick them up and let them hitchhike home with us."

"Yeehaw," she yodeled out the window.

When we got to our room, I watched Colette unpack all her toiletries. She pulled out a trunk of creams, waxes, lotions, bleaches, and concealers. The array of beauty products was endless. And expensive!

"What is all that?" I stared in disbelief at what looked like a department store counter. I read the labels on each item, which seemed to oversell more than they could deliver.

"Everything we need for our journey." She laughed again. "Salicylic acid to unclog pores. Retinol to exfoliate. Hyaluronic acid to retain moisture."

She continued checking off the list of anti-aging products we couldn't live without on this three-day trip.

"Is this what you use every day?" I asked.

"No. I use it at night, too," she answered. "Here, you need this."

She tossed me a tube of cream.

"What is it?" I asked.

"It's mustache bleach."

"I don't need that," I protested.

"Have you looked in the mirror lately? You have whiskers. Women develop dark hairs above their lips when testosterone increases in mid-age."

I shrugged. "I'm fine with mustache hairs. If that's what my body is supposed to do, then why should I stop it?"

"You've got to stay ahead of the curse."

"You mean ahead of the *curve*?" I corrected.

"No, I meant curse."

"Aging is not a curse," I said. "I'd rather age than give in to the alternative."

"I'm not giving in to death, but I don't have to give in to aging like I'm surrendering in war, either. Doesn't it terrify you to watch your beauty fade?" Colette pressed. "The quest for the fountain of youth has been pursued for thousands of years."

"Yes, I know. I wrote a college paper about it," I said.

"Wasn't that a thousand years ago?" she teased.

And then I did what any mature middle-aged woman would do. I whacked her across the head with a bed pillow. She was stunned. She hadn't expected it. In return, she did what any other mature woman would do. She whacked me back. A pillow fight ensued.

Finally, I collapsed on the floor, laughing and winded. Colette was also breathless from the feather-weight boxing match.

"I'm laughing so hard tears are running down my legs," I admitted. "I used to trickle only when I coughed or sneezed. Now it's when I laugh, too."

That made us laugh more. And trickle more.

"Here's to acting your age," she said. *Whack.*

"Not your shoe size," I returned. *Whack.*

The following day two dozen women between sixty and seventy years old assembled in the hotel conference room. The women were skinny and overweight, beautiful and plain. Some had gray hair, some didn't. Some had telltale signs of aging, and some had "work" done. But it struck me that our chronological age on the timeline of life did not determine what someone's outward age showed. What was someone supposed to look like in this stage of life anyway? Beauty and old were subjective.

The facilitator entered and introduced herself as Pauline. She was middle-aged and gorgeous, perfectly poised and polished. She reminded me of Colette. I wondered if it also took her two hours to get ready this morning.

"Ladies, I have a gift for you," Pauline announced. "Inside your makeup bags, you won't find makeup. Instead, you'll find makeup remover. Use it now to remove every trace of makeup, serum, coverup, and everything you've hidden your face with. You'll begin the weekend in your most natural form."

A screech like a wounded animal echoed across the room. It was Colette. She looked like a deer about to be flattened by a semi-truck. I knew Colette was terrified she'd have to expose her authentic self. That was on the same level as revealing her soul. I wanted to laugh. This could push her to the brink.

It didn't take much to wipe my face clean. I gave my extra cloths to Colette, who needed a pile of them. I always went for simplicity. I dabbed a few blemishes and sunspots with concealer and light foundation and called it good. But this was even a lesson for me. I, too, covered my flaws.

"Ladies, you're going bare for the rest of the weekend," Pauline said. "No beauty products or makeup. Nothing. I want you to face your face. You'll see how beautiful you are, not hiding behind products that camouflage the real you."

She then began to wipe the makeup from her face. She wasn't going to be a hypocrite. Upon finishing, she retrieved a magazine from a plastic bin beside her and held it up for everyone to see. A young, flawless model graced the cover. The bold headline read, *Age No More: Top Five Beauty Secrets.*

"What does this mean?" she asked.

"We can stop the aging process in five easy steps?" a woman guessed.

"Nope. There isn't a beauty secret in the world that accomplishes it. Think about it. What does age no more really mean?" she asked.

"Death," multiple voices called out.

"That's right. Any message that says to stop aging is not doing you any favors. To stop aging means to die. Not a very warm message if we see it for what it is."

She held up a second magazine titled, *Defy Your Age.* Another youthful face graced the cover.

"What does this convey?" she asked.

"Fight your age. Don't embrace it," another woman yelled out.

"That's right. It's telling you to fight who you are. But you can't change your age. You cannot defy aging. Anyone in the media and cosmetic industry that tells you to defy your age is telling you to go to war with yourself."

She held up a third magazine with a middle-aged woman posing on the cover. Her face was tight and smooth. Obviously, her picture had been edited. This headline read, *Sixty Is the New Forty.*

"Ladies, you're not forty anymore," Pauline said. "You're sixty. It's who you are and to be celebrated. There's nothing wrong with being your real age or showing it. It's the natural order of aging. The sooner you accept this, the happier you'll be. This is an issue of social justice. It's about fighting ageism. You can either be a part of the problem or part of the solution. Aging means being human. Aging means life. To be anti-aging is to be anti-life."

Pauline picked up the bin and dumped out a pile of beauty magazines, all with the same kind of messaging—to defeat aging.

"Ladies, the anti-aging industry perpetuates our fears of getting old," Pauline said, her voice rising with the passion of her words. "But we're not old; we're just long-lived. You can stop buying these shallow magazines. Then they can't profit from our insecurities."

She jumped up on the table where she had dumped the magazines. "Stop drinking the Kool-Aid in the so-called fountain of youth. Stand up for your age!"

"I'm standing up," I said, climbing onto the table next to her. "I'm Julia. I'm proud of my age. I turn sixty-one tomorrow, along with my best friend, Colette." I pointed at Colette. She cringed as I called out her age.

Another woman followed my lead and jumped onto the table. "We've been aging since birth!" she yelled. "We were designed by nature to change physically. There must be a paradigm shift in our society to radically embrace aging!"

"This is a youth-obsessed culture," Pauline continued. "By spending money to reclaim youth, is it really an investment? No! You're only getting a reproduction of it. And reproductions are never as valuable as originals."

It was an anti-anti-aging rally. I loved everything Pauline preached about pro-aging. The fear of aging was occurring at a younger and younger age. Kids in their twenties were now starting to use anti-aging products. Pauline discussed a study showing women who reached the age of twenty-nine already feared aging.

That's a long time to be worried about getting old. The experience of aging had been reduced to shame. Nobody wants to feel shame, so we're sold a worthless bill of goods. I vowed then to quit using any products that would mask my natural beauty or perpetuate the propaganda that my age was a liability and not an asset.

By the end of Pauline's speech, everyone had jumped up on the table, embracing the power of her message—everyone except Colette. The rest of us held hands and sang, "Make new friends but keep the old. One is silver, and the other's gold."

I woke the next morning—my sixty-first birthday—to discover Colette had packed and left. I read the note she left behind.

*Julia, it's hypocritical to stay when selling beauty has been my lifelong career. It's my passion. I love ceramides, collagen, and anti-aging acids. We're on the pro-aging/anti-aging spectrum at opposite ends. This workshop did help me discover one thing, though—how droopy my face is. I went home to schedule plastic surgery. Love your golden friend, Colette.*

I slumped to the floor. I had wanted to lift her spirits. Instead, I pushed her into getting a lift for her face. If I learned anything from this weekend, it was to stop forcing Colette to conform to my idea of beauty. Who was I to define it for anyone?

• • • • • • • • • •

## COLETTE, 63

Retirement was fabulous. I spent my newfound free time doing yoga, having chemical peels, body wraps, microdermabrasion, and Botox. I don't know how I had time to work with all these appointments. I was becoming the best of myself. I had no idea how great life could be post-sixty. The truth is, it was not as bad as I had expected. I anticipated that sixty would be as bad as a colonoscopy. I guessed I was moving up the curve of happiness.

My surgery for a facelift was officially on the books—two years after the pro-aging rally, which was as enjoyable as a boob-o-gram. I kept pushing surgery back as I wrestled with the fear of going under the knife. I didn't want to look like a car accident victim. I'd seen pictures of celebrities who had botched facelifts. The surgeon assured me I wouldn't look like that after one lift and that it only occurred after too much plastic surgery. In the meantime, as I debated in private, I continued with the quick fix of Botox.

In her attempt to be helpful, Julia suggested plastic surgeons should offer psychological counseling before any patient voluntarily went under the knife. I thought that was silly. I didn't need a shrink telling me I hated the idea of getting old. I had that figured out on my own.

"I think you've got gerascophobia," Julia told me as we walked the mall. Speed-walking indoors became a ritual of ours. We laced up our tennis shoes twice a week and trotted the corridors before the stores opened. She did it for the fitness. I did it to watch for the sales. While she wanted to improve her brain, I wanted to improve my budget.

"What's geran-soco-sobobia?" I asked trying to pronounce her big, fancy words.

"It's the irrational fear of getting older," she explained.

"No, you've got it wrong," I said. "It's not irrational."

"Your planned surgery can't be cheap. Why not invest that money in the stock market? You'll do far better financially than padding a surgeon's pockets."

"It's an investment in me."

"Why don't you just grow out your bangs a little longer instead of undergoing surgery?" Julia asked.

"Down to my chin? I'd look like a sheepdog."

"Don't you know you're a natural beauty? Just age gracefully," Julia said.

"Graceful aging is baloney. Anyone who says you can age gracefully is blowing smoke up your you-know-what," I said.

"Marilyn Monroe said she wouldn't get a facelift because it would take the character out of her face," Julia suggested.

"Oh, please. She was thirty-six when she died. I guarantee she would've had plastic surgery when she reached our age. Why are you trying to talk me out of this procedure anyway? You know I'm shallow and self-obsessed."

"Because you don't need to do this. You're beautiful just the way you are. Don't risk complications of surgery. I know someone who had it done. She had nerve damage that left her with permanent facial paralysis. She could only smile on one side. On the other side, she frowned."

"That's sweet of you to look out for me. But another Hollywood legend, Betty Davis, declared old age ain't for sissies. She's right. I can't be weak."

"I don't think that's what she meant," Julia said.

I stopped in front of a window display, looking into the mirror, pulling my skin up to mimic the final results of the facelift. Tugging my skin back made a considerable difference in wiping out the wrinkles and eliminating my sagging jowls. I appeared tired and worn out. But I wasn't. I had a lot of juice left in this body of mine. I wanted my face to match what I felt.

"What if you lowered the wattage in your bathroom light? Or smeared Vaseline on the mirror? Both of those things are safer and have immediate effects on reducing wrinkles that you see," Julia suggested with a laugh.

"I feel unseen to the world. Have you ever realized people stop noticing you when you reach a certain age? We've become invisible, Julia."

"You're only invisible if you're boring and uninspiring," she replied. "And, you, of all people, are neither of those. You're striking. And charming. And your charm comes from the inside," Julia said.

She gripped my hand lovingly, trying to convince me. "If you want another Hollywood legend to consider, look at Betty White. She was charming because of her wrinkles and fluffy white hair. Everyone loved her because she was so endearing in her old age. Be Betty."

"I don't want to be Betty. I want to be better."

"You're already better, simply by the fact you're sixty-three. Age makes us better. If you want to be a true woman, the most feminine action you can take is allowing your true self to shine without cosmetic intervention."

"Wow! That's good," I declared.

"Awww, my words are having an effect on you?" Julia asked.

"No, sorry. I saw a killer shoe sale in that window," I said, pointing at the clearance sign. "Your words have no effect on me."

"Can I give you another piece of advice to get rid of wrinkles without invasive surgery?" Julia asked.

"Yes, though I won't take it."

"Take your glasses off when you look in the mirror. You won't see a darn thing."

She couldn't convince me. The next day I went in for the facelift. I wouldn't admit it to Julia, but I was terrified. I had to sign my life away with all the consent forms. The list of things that could go wrong was unsettling: lopsided features, facial paralysis, infection, and even death. What women go through to look beautiful! For a moment, I considered backing out. But it was a fleeting thought. I wasn't going to let fear rule me.

The surgery went off without incident. But recovery hurt like hell. Like childbirth without an epidural. But as with childbirth, you forget the pain, or else you'd never get knocked up again. I was bandaged like a mummy. Nurses brought me Jell-O, which I couldn't eat. I could barely open my mouth and felt so ill it would've tasted like acid anyway.

Two days later, the burial cloths were removed from my face. They were replaced with a hideous-looking facial cap. It was a headdress I'd wear for at least four weeks. It made me look like a cloistered nun.

After two days in the hospital, I was transferred to a posh hotel to heal, and then I was given the clear to go home. I was doped up and still begged for more pain meds. I glanced in the mirror only once and was mortified by my appearance. My face looked like a picture some preschooler would color—swirled with shades of purple, blue, and yellow. My face was a Monet painting gone bad. The swelling made me unrecognizable. The incisions, stitched with black thread and crusted with blood, resembled Frankenstein. Broken capillaries dotted my face. The surgeon assured me it was all normal. Still, looking like I had gone through the windshield in a fatal car accident was unnerving. Only the accident was chosen by me—premeditated. I had willingly opted to have my face go through a hypothetical windshield. What the heck was I thinking?

I wouldn't let my daughters visit me. I feared they would be traumatized by my freakish looks. *I* was traumatized. I continued to ice the swelling and bruising with packs of frozen corn. I had to sleep sitting up, except calling it sleep was overreaching. It felt like I had been stretched beyond normal, and the itching from the adverse reaction to the painkillers was unbearable. I couldn't eat. I couldn't talk. I couldn't sleep. I couldn't do much but overcome the buyer's remorse I felt. The surgeon said it was typical to feel a sense of regret. It's the part of the brain being bombarded with so many medications. He told me it would be an emotional roller coaster. I never did like roller coasters.

But as time passed, the pain wore off, the swelling subsided, the bruising vanished, and the buyer's remorse lifted. It was not a piece of cake. After a healing process that lasted many months, I would say I looked fresher. Not decades younger, but refreshed. I was delighted with the results.

I settled back into life with a new face and outlook. Would I do it again now that I knew what I'd go through? Despite the horrible pain, being stretched beyond belief, feeling emotional lows, a temporarily disfigured face, and a long recovery process—the answer was yes! It's like childbirth. You forget the pain. But I also promised myself I'd *never*, ever have another facelift. At least for now.

• • • • • • • • •

## JULIA, 66

Spending time with my granddaughter Ayden was the most remarkable thing on earth. The greatest joy in my life was her. Grandparenting made the trials of parenting so rewarding—having a grandchild to love without having to do the discipline or hard work of raising her. Whoever said grandkids were the prize for putting up with kids was right. I got to love Ayden unconditionally and, at the end of the day, return her to Carolann. I chuckled at this well-known secret all new grandparents discovered.

Today I took Ayden to the zoo for her eighth birthday. It was a picturesque fall day. The air was mild, and the trees were flaunting their full spectrum of colors—reds, oranges, and yellows. It was splendid.

"Grammy, you look like an elephant," she said as we stood in front of the elephant exhibit. I laughed hard.

"Why? Because I'm fat?" I asked.

"Oh, no. Mommy says it's not nice to call anyone fat. You're not fat—you're pudgy."

"I am a little pudgy," I agreed.

"But that's not why you look like an elephant."

"Why do I look like an elephant then?"

"You've got the same wrinkles as an elephant," she observed. "Other animals in the zoo don't have those wrinkles. Just elephants."

"You're right. I do have wrinkles like an elephant." I laughed, considering the innocent perspective of a child.

"But it sounds mean to say you look like an elephant," Ayden mused. "So I'll say you look like a turkey."

"Why is that?"

"Because you've got a turkey neck," she said.

*Out of the mouths of babes,* I thought, chuckling to myself.

"Why do you have wrinkles and I don't?" she asked.

I gave it some thought as we stood watching the elephants stagger around. How do you explain the science behind wrinkles to a child? But I realized she didn't want the science. She wanted the story.

"Well, these wrinkles here," I said, pointing to my décolletage and hands, "are sun wrinkles from spending time outdoors. I got them from building sandcastles in the summer at the beach and planting flowers in my garden. The wrinkles grew from doing fun things in the warm sun."

She listened very attentively as I explained. Her eyes were big with anticipation.

"And these wrinkles are frown wrinkles," I said, pointing to the lines on my forehead. "They're from being sad when your grandpa died, from worrying about your mom when she was a child. And they're from crying when I see others hurting."

"I don't know if I want those kinds of wrinkles," she said, frowning.

"But you do because that means you've got people to care for and show compassion to. And when you grow frown wrinkles, the next type of wrinkles become even sweeter. Do you know what those wrinkles are?"

"No. What are they?" she asked eagerly, her eyes growing larger as I leaned in closer to share.

"These wrinkles are the greatest wrinkles you can get," I said, pointing to the lines around my mouth and at the outside corners of my eyes. "They are happiness wrinkles. They form from smiling. Do you know how I got them?"

She shook her head no.

"I got them from laughing with my best friend Colette, from being deliriously happy on my wedding day, and by being over the moon when I had a child." I grinned widely to increase the wrinkles for effect. "And best of all, I got the biggest happiness wrinkles from smiling when I held you as a newborn baby for the very first time. These wrinkles are the best."

"I want wrinkles when I grow up," she said, glowing. "Do you think I'll get them?"

"I promise you will," I assured. "Do you know how I know?"

"How?"

"Because today we're at the zoo in the warm sunshine and happily enjoying all the animals. Your sun and happiness wrinkles are slowly growing already."

She smiled at the thought. I hoped I explained the purpose of wrinkles well enough for her to embrace them and not fear getting them. We continued to walk through the zoo as she asked 101 more questions. She was so full of curiosity and wonder. Where did that wonder go as we aged?

"Would you like some ice cream?" I asked, pointing to the sign reading, *Old-Fashioned Ice Cream Parlor*.

"Yes, yes, yes," she squealed, jumping up and down. "Grammy, what's old-fashioned mean?"

"It means like an old style. Not common to modern times anymore," I explained.

The ice cream parlor was built to look like an old saloon, with dark wooden walls and swing-style doors. Vintage jars full of candy lined the shelves. Freezer cases were stocked with a variety of ice cream flavors. Ayden's eyes twinkled at the endless array of options. She bounced back and forth from foot to foot. To have this kind of boundless energy. This was a "kid in a candy store" experience with all the sweet delicacies. It took ten minutes for Ayden to decide on an ice cream flavor.

"Can I get ice cream *and* candy?" she asked, her eyes dancing with delight.

"Of course," I said, wrapping her in a warm hug.

It took another five minutes to pick out candy. Oh, to be a kid again when the biggest decisions were what kind of desserts to choose.

"So, what kind of wrinkles does ice cream give you?" she asked, watching as I licked the first bit of my ice cream cone.

"Ice cream doesn't cause me to be wrinkly. It causes me to be pudgy."

We took our seats inside the saloon. The walls were adorned with antiques and Americana nostalgia art. Ayden looked around with curiosity.

"Grammy, what's an antique?" she asked, reading the vintage sign on the wall that read, *Antiques: Buy, Sell, Trade*.

"Well, it's a collectible, like a really old piece of furniture or art," I described. "Like a table, or jewelry, or vases that are really old. You know, the big cabinet in my house is in the living room. That's an antique."

"Why do you buy, sell, or trade them?" she asked, licking the melting ice cream dripping down the cone.

"Because they have a high value due to their age," I explained. "That means they're worth a lot of money."

"So, an antique is really old and has a lot of value?"

"Yes, exactly."

"You're an antique," she said matter-of-factly.

"Why do you say that?" I asked.

"Because you're really old and very valuable."

"I guess you could say that," I said, smiling widely.

"You're growing another happiness wrinkle," Ayden exclaimed.

I marveled how this child understood that we become more valuable as we age. If only society grasped what this eight-year-old knew to be true.

•••••••••••

## COLETTE, 67

"Colette, you look amazing!" gushed Lisa, one of my former classmates. She pored over me. I loved it. "You haven't aged a day since high school. What's your secret?"

"Good surgeons." Julia coughed under her breath. She was standing next to me.

"I'm sorry. I missed what you said," Lisa said.

"Good genes," I added quickly, correcting Julia. I shot a look of death in her direction.

I was happy to receive the compliment. It's one of the reasons I got plastic surgery, to hear the affirmation of ogling women who hadn't seen me in years. And the best place to get these affirmations—class reunions.

Our high school graduating class had reconvened for our fifty-year reunion. We were having dinner in our old high school auditorium. The room had not aged well. *It needs a facelift, too,* I thought, laughing to myself.

Our class had grown smaller since our forty-year reunion ten years prior. There were more deaths and divorces, resulting in fewer people showing up. I wondered how much smaller it would be ten years from now.

As class reunions typically go, it was stiff and awkward. I kept in touch with the people I cared about. The others? If I cared about them, I'd still be friends with them. I wasn't looking to make new friends. I had enough. I strolled from conversation to conversation, pretending to be interested. It was dreadful.

The first group I approached droned on about social security. Is this what midlife socializing looks like? We were pathetic.

"I decided to collect social security at my full retirement age..."

"I collected at sixty-two. I couldn't hold off getting that check..."

"You should wait until you're seventy to get the biggest benefit..."

Listening to talk of social security was like pushing pins into my eyeballs. I moved on to another group and joined in. This group bickered about Medicare.

"I didn't sign up for Medicare on time, so I'm penalized for the rest of my life now..."

"I'm shopping around for less-expensive gap insurance..."

"Seems like premiums go up, and benefits go down..."

*When did we become so boring?* I wondered. I moved on again. The next group compared their aches and pains.

"I had my second knee replaced..."

"I'm scheduled for hip replacement..."

"I'm getting hearing implants..."

"Just got screened for prostate cancer..."

Listening to them rattle on about their dismal health issues was painful, so I left them. Finally, I joined a conversation about what people were doing in life. Julia was with this group, so I stayed.

"I'm busier now in retirement than when I worked," I told the cluster of people standing around. "I don't know how I had time to work."

"Isn't that the truth?" the group chimed in agreement.

"So, what are you doing now to find purpose in your life?" Julia asked one of the group members. Their voices trailed off as I began to tune out the conversation.

Julia and I were still so different. Julia wanted to hear about their fulfillment in life. As for me, I was doing a mental roll call, sizing up how well or poorly my classmates aged.

So many former classmates looked rough. Goodness, did I look like them? They all looked so... old. They had gray hair, and wrinkles, and faces that looked like they were melting because they sagged so much. I hoped I didn't look like them. But I couldn't. Why would I? I was aging beautifully. Even if it was with a little cosmetic help.

Julia continued to go around the group circle and listen to people's life successes—whether it was success in love, hobbies, work, or how they were finding meaning. She was engrossed in this. Maybe I needed to stop being so shallow and learn something from them.

"I believe volunteering has made me healthier. It's given me something to wake up to every day and has helped me fight off depression," one of the women explained. "I've found purpose in helping others."

"Volunteering has been proven to extend life expectancy," Julia claimed knowingly.

"I feel a sense of satisfaction knowing I'm making a difference every day," the woman continued. "I've found purpose in serving others. Colette, what about you? What are you doing?"

"Botox," I said, pulling myself out of the daydream. I realized I ignored most of what was said as I went through my classmate-aging roll call.

"Pardon me?" she said. "What are you up to in life?"

"Oh, sorry, I zoned out. Well, I'm exploring botulism toxins in our water. I'm helping to bring water to, um, the Amazon rainforest," I explained off the cuff, without a clue as to what I was talking about.

Everyone stared at me in confusion. Julia stared in disbelief.

"It's a very complex project, bringing water into a rainforest. I'd love to share it with you, but finding water where we're digging is like looking for a needle in the forehead—I mean, haystack."

I was doing nothing meaningful in life. Then, as if on cue, I was saved from additional humiliation. The speaker took the stage and interrupted the conversation as I tried to explain my fake mission in the Amazon.

"Good evening, former students. I'm here to talk to you about Alzheimer's," the speaker began. "One in eight of you will develop Alzheimer's after the age of sixty-five. One in two will develop Alzheimer's after eighty-five. Look at the person next to you. One of you will develop Alzheimer's after you reach eighty-five. That's the fastest growing segment of the population—those over eighty-five. Consider the enormity of this disease we all face."

Holy crow's feet! This was depressing. What kind of message was this for our class reunion? Everyone shifted nervously, hoping the speaker would get booed off the stage.

"And bad news if you're Hispanic. You're one-and-a-half times more like-ly to develop Alzheimer's and other dementias than non-Hispanics," the speaker continued.

I felt awful for Julia. She was more likely to get it than me. I couldn't even fathom it. It was too torturous to think about losing her that way.

"Who was on the planning committee for this?" I whispered to Julia, who appeared intrigued.

"Since I was class president," she said, "I booked the speaker." Why was I not surprised?

The speaker rattled off more grim statistics. This was ghastly. I slipped away to the beverage table. I would drown my sorrows in something stiff but discovered it was a "dry" reunion since it was on school property.

"Colette, come with me," whispered my classmate Lisa, who snuck up behind me. She was always the school rebel. "Let's ditch this like we did math class."

She led me by the elbow out of the auditorium. Lisa rounded up a few other women who hung in our social circle back in the day. We went into the girls' bathroom. Lisa pulled out a flask of tequila. We chuckled at the ridiculousness of hiding in the school bathroom, sneaking booze. It felt like old times!

"Class reunions are nothing but a comparison game," Lisa groaned, taking a swig from the flask. "We're compared to our younger eighteen-year-old selves. All of us here are doing it to each other. We're all judging how much we resemble the physique of our former teenage bodies. We lose things we want to keep, like hair. And gain things we want to lose, like weight. We judge whose boobs have gone south and whose waist has widened to the east and west."

"What's gone north?" I asked, laughing.

"Cholesterol! That goes up," one of the women answered.

"Why do we put pressure on others to look like their former selves? It's unrealistic to expect we maintain our youthful appearances," one of the others said.

"When I see people aging worse than me, it makes me feel better. Like I've got some advantage," I said honestly. "Is that harsh?"

"Yes, definitely," they all said in unison.

"The pressure comes from within. And it comes from the outside, from the media, from the judgment of others," Lisa said.

"And from the face that reflects in the mirror and screams, you're not young, beautiful, worthy, nor desirable in this stage of life," I added.

"Colette, you've got nothing to worry about," Lisa said. "You always were the prettiest girl in school. You still are."

"Do you know how I silenced the screams of aging insecurity?" I asked. My voice breathed hot after slamming another shot of tequila. I paused for effect. "With plastic surgery. The voices of self-doubt finally quieted when I got a little nip here and a little tuck there. I reclaimed a piece of youth from yesterday and preserved it for tomorrow by going under the knife."

"Colette, that's quite a confession to these women," Julia said, walking into the bathroom and interrupting our conversation. "You're not always this introspective and honest. What's gotten into you?"

"The tequila," I said before taking another swig.

"Colette, you're creating a comparison monster because everyone's judging themselves against your false standard," Lisa explained. "You've had plastic surgery, which raises the bar to which the rest of us compare ourselves. We feel like toilet water because you look forty, while the rest of us look our real age."

"But you shouldn't feel like toilet water because you look sixty-seven," Julia piped in. "This is what sixty-seven looks like. What is wrong with that?"

"Right, I shouldn't feel bad about myself when I know Colette had invasive procedures to capture eternal youth," Lisa agreed.

"You should feel beautiful no matter what you look like, especially when it's natural beauty like yours," Julia continued.

"Well, Colette, you're lucky to be able to afford plastic surgery. This is what my genes have given me," Lisa said, pointing to the deeply set wrinkles around her eyes and sagging jowls.

I laughed. "Oh, I couldn't afford it, either. I used my social security to pay for it."

"Ladies, I'm taking you back to the party," Julia announced. "There's a surprise waiting. Check out the photo booth if you want to see how beautiful you'll be in twenty years. It creates a mock photo of what you'll look like in twenty years. It's rather ingenious."

"You mean insidious?" I challenged. "Do you really want to see how old you'll look in the future?"

"You'll still be beautiful. You'll just look different," Julia said.

"Let's do it. We can compare it to the class picture taken of us at graduation fifty years ago that hangs in the hallway," Lisa said.

The six of us piled into the photo booth. The picture captured us twenty years from now. I thought it was a cruel joke. It showed us on the brink of being ninety years old, looking very old. While we all looked to be various ages today with different levels of wrinkles and gray hair, the mock photo made us all look like equals in age, despite the fact I had plastic surgery. It was disheartening.

"Here's your gift," Julia said, handing each of us a filmstrip of the photos.

"I should've run for class president," I groaned.

• • • • • • • • • •

## JULIA, 68

Mama and Papa hadn't cared for their health over the years. They were avid smokers and ate more than their fair share of fried *flautas* and *empanadas*. Because of their poor health choices, Papa had died unexpectedly two years ago from a heart attack—the ominous widowmaker.

So Mama vowed to get healthy. The doctors warned her that heart disease is the number one killer of women, and she was at risk with her lifestyle. She quit smoking cold turkey, took up walking, and lost weight, though she didn't give up fried food. I was happy to see her get a new lease on life. But while she tried to reverse the detriments of past choices, she couldn't stop the damage that years of abuse had done to her body. She was diagnosed with Stage Four lung cancer, the number one leading cause of cancer for women. Though it was no surprise after smoking most of her life, it was devastating.

Mama became incapable of caring for herself as the disease ravaged her body. Despite running a nursing home for years, I refused to put her into one. Oh, the irony! It was part of my heritage to care for my family rather than have an institution do it. It had already been over ten years since Jack died, and I forgot how hard it was to care for someone. But I also knew this was precious, limited time with Mama. I wanted to savor every moment left with her. The cancer had metastasized, and she didn't have long to live. I called in hospice to make her transition from life to death more comfortable and pain-free, as I had with Jack.

Three months later, Mama passed, and I buried her next to Papa. I was now an orphan. To be without parents was not something I had prepared for.

I was left with the task of managing their estate and sorting through the remnants of their life. I had the heart-wrenching job of clearing out their home and handing off their belongings and keepsakes as if they had no meaning. It was excruciating. I didn't want to be the one to decide how to part with their stuff. They had decades' worth of things that I couldn't bring to my house. I couldn't keep it, but I struggled to part with it. I was paralyzed in deciding how to dismantle the life they had built together. Why didn't anyone talk about how hard this was? I felt like I was smashing a glass castle and giving away all the shards of glass to anyone, anywhere.

It took months to go through every file, folder, storage box, nook, and cranny. I knew my parents' generation hid money—mattress money—so I needed to be diligent in ensuring nothing was thrown out without inspecting it first. Sure enough, I found stacks of one hundred dollar bills in obscure places. The oddest location was an empty cereal box in the basement pantry. The box was filthy and musty, but my parents did a good job concealing the money. A burglar would not steal a box of dusty cereal. I discovered their marriage and birth certificates in a rusted coffee can.

I worked strategically from the basement to the attic. It was daunting, and I was overwhelmed. Everything held meaning for them: old photos, jewelry, even locks of baby hair safely mounted in keepsake albums. But nothing held meaning for me. I didn't know the history behind any of this stuff. I couldn't identify the people captured in the photographs. And I certainly had no idea whether the jewelry had sentimental value or even financial value. It was difficult to determine what was essential to keep and what wasn't.

My breaking point was when I worked in the attic and uncovered one of Mama's most precious items. She had her wedding dress preserved and stored in a box. She had never opened the box for me to see it because she was concerned doing so would've left it vulnerable to moths. I found it ironic she had it preserved and stored away to keep it protected yet never once took it out to look at or enjoy. Now her life was over, and she would never have the opportunity to see it again. What was the point of holding on to something you wouldn't allow yourself to enjoy?

I carefully untied the faded silk ribbon that held the box together. I lifted the lid, sneezing from the excessive dust. I split open the shrink-wrapped plastic that sealed the dress. I pulled it out and fluffed the lace and silk to reveal a magnificent ivory dress. It was a vintage Mexican wedding gown. A garden of embroidered flowers lined the hem and bodice. A rainbow of roses, begonias, and violets were delicately hand-stitched onto the silk canvas. Beneath the dress in the box was a lace mantilla wedding veil, hand-stitched with scalloped edges. The dress was stunning. It was timeless. And it was something my mother kept hidden and never shared with me. It was so precious to her that she wouldn't even let me see it, yet here I was, looking at it for the first time, deciding on its fate. What was I to do with this discovery? What would I do with it other than to hold it captive in my attic as she did? Did the dress serve a purpose left in a box and forgotten over time?

The reality was I couldn't keep it. It didn't hold the same meaning for me. The importance of it belonged to Mama. It pained me to part with Mama's wedding dress. It would end up in no man's land after I donated it. But maybe I was freeing it for a greater purpose. I couldn't and wouldn't hold on to any keepsakes that would only become prisoners in my home. Otherwise, my daughter would then be tasked with the chore of unloading two generations of stuff. I didn't want to do that to her. I cried, clutching the dress in my hands. The tears fell onto the silk, leaving wet stains. I packed it back into the box and re-tied the ribbon. I placed the box in a pile that would be donated.

As I neared the end of rummaging, a box labeled with my name caught my attention. Inside was memorabilia from my childhood. I laughed at the elementary crafts and artwork I had worked so hard on as gifts for Mama and Papa. There was also a baby bib, my first pair of shoes, and even a lost tooth. *Oh, the useless stuff parents keep,* I laughed to myself.

As I rifled through the mementos, I discovered a time capsule. It was a plastic cylinder container with a screw-on cap. I untwisted it to reveal several things from my childhood, including the dried rose and the card that read, *Stop and smell the roses* given to me in the seventh grade. I unfolded a piece of paper with my childhood writing on it. It was the obituary I was forced to conceive in the fifth grade. I laughed, reading through what I thought my life would become. While many predictions didn't transpire, some things did—like having a loving family and still being friends with Colette decades later. I felt tears form as I read on. What gave me joy was balanced out by what brought me sorrow. I had written, *She stayed married to her husband for seventy years. They died hours apart, still happily married.*

"That's not how it ended," I said aloud, breathing back the tears.

I read further, *And it all went according to plan.* Ha. Not much has gone according to plan.

The most poignant part read, *There was nothing exciting about her life. It was simple, but she was happy.* Is that how I want my life to be remembered? That nothing was exciting about it?

It was a shocking statement to read that this was what I thought my life would become. That's not how I wanted my life to be. I knew I had to do more to make it exciting. I read through the list of dreams I had written down. While most were obnoxious (like skydiving at ninety) and unattainable (like marrying a billionaire), it gave me the nudge to write a new list of aspirations. I wanted to be remembered for doing good and living a fulfilling life.

After clearing out my parents' entire home, the time capsule was all I kept. I wanted to keep this as memorabilia of how to live life and not wait to enjoy it. It would be a daily reminder not to keep my beautiful dreams stored away like a magnificent wedding dress locked away in a box in an attic.

• • • • • • • • •

## COLETTE, 69

Julia showed me the time capsule she had recovered from her parents' house. It was endearing to see her juvenile ideas captured in time. And it gave me food for thought. I wanted to create my own bucket list of goals. *What do I want to do when I grow up?* I wondered.

I was in my encore years with a lot to accomplish. I liked the word encore. It's like the encore of a rock concert where the musicians saved the best for last. This was my time to put my best self forward, achieving my aspirations. I was motivated to put some ideas into action. I bought a crisp new journal and colored pencils and went to a park to enjoy the last warm days of autumn and write my list of life goals. I found the exercise exhilarating and challenging. I would push myself to achieve more. I was also coming to understand the limited time ahead of me. If I ever wanted to step it up to get things done, now was the time. This was not my parents' retirement, and I still had many opportunities ahead of me. But time was ticking. I spent two hours jotting down ideas. I finished writing and skimmed through some of my goals.

*My Bucket List: Ten Things I Want to Achieve*
1. *Read ten classic literary novels. Maybe five. Make that one.*

2. *Walk through a shoe department and not buy a single pair of shoes.*

3. *Drive to an exotic destination. (like Climax, MI)*

4. *Become a world-class ballroom dancer. Or just take dance lessons.*

5. *Discover my true hair color beneath the dye. (Maybe)*

6. *Go skydiving. (It was in Julia's childhood list of things to do. Still possible.)*

7. *Enjoy the little things in life, like dessert before dinner.*

8. *Make it a global cause to stop calling us older people senior citizens. We're just preserved kids.*

9. *Discover why senior citizens (oops, I mean preserved kids) love Bingo. Can I learn to love it, too?*

10. *Find my purpose, live without a single regret, and do meaningful things to help others (maybe that's not just one thing, but who's counting).*

My list extended beyond ten goals. When I looked at the three pages of scribbling, I knew I'd never be able to accomplish even half of the things

I wrote down. Some were too ambitious. Some were outright ridiculous. Regardless, they fired me up to start crafting more meaning into my life.

I strolled home invigorated. I reflected on my life and eagerly anticipated the life yet to come. Since retirement, I had focused on unambitious objectives but yearned to do something more meaningful. How would I begin with a list of more than three pages of ideas? I transferred each idea onto a notecard and placed them in a vase on my fireplace mantel. I'd randomly pick one daily and start on whatever was pulled out.

I selected the first card, *Embrace my fifty-plus status and renew my AMAC membership*. I had let my membership lapse after Julia signed me up. I still wasn't ready to take this on. I put it back in the vase and drew out another. The second card read, *Go back to college and finish what you started*. That was a good one. But I needed something more manageable for now. The third card I pulled read, *Write a letter to your younger self*. Now that I could do. So I retrieved my journal and pencils.

*Dear Younger Colette:*

*Can you believe it? Seventy is on the horizon for you. It's only a few months away. How'd you get there so fast, you might ask? Well, if you think time goes quickly when you're young, you've seen nothing until you reach our current age. Time is flying by. And I'm not a spring chick anymore. I'm a clucking mother hen with lots of creaks in her bones and aches in her joints but a helluva lotta advice in her brain. I have a love/hate relationship with getting old. All your life, you'll hear messages to embrace your age. Then you'll be confronted with thousands of ways to defy it. I don't know what to tell you to do. It's all so confusing. Don't try to figure it out. Just shop for more shoes. It all boils down to shoes. (You'll still love them at this age).*

*Remember when Julia had her quinceañera? Oh wait, you weren't there. You were home sick with chickenpox. Anyway, her dad switched out her shoes. That's kind of what happens in life. Getting old is like wearing out your favorite pairs of shoes repeatedly as you transition into new stages. It's hard to give up your favorite pair when they wear out, but then you step into a great new pair. And who doesn't love a new pair of shoes? Thank goodness I still don't have the same shoes I had as a teenager. I've worn some magnificent ones along the way. I've evolved right along with my shoes. I don't wear skyscraper-high stilettos anymore. They hurt my bunions and don't do my back any favors. But I made dumb choices along the way out of vanity. I'd suffer through the worst pair of stilettos because they looked good. But now, I say to hell with those, and I wear kitten heels. I fully expect that the kitten heels will be replaced with flats. But so help me, I'll NEVER wear geriatric shoes when I get really old. I swear on Imelda's grave.*

*My point with shoes is this: Do what makes you feel good. Be comfortable in your own shoes and your own skin. I can tell you dying your hair and getting plastic surgery will make you feel good about yourself, which translates to a better attitude in life. Julia feels good in her wrinkled skin. I feel good in my sculpted skin.*

*I've developed granny chic. I don't dress my age or act my age because there's no such thing as "age-appropriate," no matter what people tell you. Let me add, dear youthful self, old is not something I am. Old is something I can become if I choose to. But I choose not to be old. It doesn't mean I won't increase in age or slow down. I fully expect to. I've already slowed down in lots of ways. I maintain an optimistic attitude that aging doesn't have to be negative. Don't fear it. I continue to ascend the U-curve of happiness in life, and the view from up here is spectacular. In closing, live true to yourself. And wear whatever damn shoes you want!*

*Love, Yourself*

*P.S. Julia will tell you lip fillers and spandex are not your friends. Don't believe her!*

*P.P.S. You do not have a sell-by date. That's distasteful. I promise you won't expire like soured milk.*

# Septuagenarians
## Ages 70 – 79

**JULIA, 70**

Having worked in the field of gerontology for so many years, I had a stellar understanding of the complexity of the maze of older adult services. After navigating through the red tape of agencies and the intake process for nursing homes and home and community-based services, I was a pro. The same was true for social security. I knew all the rules and strategies of when to collect social security. I always preached to wait until you're seventy to get the most benefits. I also knew to apply three months before I wanted to collect. As a reminder, it was penciled on my calendar three months before my seventieth birthday. So, with my superior knowledge, getting the benefits in place was supposed to be a piece of cake. However, when nothing arrived in the mail today—my seventieth birthday—I called, only to discover they had lost my paperwork. I was forced to start the process over again.

After numerous phone calls that resulted in frustration over the SSA representative's obvious lack of understanding of my case, I drove the sixty minutes to the local social security office. Meeting face-to-face would speed this process up. This was how I would spend my seventieth birthday—fighting the social security system.

The parking lot was jam-packed. I was grateful to see they had a senior citizen designated parking place. I'd take advantage of my age whenever I could. Before I could snag the spot, a young kid no more than eighteen pulled into it.

"Hey, kid, do you see the sign? You're not a senior citizen," I yelled.

"I see it, granny. The sign says 'For Senior Citizens.' I'm a senior in high school and a citizen in this fine town," he justified. He flipped me off and walked away. The nerve of that hooligan. He should be grounded.

I was forced to park in a lot across the street. I scurried to cross the road when the pedestrian walk light turned red much too quickly. I was only halfway there. As I picked up my pace, a giant tractor trailer barreled down the street as if to take aim at me. My Heavens, I was going to be hit by a green machine. I felt like a squirrel going back and forth trying to decide which way to cross the road. Out of nowhere, I began to sing, "Grandma got run over by a John Deere." I belted out the wrong lyrics as I completed the journey of a thousand miles simply to collect social security. I could see the headlines now and wondered if this is where the joke "Why'd the chicken cross the road?" came from. So the retiree could live long enough to see her first check.

Upon entering the building, I faced a crowded waiting room full of bored patrons staring at closed-captioned TVs. I pulled a number from the ticket kiosk and entered the race of the waiting game. I glanced at the digital screen above the counter to discover I was only forty numbers away from being called. The upside? I was one ahead of the person who walked in behind me.

Two hours later, my number finally popped up on the screen. I felt like I had won the lottery when my number was called. I rushed to the desk, thinking that would speed up the process, and took a seat across from the clerk. The girl, who looked to be in her mid-twenties, was entirely disinterested in her job.

"Can I help yuh?" she asked without looking at me, loudly smacking gum between her teeth.

"I'm here to apply for social security," I said.

"You and a hundred others," she retorted under her breath.

The next forty-five minutes were spent arguing with this underqualified girl giving me bad advice. Feeling the heat of frustration rise, I argued back, knowing my options. As she continued to dispute them, my voice began to elevate.

"Ma'am, I'm gunna need yuh to chill out. Yuh think yur the only Q-tip I deal with who thinks they know everything about social security? Lots of bad advice from them financial planners out there," she accused.

"This isn't the advice of a planner!" I yelled. "This was the information I was given on the phone by one of the social security administrators!"

"Yuh've been misinformed," she said.

The level of contradictory information I received was alarming. I didn't even know how to resolve the problem with this inexperienced dimwit.

"This is unacceptable. I expect accurate information from you. You're all ill-trained, understaffed, and more confused than ever!" I yelled at the clerk. "Don't you know I'm a senior citizen who worked in the senior care industry, and I've earned this benefit?"

"Yup, and all the other crazy cotton balls that come in," she said.

With that, I lost it. I yelled like a crazy lady. The visitors in the building turned their attention toward me. I was creating a scene, but I didn't care. I was getting nowhere with this blockhead, so maybe a little drama would help my case.

"Ma'am, I need yuh to relax, or I'm gunna call security."

"Please do. Maybe they can help me more than you can!" I yelled.

She pushed a button behind her desk, and within thirty seconds, an armed security guard overshadowed me.

"Is there a problem?" the guard asked.

"Yes!" I yelled louder. "I need social security, and no one seems capable of helping me!"

"I understand. But if you don't calm down, I will need to escort you off the premises," he warned.

"YOU CAN'T ARREST A SEVENTY-YEAR-OLD GRANDMA ON HER BIRTHDAY!" I screamed at him.

"No?" With that, the security guard threw cuffs on my right wrist, wrapped it around my back, and locked it in my left wrist. He walked me out of the office while concerned faces stared at me being hauled off in a paddy wagon.

I had become *that* woman—the crazy old bat who stereotypically yells at people and whacks them with her purse. Except I didn't hit anyone with my purse. But I had come undone in public. Is this what a nervous breakdown looks like? I had no idea. I did feel proud in a way, like I took one for the team, for the countless irritated senior citizens who fought to get their social security benefits.

I was booked in jail for disorderly conduct. I hung my head in shame. I was a disgrace. I had acted like a child. How could I be so juvenile to end up in jail? What if I run into someone here? But who was I going to run into in jail? My friends aren't the jailbird type. Little did they know I was. I would be disowned for my antics. I had better act appropriately for my age from now on. At least I didn't have to change into a jail uniform. I never did look good in orange or stripes.

I posted bail and took a cab home. I refused to tell anyone I was arrested for disrupting the peace on my birthday. On the ride home, I heard on the radio a short news story about an elderly woman arrested at the social security office. I was more outraged that they called me elderly than I was about the story. Fortunately, they didn't identify me by name.

I was ordered to attend a court hearing a few weeks later. I wore a frumpy house dress, knee-high socks with sandals, and a plastic bonnet to age me. I wanted the judge to pity me—a feeble little old granny on a fixed income. I tried to persuade him that I was not a criminal. I'd just had a rubber band-snapping moment. Every woman was entitled to at least one in her life when she was stretched too far.

The judge wasn't convinced. As a bona fide offender of disorderly conduct, I was ordered to pay a hefty fine and sentenced to community service.

Ironically, my first social security check arrived three months later—just enough to cover the fine. And for community service, I was sentenced to work at a senior center. Go figure!

• • • • • • • • • •

## COLETTE, 71

I poured myself a cup of herbal tea and sat down at Mom and Dad's empty dining table. I opened the newspaper. I had been dreading this moment for the last week. No, that wasn't true. I had been dreading this moment my whole life.

I wrapped up in a blanket to warm myself from the chill that settled into my bones from shock. I reluctantly flipped to the obituary section. And there they were—my parents.

They had died tragically together in a car crash. I still couldn't comprehend it. The investigators reenacted the accident scene and determined it was Dad's fault. The grief was overwhelming. I also had to shoulder some guilt. I wanted to take his keys from him, but he adamantly refused. I was wracked with the pain of thinking I could have done something to prevent this. I should've just stolen his keys. Why did the elderly hold so firmly to their independence even when it wasn't safe?

Mom and Dad hadn't planned out their final wishes, so all the decisions fell onto me. I was frustrated that my parents hadn't been more prepared with their funeral planning. I was making rash decisions about something that should've been deliberated more carefully by them. Exhausted with all the sudden planning, I asked the funeral home to write their obituaries. I couldn't do it. As I sat there numb, I read their "death biographies" for the first time.

I felt suffocated. I hated death. I hated that my parents were gone. I read the lines over and over and sobbed. As I studied my parents' pictures that stared back at me, I wondered about the lives behind the portraits. Had I asked them the questions that mattered? Did I know them deeply? I realized I took my parents for granted. I hadn't told them often enough that I loved and valued them. I assumed they would always be here. And today, they weren't. I had so many more things I wanted to say to them. So many more questions to ask.

I had witnessed Julia slowly watch her husband and parents fade into death. But my parents' death was so unexpected. I didn't get to the heart of matters that mattered. I didn't want this same fate for my kids. I wanted to tell them things before it was too late. I wanted them to ask me questions, so I felt confident my legacy would live on through stories.

Reading my parents' obituaries, I faced my mortality. I was now the matriarch of the family. I was an orphan. The people who gave me life, looked out for me, and always had my back were gone. They were my anchors. Now I felt ungrounded. It was a strange feeling. I wondered if the pain of losing my parents would ever go away. I scanned the other obituaries, knowing many families were hurting over the deaths of their loved ones as well.

The obituaries ended, and the announcements switched to anniversaries, weddings, and births. The transitions of life mirrored the newspaper clippings. I glanced at the birth photos—images of new life and new possibilities in each of them. I admired the hopes and dreams captured in the faces of young bridal couples at the cusp of starting their lives together.

I turned the page to read the anniversaries. It was the smallest section of announcements. It was becoming rarer for couples to make it to seventy years, or even to forty for that matter. Death and divorce were to blame. A few long-time couples posed together, marking their golden and silver anniversaries. Knowing I wouldn't grace the newspaper with my anniversary photo made me lonely.

I had been angry with Gerrit for more than twenty years for causing the failure in our marriage. But I wasn't angry at Gerrit in this moment of my grief. I was sad that our life together hadn't turned out how I expected. I felt the urge to call and tell him I had forgiven him and, more importantly, to take ownership of my part in our marriage's demise. I had contributed in other ways to the failure. I hadn't cheated, but I wasn't the best wife. And after he left, I harbored resentment toward him for walking out on me. I still held on to this contempt two decades later, though he had moved on with his life. I had stayed mad at him all this time, but he wasn't eating my poison. I was. I was poisoning myself with my own anger. I needed to let it go and forgive him.

I called him up. Since our daughters were now adults, there wasn't a reason for us to talk anymore, and it had been a long time since we had spoken. Gerrit answered on the first ring.

"I'm sorry," I said immediately. Those two simple words started an outpouring of long-overdue apologies on both sides. The hour-long conversation of kindness, compassion, and forgiveness had released me from the slavery of contempt. I felt lighter, happier, and freer. He offered to go to the funeral with me and sit beside me. My parents were close with Gerrit during our marriage, and he wanted to pay his respects. (I would have to wear my best revenge heels. Not to get back at him, but to show him I looked great even twenty years after our divorce).

I sat in the front pew of the church for Mom and Dad's funeral. Gerrit was on one side of me. Julia was on the other. My daughters sat next to Julia. I sobbed, looking at both caskets. After the funeral had ended, everyone exited for the luncheon in the church basement. I remained frozen in my seat. Gerrit stayed with me. It seemed appropriate to finish one last piece of business with him. I handed him Granny Smith's engagement ring.

"Gerrit, I'm giving this back to you. It was spiteful to keep it. The ring belongs to you and needs to stay in your family."

"Thank you, Colette. That means a lot to me," he said sincerely. "We might not have been good spouses but we were good parents. You are an exceptional mom. I'm so grateful we got to make our peace. I care for you, Colette, and I'm sorry for hurting you. Thank you for forgiving me."

"Thank you, Gerrit," I said. I placed the ring in the palm of his hand, sad to part with the promises it was supposed to bring. He hugged me and left the church. I stayed seated, feeling at peace that our conflict was resolved. Now I could move forward and heal.

I had grown introspective, grappling with my parent's death. I realized death did that. Death showed me that time was of the essence to reflect, look inward, and tie up loose ends in life. Had I not grasped this, it would've been wasted grief. I cried harder than I ever cried. And I released myself of pain, regret, unforgiveness, and anger toward Gerrit. I felt freer than I had ever felt in my life. As painful as grief is, it's like a rainstorm washing over us to cleanse us. I had lost my parents, forgiven Gerrit, and now felt I was transformed into a different person—more loving and caring in the third stage of life.

• • • • • • • • • •

## JULIA, 72

It had been almost thirty years since quitting the nursing home. After I left, I transitioned my career to work in a multi-generational daycare center. There was compelling research about how bringing young children and older adults together in the same setting positively and significantly impacts both generations. The elderly thrived in the presence of youth. And the children learned from their older counterparts and had a greater appreciation for them. I had worked for years on this initiative and was very successful. But

I was tired and ready to hand off the reigns. I was admittedly slowing down now that I was seventy-two. I was ready to step into a new phase of life at a reduced pace.

I walked out of my office for the last time with my personal belongings jam-packed into a cardboard box. This was what my life in the workforce amounted to. A box with knick-knacks, a few family pictures, and a candy dish once filled with mints for meetings. I stopped refilling the dish when I announced my retirement. Now that empty dish made me cry. Retirement was also supposed to be lived out with Jack. He and I had made plans together for retirement. Now I was navigating the final chapter alone. Oh, how I missed him at times like this.

I found myself afraid of the abyss of this new chapter without a job. People raved about retirement, but I found it unsettling. All my adult life, I was on a career path with guard rails up to protect me. Now in retirement, the guard rails were gone, and I could go anywhere. Even off the cliff if I chose. I feared that was exactly where I'd end up. For decades I had a routine. To get up and go to work. There was no variation. I was like a lab rat. Go to work. Go home. Go to work. Go home. I knew the guard rails were waiting for me on Monday at 6:00 a.m. Life before retirement was clockwork. Life after retirement was clock-broken. I felt the anxiety of living without a schedule. I liked structure, and retirement didn't have structure. I would force myself to shift my perspective and focus on the transition positively.

Sleeping in. That would be a benefit. So the first night of retirement, I turned my alarm clock off to adjust to my newfound freedom. Sleeping in and waking up naturally to birds chirping would be the life. No more obnoxious buzzing of an alarm set to 6:00 a.m. Yet when I awoke naturally, it was 6:00 a.m. Ugh. My body had been programmed for so long to wake up at the same time I was unable to sleep in. I forced myself to stay in bed until a reasonable retirement time. What time do retired people wake up? I was a virgin retiree. I didn't know how this worked. How would I find my new circadian rhythm without guard rails and alarm clocks? I lingered in bed but was too bored to lie there any longer. I got up. The clock read 6:07 a.m. That was sleeping in, right?

I was also going to stay in pajamas all day. Just because I could. One of the benefits of retirement was I didn't have to get dressed up. And I wouldn't even brush my teeth. This was retirement, after all. I could do anything I wanted. No guard rails.

I made coffee. I read the newspaper—every single article and advertisement. I clipped coupons. An hour passed.

I brushed my teeth after all. Who was I kidding? I wasn't going completely rogue in retirement. I played solitaire with a deck of cards. Watered plants. Played more solitaire. Another hour passed.

I made toast and eggs. I never ate breakfast before, but I would now in retirement. I gave myself a pedicure. I cleaned the dust bunnies under the beds. A third hour passed.

It wasn't even 9:30 a.m. yet, and I'd accomplished more than I did on the weekends while working. Retirement was going to be great. I would get so much done. I made my list for the day of what I wanted to accomplish. I worked all day getting things checked off my to-do column. I even added things I had already completed so that I could have the satisfaction of crossing them off the list. I went to bed that night exhausted. I didn't even need to change into pajamas. Another benefit.

Day two of retirement: I woke up two minutes later than yesterday. Progress. And I stayed in bed ten minutes longer. I was doing well. I made my little checklist and felt victorious for all the red check marks to complete each task. A completed task list was like a trophy for me.

Day three of retirement: The clock read 5:30 a.m. I had gone backward with my goal of sleeping in. I was failing in retirement already. I hit a wall. Boredom was overtaking me. I didn't have anything to wake up to. There were no to-do things left on my list. I stared at the ceiling and cried. I pulled out the deck of cards and played solitaire in bed. Eventually, I dragged myself out of bed for a cup of orange juice. Okay, it was a mimosa, but who's paying attention anyway? I was retired. I opened the daily newspaper delivered to my door.

The headline read, *Retirement May Be Fatal.* No kidding! The article outlined research that the first year of retirement can be deadly—there's a spike in mortality because people lose their sense of purpose. I would need to find my new purpose as soon as possible. The data also showed retirement led to loneliness, which was as harmful as smoking fifteen cigarettes daily. That was depressing. I never smoked. I didn't want to die as if I had, like Mama.

My demise wouldn't be because of being a bored, aimless, lonely old woman. I needed retirement therapy. Was there such a thing? I needed someone to tell me this was all normal. I needed to reprogram myself to be okay with living in this space of slowness and boredom.

Colette would remind me how great retirement was. So I called her. Her cellphone rang until the recorded greeting came on. Dang it, she was still sleeping. I left a blabbering message.

"Colette, I think I need to retire from retirement. I thought retirement would be a reward, but it's turning out to be a punishment. I want guardrails, alarm clocks, and meaningful work, not just house chores, to fill my time. The time goes so slowly. How much solitaire can a woman play in a day? I will sink into the quicksand of depression and drink my days away from boredom. It'll be a slow, inactive death. Death by boredom. People will eulogize me and say retirement killed her. And solitaire killed her because it's such a solitary game. I'll be dead before the year is out at this rate. It is possible for someone to die of boredom, you know. Okay. Call me back, and if I don't answer, I'm either comatose on solitaire, drunk, or dead, which is all the same. I hope to hear from you before these events occur. Oh, and it's me, Julia."

And then it hit me. I didn't have to be a prisoner at home. I could still go places. Oh, the places I'd go in retirement. I pulled on the sweatshirt my co-workers had given me as a farewell gift. It was screen-printed with, *I'm retired. This is as dressed up as I get.*

I stepped out of the house for the first time in three days. This would be a field trip. I had all the time in the world to go places. I'd start with the library. I had scribbled down recommended books through the years, and now this would be the time to read them all. I'd check out the maximum of ten books at a time. It would be like winning the lottery. I had the golden ticket—a library card.

I treated myself to ice cream, and it was only 10:00 in the morning! I decided to go easy on myself figuring this retirement gig out. I could enjoy ice cream every day if I wanted. I would be compassionate with myself. I was rigid and too hard on myself. I needed to give myself space to make mistakes.

There was no roadmap in the journey of life. And certainly not in retirement, where it turned out to be the wild, Wild West. People settled into retirement in various ways. Some had a purpose, and others had none whatsoever. Some got lost, and others found a new path. I knew I had a lot of time to navigate my future on the autobahn of retirement, one step at a time.

As I licked the melting ice cream, I vowed to give myself a year of doing nothing in retirement—to embrace "nothing-to-do-ness." I would not make any major decisions in the first twelve months post-career. I wouldn't commit to any part-time work or volunteering, or service. I would allow myself to feel boredom and be okay with it. To slow down. No, I would slow up. But that didn't sound right. I would grow up. But I was too old to grow up, so I decided to bloom up. But then I sounded like a plant. So I changed it to glow up. That felt right. I was going to glow up in retirement.

I wondered if I was tipsy from mimosas, wired from too much ice cream, or buzzed from the newfound freedom I was experiencing. I wasn't sure. But in that moment of eating ice cream for breakfast, I knew I would be okay.

· · · · · · · · · ·

### COLETTE, 73

"I've become my mother," I groaned. I had boarded the motor coach loaded with loud, cackling, red-hatted women eager to take a road trip for a week of casino luck and beach bathing. We were going to the Jersey Shore.

I wasn't a gambler. I detested it. I had watched Mom waste Dad's hard-earned retirement savings on bingo cards, hoping for the windfall that never came. She would sit for hours stamping rainbow-colored ink daubers in a high-stakes game of bingo on Friday nights. I refused to be like that. Yet now I was channeling her by going on this casino getaway with Julia. I never thought it would happen to me. But it had.

Julia twisted my arm to join the Red Hat Society with her. She had even become a Queen as part of this mad-hatter association. She promised it would provide fun social opportunities, especially as we aged.

Becoming a member of the Red Hat Society required doing things with them. It wasn't enough that I could sign on the dotted line. There were outings. Chapter meetings. Even a pledge of agreeing to uphold the spirit of the RHS and greet my age with verve, humor, and style. It was a sorority for old women. To participate, I had to wear a red hat and gaudy purple clothes. At least I had a red hat—the one Granny Smith gifted me. It had been years since she passed away, and the hat was still a precious possession. I came to appreciate it even more as time went on. So I donned my red and purple garb to identify myself as a member of this ostentatious group and got on the bus.

As I was analyzing and judging the group, I was taking too long boarding. "Keep it moving, toots, the slot machines are waiting!" a woman behind me yelled, hurrying me along. I fumbled down the narrow aisle. My oversized red-brimmed hat bumped into the overhead bins, and my rear end brushed against the shoulders of the seated travelers.

*Travel is for small people,* I concluded silently. I was no longer the slim-framed giraffe of my younger years. I had gained thirty pounds since menopause. I had become my mother in dress size, too.

I found two empty seats beside each other and snagged them for Julia and myself. I hoisted my bag into the overhead compartment and took the seat by the window. I saw Julia making her way toward me behind another woman who sported an enormous red-brimmed hat—bigger than mine—purple leopard-print leggings and a green sequin shawl, complete with a purple feather boa. It was obnoxious. She sat down next to me.

"Hello, *señorita*. I'm Rosario. I sit here, *si*?" She asked in a thick Spanish accent.

"It's saved for my girlfriend. She's com—"

"No, no, you have new girlfriend," the woman interrupted, claiming the seat next to me.

I glanced at Julia, who nodded in understanding. She took the seat on the other side of the aisle.

"You have a name?" the woman asked.

"Colette."

"Rosario pleased to meet Colette," she said, shaking my hand vigorously.

"*¿Qué tal? señorita,*" I replied, trying to sound fluent in Spanish. I knew a few words of the language, having been immersed in Julia's family my whole life.

"*Estoy muy bien. ¿Cómo está?*" Julia broke out into Spanish, and the two of them chatted across the aisle for a few minutes, laughing like schoolgirls. She then turned to me, speaking in Spanish.

"I have no idea what you just said," I confessed.

"Imposter Hispanic," she joked.

"I am not an imposter. I can say ¿*Dónde está el baño*? And *mas vino*. That's what's important anyway—Where's the toilet? And more wine."

Rosario laughed hard, her brown teeth showing widely with her smile. "You need take Spanish lessons. Learn new language."

"I can't learn Spanish at my age," I said.

"*No es verdad*. Not True. Enough stifling your potential. Stop self-limiting thoughts, si. I learn French after retirement. Rosario learn new language at my age. Colette learn new language at your age. What Colette's age—feefty?"

Oh, I liked her already. We would get along just fine. She thought I was fifty. I wasn't about to admit I was seventy-three.

Rosario revealed she was ninety! I was shocked she'd admit that. Out loud. In public.

"What's your secret to looking so good?" I asked.

"How you say 'good pair of pants'?"

"Jeans."

"Si, genes—the Gloria VanderBilt ones." She laughed, cracking herself up with a bad joke.

She was spunky. And different from any other ninety-year-old I knew. Not that I knew many. She shared she was a tango instructor. I wasn't sure whether she was pulling my leg. She was appalled I didn't know how to dance, let alone speak another language. She said there was a Latin nightclub near our hotel, and she would teach me how to tango. After a few margaritas, of course.

"What's your secret to staying so active?" I asked.

"I enjoy good health cause I exercise my tushy with spicy dance and cheeky-cheeky. You don't use it, you lose it," she warned. "I also engage in brain aerobics. I take French lesson and cooking class, and today decide where I want to go next, si."

"You're the most active ninety-year-old I've ever met," I admitted.

"Senorita, call me seasoned adult," she said. "I spicy-spicy things up. I decide how to age, not based on limitations of ageist society but on how Rosario decides. Rosario lives outside the shadows of expectations. Rosario wants *los nietos*—my grandchildren—to see possibilities in life no matter what Rosario's creeky bones say. If I still tango at ninety, then I teach about living life to fullest."

She closed her eyes and paused. The pause lasted so long I wondered if she passed to the other side, right there in the seat next to me. I began to worry. I don't do spontaneous death of old people well. I took a compact mirror from my purse and held it under her nose to see if she was still breathing.

"You try to grope me? Get in own seat," she said, staring at me with one eye open.

"Just checking to make sure you're still living. I don't even care if it's to the fullest. I just want to make sure you're alive," I explained with a laugh.

"Rosario don't die on tour bus. Eiff. What you take me as—some kind of decrepit old woman?"

"Not at all."

"Good. Rosario sleep now."

"It was nice talking to you," I said. "And by the way, I hope to wear leopard leggings like you when I'm ninety."

"Gracias. You and me—new friends. We tango later."

She slept until we reached the Atlantic City casino and hotel—our home for the next three days. Forty women in red hats stepped off our bus into the heat of the coastal sun. We were quite the motley crew with our hideous hats and purple accessories. Our first stop was to the bathrooms. With a bus full of older women with weak bladders, using the bathrooms first was like hitting the jackpot.

For the rest of the weekend, Rosario and I were like sisters. She kept her promise and taught me how to tango. Or rather, to take a few steps of a muddled Latin dance with my two left feet. She encouraged me to take lessons when I returned home. She made me promise I'd challenge myself and keep my brain sharp by doing new things, including a little more "cheeky-cheeky."

"You be young in heart. You be smart with choices. You not get this lesson in life wrong. You can age however Colette chooses. It's all here," she said, tapping on my heart. "But first, Colette learn to tango."

And so there it was. I was going to get my tango on at seventy-three.

•••••••••

## JULIA, 74

"Grammy, why are we going to a cemetery to celebrate your birthday when it's not even your birthday?" my granddaughter Ayden inquired. She was sixteen now and blossoming into a beautiful young woman.

"Because I want to enjoy a picnic to celebrate my life, and since my birthday is in the winter, it's too hard to do it with snow on the ground," I said. "So I'm creating an early bird celebration today. We're going to pick out my final resting place."

I walked through the cemetery holding her hand. I carried a picnic basket in the other. My daughter Carolann and her husband lagged, taking their time walking past the weathered tombstones. I wanted Colette to join us, but she refused to go to a cemetery for any reason—even a funeral.

It was a crisp late fall day. The leaves had fallen and littered the earth in shades of rust and brown. The scent of decomposing leaves filled the air. It was quiet, except for the dried leaves crunching under our footsteps. It was peaceful. Something about cemeteries gave me that sense of serenity.

My new cellphone rang in my pocket, disrupting the preferred silence. My phone was so new I struggled with figuring out how to answer it. Ayden grabbed the phone from me and, like an expert, touched the screen and answered it. Amazing! Kids and technology these days.

"Hi, Colette. Grammy is buying real estate in the cemetery," Ayden said. "We're shopping for land right now."

Ayden handed me my phone.

"I would've taken you to an insane asylum if you wanted to do crazy," Colette joked.

"I'm shopping," I acknowledged, laughing.

"At a cemetery?"

"Yes, and I'm also buying a plot for you."

"They better give you a buy-one-get-one-free deal," Colette teased. "I won't take up too much land. You know I want to be cremated."

"Only the finest for you, my dear—a clearance-priced grave," I joked back. "My doula told me to do this."

"Your doula? Aren't you a bit old to be having a baby?"

"Not that kind of doula. An end-of-life doula. She's helping me plan my death and end-of-life affairs so I can pass dignified."

"A death doula? Only you would hire the grim reaper. Don't you think it's morbid to bring your family to a cemetery for a picnic?"

"I'm picking out my burial place. When I go to Heaven, I won't leave my family in Hell trying to figure out my affairs. It's worse for them to make burial decisions when they're grieving and I'm gone. So I'm doing them a huge favor," I explained.

I knew that 60 percent of people lacked a will or had their estate affairs in order. I wanted to lead by example for my family.

"Why'd you call anyway?" I asked.

"Good grief. I don't remember," she confessed with a chuckle. "I'm having a senior moment."

"Why don't you call it a junior moment when young people forget something?" I inquired. "I'll call you later after I put a down payment on our future homes."

I handed the phone back to Ayden for her to show me how to end the call.

"Here, I'll let you hang it up. I can't figure it out."

"Grammy, you sound so old-fashioned," she chided. "You don't hang up a cellphone. You turn it off."

I didn't see the difference. But apparently, it made me sound not very cool to want to hang up my cellphone. I took her hand again and followed the groundskeeper to the burial plots ready for new owners. He stopped at a clearing.

"This plot here is a beautiful location with trees that overlooks the pond. I think you'll like it," he said, spreading his arms wide to show off the land.

"You realize I won't be looking at the pond or trees when I'm pushing up daisies," I joked.

"Of course, but your family will be. They get to enjoy the scenery," he replied.

"No, we won't," Carolann interjected.

"Because you won't be coming to visit?" I questioned.

"Because we'll be too sad to enjoy the scenery," she clarified.

Her eyes welled up in tears as we talked. She wrapped her arm around my shoulders and squeezed me. It was hard for her to imagine not having me around. I understood her pain. I was a daughter who ached having my mother gone. I knew how it felt. But I wanted to make my death easier for her when the time came. Hopefully, she could appreciate this setting before I was lying beneath it, and the beauty was lost in her eyes. The landscape would change for her once I was buried here. She wouldn't be able to look beyond the sorrow of my tomb and recognize the beauty of the surroundings. She would only feel the loneliness, and today I wanted her to see the loveliness.

"Give me time to talk to my family," I requested of the groundskeeper. He nodded and left us. I set the picnic basket on the ground and pulled out a blanket. I asked Ayden to spread it on the grass. I took out a bottle of sparkling grape juice and a decorated birthday cake. My son-in-law poured the non-alcoholic juice into crystal goblets.

"Mom, don't you think this is all a bit much?" Carolann asked. She looked uncomfortable with this unconventional picnic.

"Why? Because I want to share this moment with my family?" I replied. "This is my final resting place—the last place I'll ever be on Earth. I want to take it in with all of you. Who knows when I'll return here? But when I do, I won't be alive to enjoy it."

My family sat down reluctantly. They weren't embracing this quite like I was. I pulled out a packet of papers from the picnic basket. I handed them copies of my trust, advance directives, durable power of attorney, and other legal documents.

"What's all this for?" Carolann asked.

"People do not adequately prepare for death. I'm giving you copies of my last wishes, a do not resuscitate order, and funeral arrangements, even down to the final details of the songs I want to be played."

"Mom, are you dying?" Carolann asked in a panic. "Is that what this is all about?"

"We're all dying. We just don't know when," I replied gently. "I want everything in order to take the burden off you. I don't want this to get tangled up in probate court. I don't want to be on life support if there's no chance of survival. I don't want fights over who gets my belongings. I'm doing this for you, so you don't have to make the decisions when I can't."

"I hate talking about this stuff," Carolann said.

"You and the rest of the world. But burying your head in the sand doesn't change the outcome of burying me. Death requires tough decisions, and I've outlined all mine in these pages."

"I'll read through them some night when I have insomnia," Carolann said, mustering a laugh.

"Let's toast," I said, holding up my goblet. "May the dash carved on our tombstones between the date we're born and the date we die be long and filled with abundant health, happiness, and purpose—a dash full of joy, goodness, and love. A dash filled with hope in knowing the end of the dash isn't the end."

"What a beautiful toast. Here, here!" my son-in-law bellowed, his words echoing through the stillness of the cemetery.

"To life and death," I added.

We toasted our wine goblets, the crystal clinking together. I lit the birthday candles.

"Have you ever considered that your death date comes around once every year, too, yet you pass over it simply because you don't know when it is?" I asked.

"Grammy, you should make a wish as if it is your birthday," Ayden chimed in.

I closed my eyes and quietly wished that my remaining years would be met with courage. I knew my time left would be full of loss. What an oxymoron that was—full of loss. I pondered the statement—the loss of ability, health, and loved ones. The losses would be abundant. I would soon enter a season of minimization. The things that filled my life—material possessions, the companionship of friends and family, health, even my abilities—gradually waned to prepare us for moving on to the next life. This diminishment gave us a yearning for Heaven that may not have existed as deeply if our lives were still as abundant as they were in our youth. The simplicity of the next season of life would allow me to let go more easily. I had begun to weep as my thoughts pondered the exit of this life.

"Grammy, you're crying. We're not burying you here today, you know," Ayden said.

"Of course not. We're celebrating life today," I said. I wiped tears from my eyes.

"So if the dash is about our life, then why is the obituary, which is supposed to describe the dash, so boring?" Ayden asked.

"Oh, you are a smart cookie. I don't know why they do that. Maybe you can write a more interesting obituary for me."

"What should I say in it?" she asked.

"Well, look at the beauty of autumn all around you. The seasons change in nature. They change in life. They're all beautiful. I transitioned from being a little girl to a young lady, to a mother, and now to a grandmother. They're all beautiful seasons of life. And someday, I'll move to another season of life—the afterlife in Heaven.

"You won't be able to see me then. But you can come to this spot where my grave will be, and you can talk to me. I'll still be with you in spirit. You won't see my physical body anymore, but my spirit will still exist. Does that make sense?"

"Yes," she said. "Grammy, are you afraid to die?"

"No. Death doesn't scare me. Now that I'm older, I'm less afraid of it. I was scared of dying when I was young, but not now."

"Will I be scared of death when I get older?" Ayden asked.

"You won't. When you get older, you understand death is just a part of life. The mystery of it makes more sense the older you get."

"But I'll miss you," she said sadly.

"I know. But you'll feel my love when you think about me. And it's times like this you'll always remember. Someday you'll get a big chuckle remembering this early birthday party where we ate cake on my gravesite. That can go in my obituary."

Ayden laughed. My family began to relax with this unconventional celebration. Death was not an easy subject for families. Too many families were unprepared for death—even when they knew the end was in sight. It's necessary to have these conversations. We cannot deny death. It's easy to pretend we'll somehow escape the outcome. But if we could just talk about it, we could accept its reality more easily. It is simply the destination of this remarkable journey we're on.

• • • • • • • • •

## COLETTE, 75

I was seventy-five and learning tango. In preparation for my lessons, I carefully shopped and tried on dozens of ballroom shoes. I finally settled on a pair of black satin Latin shoes. They were strappy with a three-inch heel. They might have been too high, but I didn't want to sell myself short. I was up for the challenge of too-high ballroom shoes for my lessons. Since Rosario had encouraged me to take up dance lessons, and it was on my bucket list, it was time to find out if I could be a granny dancing sensation.

My first tango lesson was with an Argentinian man chiseled like a marble statue. Leonardo DaVinci himself may have sculpted his body. His white T-shirt was glued to the curves of his chest and abs. And his buttocks and glutes were carved into his tight black pants. I broke into a nervous sweat but was too old for hot flashes. This mythological creature had an effect on me.

"What do you want to get out of dance lessons?" he asked, his thick accent dripping with sex appeal. I swooned at his voice and his tanned skin. I could still spot sexy when I saw it. That didn't go away no matter what age I was.

"I want to shake things up, light a fire," I laughed. I wasn't sure what flame was still left burning. My sex life had been on life support for decades, but maybe tango would reignite passion in me.

To add to his already dripping sex appeal, he knew how to woo me—calling me seductive things like *mi vida*. It was nice to be romanced, even if I was paying him to do it.

My first dance lesson was awkward and clumsy. I was unbalanced and unsteady. I should've bought two left shoes to match my two left feet. I was slow and stiff. My rickety old body didn't have the flexibility and coordination it once had. My right elbow creaked and my left knee clicked. I was out of my league and out of shape compared to the other dancers engaged in lessons.

"*Mi amor*, you are the best seventy-five-year-old I've ever taught," he encouraged.

I knew he was full of poppycock. "I'm the *only* seventy-five-year-old you've ever taught," I joked.

"You've got embers inside of you just waiting to be fanned into fire," he gushed.

The lesson continued with my two left feet tripping over themselves. No matter how beautiful the ballroom shoes were, they didn't match the feet inside them. And then it happened. He dipped me. I lost my balance. My foot got tangled. I fell to the floor and felt the pop. I knew immediately I had broken a bone in my right foot from the pain and sensation. I lay crumpled in terrible agony.

The X-rays revealed a break in two places. The emergency room doctor said it wasn't uncommon for women "of a certain age" to break bones due to osteoporosis. I had to have surgery to piece my foot back together with rods and screws. The doctors thought I had a screw loose for taking up tango at my age. I surmised they screwed them in extra tight in my foot to prevent me from wearing ballroom shoes again.

That was it for tango. My aspiring career as a seventy-five-year-old ballroom dancer was over. I hadn't even broken in my ballroom shoes yet, but I had broken my foot.

"You will have to trade your ballroom shoes in for a supportive shoe," the doctor ordered. "After everything heals, get fitted for a good shoe, or you'll have chronic foot problems and pain the rest of your life."

"This is terrible news," I said to the doctor.

"I know. I'm so sorry you broke your foot."

"I'm not talking about my foot. I'm talking about having to trade in stilettos for orthos," I clarified.

Eight weeks later, I got fitted for a pair of geriatric marshmallow puff shoes—like the stereotypical old-lady orthopedic style. They were even called "Bingo Beige" on the Pantone color chart to represent the population that wore them. The shoe specialist recommended I go with the Velcro style with an extra thick arch. When I tried them on, it was like walking on a cloud that melted with each step. They felt heavenly. But they looked hideous.

Julia had already succumbed to wearing puff shoes like these—not because she had to but because she *wanted* to. If I had to surrender to these shoes, I was going to at least look like a fashionista donning them.

It's revealing how a shoe style can give your age away. So, I did what any sassy seventy-five-year-old would do; I sassied them up with bling. If I had to wear them, the least I would do was look like a fashion queen. I painted them red with leather paint and glued on silver craft rhinestones. The shoes were now bejeweled and glamorous. They were flashier than the ballroom shoes I had given up. Without even knowing it, I would start a shoe sensation.

• • • • • • • • • •

## Julia, 77

I noticed I had become invisible since reaching my senior years. At one time, men paid attention to me. They checked me out, glanced at my cleavage, and did a double-take. Now I was never noticed. They didn't see me like they did when I was young and voluptuous. At this age, my breasts hung to my belly button. A man wouldn't even know where to locate them.

"You need to get back in the saddle again with dating," Colette informed me. "It's been over twenty years since Jack died. Doll yourself up with a short skirt, revealing blouse, and pair of kitten heels and put yourself back on the market."

"Oh please, that ship has passed," I laughed in protest.

Colette and I had met up at a coffee shop. We were never short of things to talk about. If we did run out of conversation, Colette would attempt to be a comedienne, like now, in determining whether I should date again.

"You're only as old as you feel," Colette said. "Age is just a number."

"Colette, you sound like me," I teased. "It sounds dreadful to put myself back into the meet market after all this time. Or is it a 'meat' market?" I asked, still laughing. "The last time I went on a date, I was in my thirties with Jack. I don't know how to do it anymore."

"Do *it* or date?" Colette joked. "They're not the same thing. But they're both like riding a bike. It comes back to you."

"I can't imagine putting myself in the dating scene again," I said. "At this age, I'm too set in my ways. I don't want to cook for anyone in the kitchen. Or cook things up in the bedroom."

"Good grief, Julia, you sound like you're ninety."

I filled my coffee cup with cream, no sugar. I was worried about developing diabetes, so I recently cut sugar from my diet. Colette poured teaspoons of it into hers and grabbed a newspaper.

"I know the best place to find a man who's lonely, needy, and desperate to have a woman in his presence," she said.

"Where's that? Prison?"

"Better," she quipped. "The obituaries."

I laughed loudly. "That's better? A dead man is the answer to finding love?"

"Not a dead man. A grieving husband. You want to hunt for a widower."

"Scrolling through the obits to find a grieving widower whose wife has died? That's your answer to finding love?" I groaned at the absurdity of it.

"Think about it. You're guaranteed he's single, available, and needs a little lovin' to help him through the rough patch of grief. It's brilliant," Colette explained.

"It's disturbing."

"It's modern dating."

"It's morbid romance."

As I sipped the bitter coffee that desperately needed sugar, Colette combed through the newspaper, making side notes next to each woman whose obituary was profiled. She talked under her breath: "Too old... Sounds dull... Not adventurous enough..."

"You're judging the quality of a grieving husband by his dead wife's obit?" I asked incredulously.

"Uh, yeah. It reveals a lot about his life. For example, if she had a long, drawn-out illness, he's obviously a loving, dutiful husband who cared for her. You want this kind of loyalty and someone to take care of you when you get old and sick."

I groaned at her ridiculous assumptions.

"Well, what if he gets old and sick first, just like Jack did? Then I have to play caregiver again."

"You'll care for each other," Colette said, pleased with herself for coming up with a solution for my life. She returned to obituary surfing.

"I found him!" Colette shrieked, still talking in broken phrases as she read. "Leaves behind devoted husband... Lots of loving grandchildren.... Enjoyed travel."

"How sad," I said.

"How wonderful!" she exclaimed. "Visitation is from 6:00 p.m. to 8:00 p.m. tomorrow, which fits perfectly with my schedule."

"I am not going to be a part of this," I objected. "This is madness."

"Julia, what do you have to lose?" Colette insisted. "We can make a brief appearance. Pay our respects. You know—check him out. I'm picking you up at 6:00 p.m. You better be ready. Wear something black and seductive that shows off your cleavage."

Colette finished her last sip of coffee, handed me the newspaper, and left the coffee shop. I glanced curiously at the obituary. This was not a good idea.

The next day Colette promptly arrived at 6:00 p.m. I begrudgingly got into her car. I still found the idea ludicrous, even if I was slightly intrigued. I wouldn't admit it to her, however.

"You're wearing a turtleneck," she accused. "How's that seductive?"

"That's as good as it gets for me," I said. We argued all the way to the funeral home about the definition of seductive. We arrived, and I got cold feet. Colette nearly dragged me in.

"Are you here for the Jones or Johnson funeral?" the mortician asked. I looked at him with uncertainty. I had no idea.

"Jones," Colette answered confidently.

"Please sign the guest book," the mortician instructed, leading us to the Jones' side of the funeral home. Colette smirked as she signed, giving us fake names. She was so proud of herself for playing matchmaker at a wake.

"Very well. Right this way, Dottie and Gertrude," the mortician said, reading the phony names Colette had added to the guest book. He pointed us in the direction of the Jones' memorial service.

"I sure hope you put me down as Dottie. I refuse to be called Gertrude," I whispered.

"Sure, whatever," Colette dismissed flippantly, waving her hand at me.

We approached the weeping crowd inside the parlor. The guests wiped tears and hugged—familiar sights at any funeral. We took our place in the receiving line that led to the casket. I was curious to see the man's dead wife. She was who I would have to compare myself to. *This is insane*, I thought, pushing the crazy suggestion out of my mind.

I listened to the well-wishers pay their respects:

"I'm so sorry for your loss..."

"She lived a good life..."

"In peace now..."

What was I supposed to say? Call me when you've forgotten her? Or maybe, I'm sorry for your loss. Can I take your loneliness away? Is that what you say to a grieving widower you want to date?

My hands perspired as I waited nervously to meet Colette's grieving man of my dreams. When we were up next, a very old lady, severely hunched over, greeted us.

"Thank you for coming. How did you know my husband, Frank?"

"Frank?" I asked, confused. I looked from her to the casket. Lying in repose was not a woman my age but a very old man—her *dead* husband.

"Uh, we went to high school together," I ad-libbed awkwardly.

"Really? You look too young to have gone to school with my Frank," she said.

She looked more confused than me. I didn't even try to explain. Colette elbowed me to move on when we discovered the grievous mistake of who was actually in the casket.

"I'm so sorry for Frank's passing. He was a lovely person," I quickly told her and rushed to take my place on the leather kneeler beside the casket. I said a brief prayer of forgiveness.

"Oh, God, please pardon me. This was all Colette's idea. She made me do it," I prayed under my breath. Colette hurriedly plopped down beside me on the kneeler.

"Rest in peace, Frank Jones," she whispered to the dead man. "Sorry it won't work out with Julia. But Julia's picky. She likes men who don't just have a soft heart, but a heartbeat."

"How did you screw this up?" I whispered tersely to Colette as we lingered at the coffin, paying our respects to the wrong person.

"I thought the last name was Jones. I guess it was Johnson," she whispered back, bowing her head and making the sign of the cross like she was praying.

"I told her I went to high school with him," I whispered.

"That's the best you could come up with?"

"I choked under pressure," I confessed.

We bid our final farewell to Frank and returned to the entrance to find the Johnson visitation.

"We were confused about who we were here to see," Colette apologetically told the mortician.

He eyed us suspiciously. "Sign the guest book," he said for the second time without smiling.

"Should we cross out our names in the other book?" I asked him.

"Leave it!" he snapped. It seemed like a legitimate question to me.

Colette approached the guest book and waved me over. "What are our names again?" she whispered.

"You were Gertrude. I was either Dollie or Donnie," I said.

"I thought it was Daisy."

"No, it was Dolly," I argued in hushed tones.

"Ladies, is there a problem?" the mortician sternly asked. He seemed to sneak up on us and appear suddenly. We jumped.

"No," Colette answered. "All set, thank you."

"Just go with Daisy," I whispered to her.

Colette signed our names—Gertrude and Daisy. The mortician looked at the signatures and gave us a disapproving glare but ushered us in any way. Once again, we took our place in the receiving line. I decided I'd be gracious to the grieving husband, but in no way was I going to try and hit on him. My nerves were too rattled after the last exchange.

"Mr. Johnson?" Colette asked happily as we approached the sad widower, ensuring we were at the correct funeral this time. He nodded.

"I'm so sorry about your wife's passing," I said.

"Thank you," he said. "She was a remarkable woman. The love of my life. My best friend. My soulmate. I can't imagine living a day without her. No one can replace her." He broke down in a torrent of tears.

"Oh, don't be so sure," Colette said in a cheap attempt at consoling him. "There are plenty of wonderful women you could meet. In fact, let me introduce you to—"

Mr. Johnson excused himself from the receiving line, sobbing hysterically. The others in line followed, crying harder as they watched him lose his composure. They handed each other tissues and embraced in hugs. They offered tissues to us, too. I dabbed at invisible tears.

Colette and I took a spot on the kneeler to pay our respects to another stranger in a casket.

"They were clearly madly in love, the way he broke down," I whispered, bowing my head. "I don't have a chance against her."

"You're right. She's gorgeous, even dead." Colette said. The insult was not lost on me. "I wonder who did her face. I need to find out who her surgeon was."

Colette peered closer at Mrs. Johnson's face; her head was now nearly inside the casket.

"Ma'am, if you're going to kiss her goodbye, please do it now, so the rest of the line can move along," the mortician scolded, performing his sudden reappearing act again.

Colette was forced to put her lips on the dead woman's cold and lifeless forehead and give her a parting kiss. She came back to the surface looking as pale as the corpse. The blood had drained from her face. I patted the deceased woman's hands wrapped in a rosary, comforting her as if she was alive.

"You were a wonderful wife," I told her. "I promise I'm not going to steal your husband from you. He still loves you very much."

Colette and I—bona fide funeral crashers—said one final prayer, asking God to pardon our transgressions in trying to date dead people and their spouses.

"Father, forgive us, for we know not what we do."

• • • • • • • • • •

## COLETTE, 78 1/2

I had stumbled upon instant success with my bejeweled shoes. When I wore them, people complimented me, a conversation followed and then I would be commissioned to make a pair. Through word of mouth, I made dozens of pairs a week. Only by accident—literally—did I discover I was sitting on a gold mine of an idea. And I invented Spry Shoes. I had become an encore entrepreneur. That's what people who become business owners after the age of fifty are called. I had been dubbed the title because, like a special performance at the end of a concert, encore business owners saved their best act for last. This was my last gig. My encore. Plus, I was afraid of running out of money. I was a spender and I didn't want to give up my standard of living. I didn't want to outlive my money. I feared it more than death.

I began to build my encore career on a shoestring budget which meant getting educated about running a business. I had quit college and never graduated. It was one of my few regrets in life, and I didn't have many. So I enrolled in a local university to get a business degree. I was labeled a nontraditional student, which I believed was cryptic for an old learner. I discovered I was a better student this time because I returned on my own dime. I took my education seriously, unlike students fresh out of high school who wasted their parents' money partying and skipping classes (not that I knew anything about that kind of reckless behavior).

I was eager to learn. I didn't skip classes or party like young hooligans. I loved college. I raised my hand to give answers. I asked smart questions. I turned homework assignments in early and completed extra credit. I felt like the perfect college student, except pimples were replaced with wrinkles.

I found that going to school and running a business were taxing on me. At this age, I didn't have the same energy I once had. I got fatigued easier and couldn't pack in as much in a day. It was part of the aging process. But slowing down frustrated me. I couldn't accomplish as much as I used to. My shoe business was booming, and I hired full-time staff to help with the orders. We had gotten a large order out of the blue, and I needed help fulfilling it. It was a good problem to have. I just didn't have the stamina to work this hard.

I was set to walk across the stage with honors and receive my diploma. It was a small college, and most of the students on campus knew me because I was the oldest student enrolled. In fact, I was the oldest student ever to attend. Due to this distinction, I was asked to give the speech at the commencement. I wrote and rewrote my speech and tossed out many revised versions. This was an important moment, and I wanted to impart some wisdom to these young guns just starting in life.

On commencement day, I wore a cap and gown and a pair of bejeweled Spry Shoes. I welled up with tears as I approached the stage. I walked to the podium, adjusted the microphone, and took a deep breath. I scanned the audience for my family, and my heart burst with pride upon seeing them.

"I know many of you are shocked to see an older woman receive her diploma," I began. "You're probably thinking I should be pushing up daisies and feeding the worms; or swimming with fishes by kicking the oxygen habit. But I'm not. I'm still counted in the census. I was asked to speak today—not because I'm famous, and not because I've achieved some great notable accomplishment, but because I'm considered old. I'm the oldest student ever to take classes at this college. I'm seventy-eight-and-a-half years old." It was important to throw in the half. Every day counted at my age.

The audience applauded. I had captured their attention, and now I was going full throttle to inspire them. "I pride myself on the fact that I went back to school, not because I'm doing it in my seventies, but because I'm doing it at all. Why should my age matter? When will society not give it a second thought that older women want to achieve their goals? Why is receiving a diploma at my age such a noteworthy and far-reaching accomplishment that I've been invited to speak about it?

"But I was invited. So I will speak. Who cares how old I am finishing up college? Who cares that I'm the oldest student to walk this campus? I sure as heck don't. What I care about is that I'm fortunate to have the mental capacity to pursue higher education. I'm as fortunate as you. We all want the same things in life—health, happiness, and prosperity—regardless of age."

I felt the adrenaline build in me as I spoke to the predominantly youthful crowd.

"You can have all of this, even when you're as old as me. But let me tell you, you have to work at it like any good thing in life. Take care of your bodies today; you'll need them healthy tomorrow. Save your money early; you'll need lots of it for rainy days ahead. Living is so much more expensive than you think. Plus, you'll want to save for a facelift," I joked.

I wasn't sure if that elicited a chuckle or a groan. As new wisdom came to mind, I went off script.

"Step into my shoes momentarily," I invited my listeners. "My generation—we had to work hard for whatever we wanted. It didn't get handed to us. The sooner you learn that the better off you'll be.

"Make yourself happy today. Because if you're not happy today, you won't be happy when you're old. You have to seek it out and choose to be happy. That is one of the great lessons of life. Happiness comes from the inside. You can try to find happiness from external circumstances, but they're all fleeting. Oh, how I wish I knew half of what I know now at your age. I thought I knew it all. I realize I knew nothing. Nothing worthy, at least."

I paused and soaked up the limelight, not wanting this to end.

"People laughed at me when I told them I was returning to college. What's so funny about an older woman wanting to strengthen her brain and stay sharp? What's funny is not using your brain to pursue greatness every single day. As far as I can tell, if I'm still breathing, I'm still living. Too many old people give up too early. They give up on life, setting goals, and growing."

I was close to wrapping up but wanted to linger a little longer, sharing random thoughts.

"It is never too late to teach an old dog new tricks. But let me clarify I am NOT an old dog. What is the meaning of the word old anyway?" I asked. "The dictionary gives a few definitions. And yes, I had dictionaries in my day."

That got a chuckle from the crowd.

"One of the definitions of old is to be used for a long time, as in worn out, shabby, tattered, moth-eaten, ragged. But just because something is used for a long time, like my seventy-eight-and-a-half-year-old body, doesn't mean I'm worn out, shabby, tattered, or ragged.

"I'll finish with these poignant words. Let's put a new framework around growing old. Drop the word old. Let's call it growing. We aren't done growing until we're on the wrong side of the grass."

I finished my speech and earned thunderous applause and a standing ovation.

The department dean closed out the commencement and congratulated us on our achievements. When my name was called, I walked across the stage, showing off my blingy shoes. The dean handed me my degree, and I switched my tassel. I was *finally* a college graduate! It only took a lifetime to get my degree!

While the rite of passage traditionally involved students throwing their mortarboard caps into the air, my graduating class planned a surprise for me. Instead of dozens of caps flying into the sky, I watched a glittering wave of shoes fly heavenward. My fellow students honored me with a salute of Spry Shoes. I had never felt so esteemed, especially by young adults who respected me, as my bejeweled shoes rained down from the sky.

# Octogenarians

## Ages 80 – 89

# C OLETTE, 80

I received a postcard in the mail from a Florida retirement community. It was offering an all-expenses paid trip to tour their resort in exchange for attending a presentation about the amenities and benefits of owning a condo in "one of Florida's most luxurious retirement neighborhoods" as the postcard described.

I was so excited it was free. I was determined to go and wanted Julia to tour with me. She warily read the postcard. She said it looked like a sales gimmick and had all the trappings of a scam—there was a limited time to respond, a limited number of people they'd accept, and rock-bottom prices offered only to me. She cautioned she had seen enough seniors get scammed to know they were most victimized by these scarcity tactics.

"There's no such thing as a free lunch," Julia warned me.

"Maybe not, but what's the harm?" I asked.

"You'll be suckered into buying one of these overpriced condos," she said.

"I have enough willpower not to get duped."

"Believe me, these condo communities, like timeshares, exert high-pressure sales tactics," Julia explained. "It's very hard to walk away without getting sucked into their convincing sales pitches."

"Julia, you've always been the voice of reason. You're much stronger than me. Go with me then, so I don't get pulled in."

"You sure are a pea in my shoe," she said bluntly.

"Please go with me," I begged. "It won't cost a thing. They pay for everything."

"You need to read all the fine print before we go and make sure we don't get scammed," she insisted.

It took a lot of pleading, but Julia finally agreed. I knew she was strong enough for both of us to withstand the hurricane of pressure they would use. She would be my anchor to ensure I didn't get blown away by it.

When our flight landed, a driver from the resort was waiting for us at the airport. He was pleasant and courteous. He loaded our suitcases into the van and handed us pineapple drinks with decorative umbrellas. I was impressed. Julia was skeptical.

When he pulled into the entrance of the resort, I noticed it was a gated community and very swanky. A sign read, *The Laurels of Naples*. It was atop a waterfall of clear aqua water, flowing down into a colorful koi pond. The bright foliage surrounding it was spectacular.

Upon arrival, the driver transferred our suitcases onto a golf cart, and a concierge greeted us. We were escorted to a two-bedroom, two-bath condo overlooking the central pond with a fountain.

Our concierge brought in our bags and offered us another pineapple drink with an umbrella. They were going down easy.

"I'll let you relax for a bit. I'll come back in an hour to start the tour," he said, closing the door behind us.

"Look at this place, Julia!" I squealed. "I think I've died and gone to Heaven. This isn't a scam."

"Maybe not, but like I said, they will do an intense sales presentation," she warned. "You better have the resolve of steel not to buy into it."

"I won't. Besides, that's why you're here."

An hour later, the concierge reappeared with another round of pineapple umbrella drinks. Thank goodness the liquor was included in the expenses paid. During the tour of the grounds, we saw multiple pools, a golf course, tennis courts, and clubhouses. Activities were taking place, peppered with residents actively engaged. It was a vibrant atmosphere that appealed to both Julia and me. But we were not there to buy a condo. We were there to take advantage of a free weekend getaway.

The concierge led us to the presentation room. Two other couples joined. They also had pineapple umbrella drinks in hand. Maybe that's how the sales agents would wear us down—loading us up on rum. The presentation was fast-paced, high-pressured, and intense, just as we suspected. And it dragged on forever. I was eager to get to the pool. I asked if they could speed it up.

"We could," the presenter replied. "But if you read the fine print, it says you must listen to the *entire* presentation, or you'll have to pay back the entire trip."

"Didn't you read the fine print?" Julia whispered to me.

"No. It was too fine for even my magnifying glass," I said.

We were there for hours. Then they separated Julia and me to try and sell us one-on-one.

"Promise me you won't buy," Julia quietly urged as they ushered her into another room.

"Pinky promise," I swore. I sure hoped I wouldn't cave. I wondered if I had a strong enough backbone for this.

The sales agent pushed me hard. He was weakening my boundaries. He hammered away at me as if I was the marble and he was the pick.

"I'm not sure I'm ready to commit to this high-ticket purchase," I explained.

"But this selling price is the best you'll ever get. It's only available while you're down here. As soon as you return home, we can't offer you the same deal again."

"I'm going to need more time to think about it," I lied. I didn't need more time. I wasn't going to buy because I had pinky-promised Julia. They could see I wouldn't cave, so they gave up, and I was finally reunited with Julia. In her hand was an even larger drink than before. It was in a coconut shell with two umbrellas.

"Wow, how'd you get lucky enough to score that fancy drink?" I asked.

"I bought a condo."

So much for Julia's resolve. I had a stronger backbone than she did.

• • • • • • • • •

**JULIA, 81**

My daughter Carolann was more shocked than anyone by the news I was moving to Florida. I convinced her of all the reasons why this made sense. The cold was brutal on my arthritis; she no longer lived near me; if I was going to take a risk for once in my life, this was going to be it—and I better hurry because I didn't know how many more years I'd have left to step out of my comfort zone. It all sounded reasonable to me, even if it didn't to anyone else.

The easiest part was letting go of my home in Michigan. I had to sell it to afford the condo in Florida. But I embraced this change as a new opportunity. I had lived in Michigan my whole life. This was my chance to fly from my own coop. My home sold quickly. The opportunity to downsize and minimize was freeing for my soul. I packed up my belongings and hired a moving company to transport everything. They would haul them the 1500 miles from Grand Rapids to Naples and get a head start before I jumped on a plane to fly down.

The hardest part was saying goodbye to Colette. She said she couldn't say goodbye to me because it would break her heart. I was disappointed she wouldn't drive me, but I understood. I needed to do this by myself anyway. I had to fly out of the nest, spread my wings, and land on my own two feet. There weren't many risks I had taken in life. This was the biggest. It required pulling up my big-girl underpants.

Though Carolann had moved out of state, she did return to help me close up my house. She offered to drive me to the airport. My heart pounded with anxiety during the ride. My farewell to her wasn't as difficult because we had already experienced it when she moved away. She hugged me at the kiss-and-fly drop-off and drove away.

With my heart in my stomach, I pulled my carry-on luggage through the airport. I was already missing my community, my home, and Colette. I wished I would've had closure with her.

As I stood in line waiting to get through security, I heard my name called through the PA system, asking me to return to the ticket counter. I dashed back, uncertain what the problem was. And there stood Colette. She raced up to me and threw her arms around me.

"I couldn't do it. I couldn't let you leave without seeing you off," Colette cried. "I thought it would break my heart to say goodbye, but *not* saying goodbye hurt worse."

We cried and said our goodbyes. I walked away and didn't look back for fear I'd never want to leave. I boarded the plane and took my seat. I felt wistful. I kept telling myself change is another word for opportunity. Why was I trying so hard to convince myself? Had I made the right decision? Would I be okay? Uncertainty bombarded my thoughts.

A few hours later, I landed in Florida. I exited the airport and breathed in the warm, humid Floridian air. It smelled delicious. This was why I had moved away from Michigan. I had grown tired of the cold winter months, and the older I got, the harder it was on my arthritic body. There were far more benefits in moving down here than staying in Michigan. It would just require an adjustment period.

While I tried to be positive, tears flowed down my cheeks when my taxi driver pulled into the condo community. I saw so many residents playing games, lingering together, and engaging in group activities. I never felt lonelier. I was the new kid on the block. I was eighty-one, hoping to make new friends. Would these people embrace me? It was hard to break into social circles at my age. I had the same insecurities as a kindergartener walking into the classroom on the first day of school.

The taxi driver parked in my driveway, unloaded my luggage, and drove off. I stood on the sidewalk, staring at my new home—my new future. I had opportunities waiting. I would need to shift my outlook from fear and doubt to excitement and possibility. I carried my suitcase to the front porch and sat down. I pulled off my winter boots and exchanged them for flip-flops. It's like what I had just done with my life—swapped it for something completely new. I hoped I wouldn't regret this.

Just then, a nice-looking older gentleman pulled into my driveway in a golf cart and introduced himself. He wore a fedora hat, a white linen shirt, and khaki pants. I liked his style.

"I'm Michael," he said, flashing a smile so perfect it could be in a toothbrush commercial.

"I'm Julia," I replied. I eagerly shook his hand and smiled in return.

"You must be my new neighbor," he said. "I'm part of the Welcome Wagon. Let me help you with your luggage."

He grabbed it and brought it inside the house. Then he handed me a card with his number on it.

"Let me know what you need as you get settled in," he said with a wink. "I'm here for you."

I knew then that I was going to be just fine.

• • • • • • • • • •

## COLETTE, 82

I joined a local library book club called "Beers & Books." I was not a book reader—that was Julia's whacked-out sense of fun—but the beer part caught my attention. Where there was beer, there must be men. The library even provided the brews. They were motivated to bring together non-enthusiastic book readers like me and turn them on to reading. However, whether I'd renew my library card depended on how good the beer and men were, not on how great the books were.

In our first meetup, I grabbed a bottle of stout. I wanted to make an announcement, so I used a pen to clink my glass like I was making a toast. The group, all seated in a circle, quieted down and turned toward me.

"I have two announcements," I began. "First, today is my eighty-second birthday."

They all clapped. Except for a grouchy-looking twenty-something girl.

"Secondly, I'm moving to another country, and I need your help deciding whether to choose Greece, Italy, Costa Rica, or Japan."

Everyone sat silent. Dumbfounded even. Now mind you, I had never met these people before, but I was looking for their objective opinions and trustworthy advice.

"Reading has opened up a whole new world for me," I explained. "I read the book *The Blue Zones.* Okay, let me clarify—I glanced at the table of contents. But I discovered the cities of Ikaria, Sardinia, Okinawa, and Nicoya have huge populations of residents who live well beyond one hundred years old. In order to live that long, I need to move to one of these countries."

"And you want complete strangers to help you decide how to pack up your entire life, move to a foreign country, and live out the rest of it?" the grouchy twenty-something asked. She smirked with a look of disdain.

"Exactly," I said. This wouldn't be so difficult, after all. "I figured some of you might've traveled to one of these destinations and could tell me which one would be the best for me to move to permanently."

"What are you, like eighty-five?" the same girl asked, rolling her eyes this time. "Aren't you too old for that now?"

"Thank you very much, but I'm not *that* old. As I mentioned five seconds ago, I'm only eighty-two. Clearly, you must have hearing loss or dementia," I said with snark.

"Maybe you could start adapting your lifestyle first to see if you can incorporate the Blue Zone lifestyle habits," she advised with even more snark. "You realize it doesn't have to do with the actual city but the lifestyle choices the residents made over a lifetime, right?"

"Ahhh, so you know the book?" I asked. "You will be a great mentor for me. And yes, I could start with overhauling my entire life first, report back to you at next month's book club, and provide an update on how quickly I've turned the direction of my life to decide the best city to move to."

It seemed relatively simple to me. But the rest of the group had no advice at all. They were very disappointing.

After the meetup, I made the decision to become a Blue Zone groupie. Maybe it was a little late to start making healthy choices at eighty-two, but I thought about my financial advisor's advice that it's never too late to save. I figured it worked the same with cramming in healthy habits in the last decades of life. I read the book cover to cover—that alone was already a radical change in my life. The book identified the lifelong habits of the oldest and healthiest people on earth. If the centenarians incorporated these principles into their daily lives, I would too. The "Power Nine" principles included:

- Move Naturally

- Purpose

- Downshift

- 80% Rule

- Plant Slant

- Wine @ 5

- Belong

- Loved Ones First

- Right Tribe

I'd start by joining the local senior citizen recreation center to incorporate the principles. It was like a country club, but only for people over the age of sixty. The first principle I'd tackle would be to drink wine. I ordered a glass of Merlot. I learned Resveratrol, an antioxidant in red wine, was healthy for you. It raises your HDL cholesterol and promotes relaxation. I figured the more, the better, so I ordered another. These Blue Zone gurus drank red wine at 5:00, and lots of it. It was only 3:00, but getting a headstart meant I got healthier sooner.

The disclaimer in the book on exercise warned, *Before beginning any new exercise regimen, consult a healthcare professional.* In eighty-plus years of living, I never did this. Whoever went to the doctor to find out if you should start exercising? "It's a waste of time and health to exercise," said no doctor ever. The book discussed in depth how this population of centenarians and supercentenarians were very active, not by exercising, but with routine daily activities. They moved naturally. So I got off the barstool and moved to the other side of the bar to get my next glass of wine. This was natural movement.

The book promoted *hara hachi bu*—something about eating 80 percent. I didn't speak Japanese, so the term didn't make sense. I ordered a big fat steak cooked rare, a large basket of deep-fried onion rings, and strawberry cheesecake with chocolate glaze for dessert. I feasted until 80 percent was gone. I was stuffed to the point of feeling sick. I didn't quite understand how this was a good thing, but I was following the healthy eating habits of hara hachi bu.

The book taught me it was important to downshift, or reduce stress in life. Stress was a natural killer, so I needed to ensure my stress levels were under control. I didn't have much stress since retiring. And sitting here reading a book and drinking red wine was indicative of my stress-free life.

Loved ones first, right tribe, and purpose were the principles I already had nailed. I spent lots of time with family, and they came first in my life. My tribe was Julia and my family. And my purpose was to live to be one hundred.

Where I knew I would struggle with the Power Nine was having a plant slant by eating more plants. This was going to be tough. I loved meat, especially thick, red, juicy steak. So I decided I'd switch to grass-fed beef. If the cattle were eating plants, then their plant-based nutrition could be passed on to me if I ate them. And I would slant toward plants through the beef I ate.

Belonging to a faith-based community was the last of the Power Nine. Julia was a devoted Christian. I admired her faith and her trust in God's plans for her life. I fell more into the holiday church-going category. I struggled with the more profound questions of faith. They hurt my brain in trying to understand deep theological mysteries. I believed in God and knew I'd reach Heaven. But to improve this Power Nine principle, I could get baptized again. I was baptized as an infant but maybe I'd get baptized as an adult. I couldn't be saved too much, I figured.

After I finished my third glass of wine and packed up a doggy bag with my 20 percent remaining food, I needed a nap. I couldn't fathom why napping wasn't a Power Nine principle. This was the best part of my day. To think I had resisted naps when I was a kid. How could I have been so ignorant in rejecting this luxury? I questioned why naps weren't added to the nine healthy habits. Maybe in the next edition, the writers could scratch off the plant-slant theory and replace it with "nap slant" instead. At any rate, I would start the practice before the revised book was published.

For the next four weeks, I worked diligently towards my goal of embracing the Power Nine principles. I wanted to report back to my Beers & Books trusted advisors and share how well my health was improving. At our next meetup, I grabbed a bottle of beer and once again clinked the glass. The circle of attendees turned toward me.

"The Power Nine principles are working," I announced. "I'm confident I'll live to one hundred and beyond because I have begun adopting the habits of the Blue Zone peeps."

As they had done before, the group clapped. Except, of course, the twenty-something.

"There are two principles I'm struggling with. The first is belong. My best friend Julia encouraged me to read the Bible more as part of the belong principle. Holy cow, it's a big book! It will take me the rest of my life to finish, but I'm determined. It's like cramming for the final exam. And that is my new sense of purpose—to finish reading God's Big Book before I go to Heaven. If you haven't read it, I encourage you. There are scandalous stories in there. The story of David and Bathsheeba—geesh!"

The group nodded in approval and understanding. They seemed to already know the Bible, so they must be more saved than me.

"But the Power Nine kicking my butt is hara hachi bu. It's a Japanese term for eating 80 percent. I've packed on ten pounds since starting this. I don't think that seems right."

The twenty-something girl who rolled her eyes at me last time didn't feign her irritation with me this time, either. "Um, I think you got that backward," she piped up. Her words dripping in disdain. "You don't eat 80 percent of the food. You only eat until you're 80 percent full."

"Ahhh, that makes sense. Wow. I've been overeating for the past month. No wonder I gained ten pounds."

I finished my announcement, leaving 20 percent of the beer in the bottle. I was on my way with healthy steps like this. Now I knew how to live to one hundred and beyond. I was developing another Blue Zone right here in Grand Rapids, Michigan.

• • • • • • • • •

## JULIA, 83

Michael and I became fast friends. He lived directly across the street from me. He helped me unpack and get settled. He introduced me to his friends; shared the best activities to get involved in; and if I was looking for love, he cautioned me on which men to steer clear of.

Michael was a refined man. His skin was tan and weathered. Sun had left its mark after living in the Sunshine State his entire life. He had a bald head under the fedora he wore most of the time. He was handsome but was the type that didn't care, even if he knew it. He was three years younger than me.

It didn't take long before our friendship blossomed into a more romantic relationship. I never dreamed that I'd find love again so late in life.

"You're a cougar," Colette joked. She was right. I was technically a cougar at the ripe old age of eighty-three, dating an eighty-year-old man.

Colette warned me about sexually transmitted infections in retirement communities. She sent me articles about the rampant spread of STIs in Florida. The statistics were alarming. The articles discussed the promiscuous paradise amongst the geriatric population and the bustling black market for Viagra.

"If Michael's a gigolo, you need to protect yourself," Colette lectured. Michael wasn't a player. He was the quiet type and didn't get caught up in the dating scene here—which, yes, there was one, just like with any other population.

"Don't worry, the only crabs I'll be catching down here are the ones that burrow in the sand."

"But what about "key swap" parties?" she asked. I explained this was all sensationalism and propaganda.

"It's a gimmick to make retirement communities sound more salacious to increase sales," I explained. "Most of the golf carts we drive have a universal key, so it doesn't matter which key you swap because everyone still returns home to their own homes in their own golf carts."

I think she was disappointed that the rumors were a result of bad media reporting and urban legend. She wanted to believe I was getting frisky and throwing wild and raucous house parties down here. It was so not that.

"Michael and I aren't even consummating our relationship," I shared.

"You're kidding me? Why?" I could hear the shock in her voice.

I explained Michael went through a gray divorce. Or, as he called it—the silver shit split. He had no interest in remarrying. Michael was looking for companionship, but after a forty-year failed marriage, he didn't intend to tie the knot again. He was safe and kind and protective—a true gentleman. Over the years, it seemed like all the good guys had been snagged, but I found one. I got a great catch, even at the age of eighty-three.

Our relationship had evolved to where we were an exclusive couple. But sex was on the slow burner for both of us. It wasn't important at this stage of our lives. Instead, we wanted intimacy through non-sexual touch like holding hands and spooning. In truth, I think the cobwebs down there might've been too thick to get through.

Michael and I were more fulfilled cuddling in the sack than romping in it. We found satisfaction in this unconventional intimate relationship. And we were emotionally and physically connected.

We embraced the LAT—living apart together—lifestyle. Many nights we would fall asleep with our legs and arms intermingled like pretzels, and in the morning, he'd return to his condo across the street. We'd reconnect later in the day for a sport or activity. We'd have dinner, binge-watch TV, and snuggle in bed to enjoy our closeness. We enjoyed pillow talk. We connected through good, intimate conversation. We closed out the day wrapped in each other's arms without any pressure to perform sexually.

Like Michael, I didn't want to get married again, either. I had been on my own far too long. I wasn't sure I could adjust to giving up my freedom and independence. I didn't want Michael rearranging my life or telling me what I needed to do. That time of life when I would've been capable of sharing a home with someone had long passed. I was too set in my ways to change my lifestyle now.

As we lay in bed together once again, I reflected on what Michael and I had. Our relationship was perfect. Per our usual routine, we were in bed by 8:00 p.m., shared a long intimate kiss, and went to sleep. This was our version of late-night, steamy romance.

• • • • • • • • • •

## COLETTE, 85

Since Julia had moved to Florida, I was lonely. I had a harder time adapting to her move than she did. We talked on the phone constantly, but it wasn't the same. I missed seeing her beautiful face and being in her presence. She had always grounded me, and I didn't truly appreciate her until she moved away.

I tried spending more time with my daughters. But I had raised them to be fiercely independent, and their lives were too busy to give me the companionship I desperately needed. I didn't fault them. It wasn't their responsibility to entertain me since my best friend had relocated across the country. I felt pretty isolated and would not allow myself to die of loneliness. I decided to have a late-life crisis. If people could have midlife crises, I could have a late-life one.

First, I bought a fur baby. I found myself the perfect rescue dog. Leo was a genuine mutt. I didn't want a puppy. They were too much work. I wanted a dog that was already trained and who would be a loyal friend.

I also took in a college student. I offered free room and board in exchange for housework. He would manage the house cleaning, yard maintenance, and various chores as a trade for rent. He had the entire basement to himself. The idea came from a newly launched program local colleges were adopting to build bridges between generations. The program saved the college student money and gave the homeowner free chore services. I had been alone for a long time, so having someone live with me would be a big change. But I figured I had nothing to lose with this arrangement. I needed help with my house, so I was fine letting a perfect stranger move in.

After filling the empty holes in my life with a dog and a roommate, the next step of my late-life crisis was to give up all anti-aging efforts. I was eighty-five years old, and it was time to stop chasing the elusive fountain of youth. Julia would be so pleased. I quit Botox. I stopped getting my hair colored. I dumped all my anti-aging products, except for moisturizer (I couldn't have dry skin after all. I wasn't that unreasonable). Cold turkey. Done. Adios. I would allow my wrinkles and gray hair to return once and for all.

I went to a new salon named, *The Silver Lining*. I'd let the talent of a stylist figure out how to transition my hair back to gray. They touted themselves as hair artists—experts in helping women achieve their best silver look. I had kept my straight hair long all these years. To grow out the gray from the artificial color would look ghastly. Plus, I had been coloring over the gray for decades. I didn't know what it would look like without some help restoring it.

Sitting in the stylist's chair, I felt wistful, letting her perform a gray makeover. Would I look like the woman I always feared—old? I remembered

Granny Smith sitting in the chair while I did her hair many years ago.
Now I was the old woman getting her hair styled. I wondered if this young
woman held the same negative stereotypes about old people that I once
had. Did she see me as an old woman like I had seen Granny Smith?
Because I wasn't old. I just happened to be stuck in an old person's body.
It was ironic to see how the tables had turned.

The hair artist shared that gray was growing in popularity, and she
colored lots of women's hair gray nowadays—especially twenty-year-olds.
She said I was very trendy, allowing my hair to go gray. Who knew?

The stylist was certainly up to date with current trends. I asked 101
questions, wanting to challenge her since this was my profession back in
the day.

"Does plucking gray hair keep them at bay?" I asked.

"No," she said.

"Does plucking one hair mean three will emerge?"

"No."

"Is gray hair caused by chronic stress?"

"The jury is out."

"Can a bad diet and smoking cause gray hair?"

"Absolutely."

The conversation was eye-opening. She debunked many of the myths I
clung to. As she worked, she promised I would love my new look—that I
would be striking with long hair fully shaded silver. She said it would be
drastic, but I'd grow into it. I liked the sounds of that.

She dried and styled my hair with my back to the mirror so I couldn't see.
She wanted to do the big reveal after finishing her work. Upon completion,
she spun me around in the chair. I gasped at my reflection. I was beautiful,
but it didn't look like me. I turned my head in different directions to see it
from various angles. I couldn't believe it. I did look stunning! Undoubt-
edly, I would have to get used to this—a full head of gray hair!

It only took until I was eighty-five before I saw the real me. I was so
pleasantly surprised by the flowing silver streaks that I wished I had done
this sooner. I was delighted, and I wanted to show off my new tresses.

"Like I said, it's very trendy, and you look stunning," the stylist complimented. "You look ten years younger."

"That puts me at seventy-five. I'm not sure if that's an improvement," I joked.

"You look amazing and younger," she said. "You're quite the silver fox."

"And you mean to tell me twenty-year-olds pay for gray?"

"Yes, and they pay a pretty penny, too."

"Now you're going to tell me seniors pay to get tattoos," I said.

She laughed. "Yes, and they pay a pretty penny."

"I'll add that next to my list," I mused.

When I said I wanted to show off my new look, I meant it. Two days after my transformation, I booked a flight to see Julia. We hadn't seen each other since she had moved four years ago, though we talked daily on the phone. I hadn't told her about my makeover. I wanted to surprise her.

I had a bounce in my step when I entered the airport. I discovered one benefit of being a senior was going through airport security without hassle. Air travel catered to the geriatric population. TSA regulations didn't require travelers over seventy-five to take off shoes, belts, or coats for airport screening. What a benefit to not strip down in the airport. Or maybe the TSA staff didn't want to see the ugly bunions on my feet or the flabby skin hanging from my arms. I suspected these exceptions weren't about my comfort but theirs.

The agent waved other travelers through the security screening area without incident. I, however, set off alarms. The security booth flashed like a fire truck. It sounded like it was about to explode. I half expected smoke and flames to shoot out. Of course, all eyes turned to me as the security sirens blared.

The TSA screener required me to go into a private room with a male and female security agent for a full body pat-down. That was the most action I had gotten in years. The culprit was not the rods from my foot surgery years ago. It was the bling on my Spry Shoes. Go figure!

"Sorry for the inconvenience, ma'am," the male security agent apologized.

"It was my pleasure," I quipped. "Everyone ought to try getting screened like that at least once."

As I snaked through the terminal, I saw Julia waiting by the baggage claim. I quickly walked toward her in anticipation of her response. She looked right past me. She didn't recognize me. I stopped right in front of her.

"Colette!" Julia squealed in disbelief when she realized it was me. "Oh my gosh! Who are you, and what have you done with my best friend?"

"You like it?" I asked, spinning around.

"You're gorgeous," she said. "I didn't know it was you when I glanced at you."

"I could tell," I said, laughing aloud. "I finally figured it was time to make friends with my true self before I take my last breath someday."

"You wanted to make sure God recognized you when you went to the pearly gates," Julia joked.

"Exactly. I didn't want to end up in the wrong afterlife," I conceded, still laughing.

"Seriously, you're an imposter!" Julia exclaimed. "I don't know what I'm more shocked about—the fact you went full gray or that you have a dog and a roommate."

"It didn't work out," I said. "I gave him back."

"I thought you loved that little dog."

"I do. I was talking about the college student. I gave him back to his parents."

"What happened?" she asked.

"He peed on the carpet."

"I mean, what happened to the college student?" she corrected.

"He peed on the carpet," I repeated. We shared another hearty laugh.

"I don't know if I've told you enough over the years, but I'm so proud of you," Julia said.

"Well, you bitched at me for years about going natural. I couldn't ignore your incessant nagging forever," I teased.

"The squeaky heels get the oil," she said.

"I think you mean squeaky wheels?"

"When you reach our age, it's the heels that squeak," she retorted.

It was so great to be in Julia's presence again. I had missed her more than I realized. It was such a blessing to have a lifelong best friend like her. No matter how much time or distance separated us, we always picked up right where we had left off. That was authentic friendship.

• • • • • • • • • •

## JULIA, 87

Boredom is not an option. That was the slogan at my retirement community. But it was an understatement. The senior activities and social scene had the energy of a toddler jacked up on a double shot of espresso. Sometimes it was exhausting living here because of everything I got involved in—or what my neighbors pushed me to do.

I learned how to play pickleball and use social media. I even learned bow hunting (just in case I ever wanted to hunt for my next meal). I felt like I needed a vacation from this perpetual vacation. I was constantly engaging my brain. The activities director would remind us about the research that cited mental aerobics were good for brain health and could ward off dementia. It wasn't proven, but I wouldn't take any chances. As a Hispanic, my odds of getting dementia increased exponentially because I was over the age of eighty-five, and my heritage put me at greater risk. So I did what I could to fight back by participating in many activities. Usually, I hesitantly agreed. But I always ended up having more fun than I anticipated.

The next adventure I found in the residential newsletter. The publication welcomed new residents, bid farewell to those who moved and paid tribute to those who died. I read the obituary section faithfully.

Tucked in the obituaries was an advertisement for a comedy contest. The headline read, *Stand Up Comedy—Make America Laugh Again*. Advertising a comedy night seemed a little out of place in the obituary section. Maybe that was part of the humor. I read the ad further.

*For one night only, compete in the first comedy contest for a chance to win 500 dollars. All humor is welcome—clean or dirty. If you haven't heard it by now, you aren't old enough to compete.*

What if I could be funny for just one night? Did I have it in me? Could a dry, first-time performer at eighty-seven make a crowd laugh? Anything was possible. I'd challenge myself to find out. I had always led a vanilla life except for a few incidents of insanity peppered in. I didn't have the wit that Colette had. Or the adventurous streak. It came easily for her. For me, I felt out of my comfort zone, pushing myself. I often equated our relationship to her being the kite and me being the anchor. That's what made our friendship rich. We balanced each other out. But at this stage of life, it was now or never for me to be the kite. I had better be funny now, or I might miss the opportunity to ever be funny.

I reserved a spot in the comedy lineup. I had two months to prepare my material. I rehearsed with Colette, who listened on the phone as the jokes fell flat. She was brutal in telling me when I wasn't funny. I practiced again and again with new content.

I didn't even let Michael get a sneak preview. I wanted him to hear it fresh when I went on stage. For the most part, my humor crashed and burned. But I didn't care. I was doing it for the fun of it. I was stretching myself to prove I could be a little funny.

In typical Colette fashion, she surprised me with a gift to congratulate my efforts. I opened the card.

*Julia,*
*Break a hip. Oops, I mean, break a leg.*
*Love, Colette*

Inside the accompanying gift bag was a hot-pink T-shirt adorned with rhinestones in big letters spelling out, *I'm a virgin*. And in small letters underneath, *But this is an old T-shirt*. I loved it! I would wear it for my comedy performance and sparkle like a virgin comedienne under the stage lights.

It was no surprise that I was the oldest contestant. At this point in life, it wasn't often that I wasn't the oldest of everything. They put me last on the list of performers. Maybe so people wouldn't throw tomatoes and walk out at the start. But Michael complimented me by saying they saved the best for last.

I watched all the performers ahead of me. The gentleman just before me had some witty one-liners that got the crowd roaring with laughter:

"An elderly couple went to the movies and snuck in a box of Jujyfruits. During the movie, the husband got down on the floor, searching under his seat. 'What are you doing?' the wife whispered tersely. 'A Jujyfruit fell out of my mouth. I'm looking for it,' he replied. 'Forget about it,' she said. 'But I've got to find it,' he insisted. 'My teeth are in it!'"

Everyone laughed. He continued with his jokes.

"You know you're old when you and your teeth don't sleep together. Speaking of sleep, I discovered the key to structured retirement—a rigid nap schedule."

The audience cheered as the jokester took a bow and exited. He would be a tough act to follow. I walked to the stage and slowly climbed the steps. My knees were rickety, and I felt them buckle with nerves that overshadowed my confidence. Michael sat in the front row, beaming with pride. He was my biggest cheerleader and promised to laugh even if no one else did. Now that's love!

I pulled the mic off the stand, and without hesitation, I let it all out. Years of humor, hidden inside of me, came bursting forth.

"Aging will find you. Getting old will find you. Wrinkles and age spots, and gray hair will find you. But who said it has to be a bad thing? There are many upsides of going down over the hill. Here's how I see it—if I could see through the cataracts."

The audience laughed, and I was just getting started. Maybe I wouldn't crash and burn after all. I continued. "They say—whomever *they* are—you've reached your peak at forty. You're at the top of your game, and when you turn fifty, apparently, it's all downhill from there.

"But I've learned there's an upside of going down over the hill. When you turn fifty, even if your friends and family forget your birthday, AARP won't. AARP will be there to remind you. Months before your fiftieth birthday, membership applications will flood your mailbox, boldly acknowledging you're eligible to join the prestigious discount club. AARP won't let your fiftieth slip by the way family members do. At the same time, you'll finally discover a benefit to being married—your spouse gets an AARP membership for free. That's the upside of going down over the hill.

"In your sixties—somewhere after sixty-two—you'll enjoy the sweet reward of having some of your hard-earned money returned to you. It's like a paycheck without having to work. It's called social security. Forget the blood, sweat, and tears from working tirelessly for decades. You will eventually be repaid a pauper's pittance of the money you loaned interest-free to the government. You'll enjoy a paycheck for the rest of your life without ever lifting a finger again. That's the upside of going down over the hill.

"In your seventies, you'll likely be widowed or divorced, maybe even twice. But you'll enjoy the largest classified dating section for seniors—the obituaries. It's a free dating platform. No joke. I've tried it. You'll bypass the interview process of a first date by reading up on how many children, and even great-grandchildren, the widower has. You'll learn how loyal they are. If the obituary reads, *Survived by a devoted and loving spouse*, they must be a good catch. Plus, you can check out the prospect anonymously by attending the wake of their deceased loved one. And you'll find out how good-looking they are because they'll never look worse than they do at their spouse's funeral. If you find them attractive then, you know they'll only get better looking. The obituaries are a fabulous dating resource. And that's the upside of going down over the hill.

"When you're in your eighties, eighty-five never looked so good. That's the percentage you'll pay on your Denny's bill as a senior. Flash your ID—in case there's any mistaking you as an older person—and you'll save 15 percent on all-you-can-eat pancakes, saving you a whopping sixty cents. The amount of carbs you'll consume over the course of a year can be consumed in one day for the low cost of a few bucks. Paying 85 percent rather than 100 percent of the bill on your bottomless pancakes is a great thing. And that's the upside of going down over the hill.

"In your nineties, you'll enjoy the ride down the hill at breakneck speeds—until your car keys are taken away, of course. And then the upside is you'll live like a king or queen with chauffeur service. Ladies, you'll be driven to the grocery store to stock up on pads—the incontinent ones. Men, your driver will take you to the urologist, who'll make you cough. And ladies, I'll let you in on a little secret—it's not a vocal chord checkup. This valet service is all done with the luxury of a personal driver. In addition, being unable to drive means people run all your errands for you—like getting one bag of groceries and fourteen bags of prescriptions. That's the upside of going down over the hill.

"When you finally reach one hundred, you will be bestowed a special title—centenarian. You'll enjoy the rewards of a triple-digit age, as exciting as when you turned double digits as a kid. You'll also receive a special letter from the president himself, with his original photocopied signature. And while the White House website admits their letter office is swamped and it may take several months to receive your acknowledgment, the government is truly looking out for your best interest. They want you to stay in the race as long as possible, to receive the special recognition that you've crossed the one-hundred-year milestone. And when that certificate finally arrives, you can say you've lived long enough to see the day when something good came out of the White House. And that's the upside of going down over the hill."

Michael laughed heartily all the way through my monologue. And so had everyone else. As I left the stage and returned to my seat, the audience rose for a standing ovation. Who knew I had such humor bottled up in me for eight-seven years? I won the comedy contest and the 500 bucks. And the biggest prize—allowing myself to be the center of attention. It stretched me out of my comfort zone and enjoy the limelight. I was proof you could teach an old dog new tricks.

• • • • • • • • •

## COLETTE, 88

I've never seen a hearse pulling a U-Haul trailer or an armored truck leading a funeral procession. The money and possessions I had accumulated in life couldn't be taken with me. They were given to me to ensure my needs were met. And the rest that overflowed beyond my needs were meant to share with others. With the sudden and instant success of my bejeweled Spry Shoes, I hit a significant windfall. After getting my business degree, I negotiated a savvy deal with a shoe manufacturer who bought my Spry Shoe company. I cashed in for a seven-figure payout. It was like winning the lottery. But I had no need for that kind of money at this point in life. What was I going to do with all of it?

I thought about Grandmother Imelda and Granny Smith. Imelda was loaded and gave none of it to her family to enjoy. Granny Smith had barely anything, but she shared her estate with her family so they could enjoy her generosity. Small as it was, she gave all she had. I kept this paradox in my heart. I wanted to be the kind of generous woman Granny Smith was.

The most important people in my life—my family—would be the bene-
ficiaries of my wealth. But I didn't want them to receive it upon my death.
I wanted them to have it while I was alive, so I could watch them enjoy it. I
didn't understand how some could accumulate wealth and keep it hidden
away until their death instead of sharing it with loved ones during their
lifetime. I wanted to pass down both a rich inheritance and a rich legacy.

None of my loved ones—not even Julia—had any idea of the wealth I
had acquired from selling Spry Shoes. I knew it would blow them away.
And I wanted to experience the fun in telling them. So for my eighty-eighth
birthday, I flew my daughters to New York City. We stayed at a swanky hotel
and ate at a five-star restaurant.

"Mom, are you sure you can afford this?" Nora asked worriedly. She gave
Valerie a troubled glance. "You need to ensure you've got enough money to
live on."

I laughed. "Oh, my dear, you only live once, and I want to spoil my family
while I'm still here."

I knew the girls were anxious, thinking they would have to take me in if
my monthly finances came up short after this extravagant weekend. For my
birthday dinner, we dined like royalty. When the dessert course arrived, I
told them I had news to share.

"Mom, we think we know what this is—it's your last meal with us,"
Valerie piped up. "Whatever your terminal illness is, we will ensure you're
taken care of. We'll help with your care, pay the medical bills, whatever you
need."

"Darling, that's not what this is about." Again, I laughed out loud. They
had mistaken the intent of this getaway weekend.

"You're not dying?" Nora asked.

"Not anytime soon," I replied.

I could sense their relief that I wasn't on my last breath. At least, I hoped
it was relief.

"You've made such big changes these last few years, like going gray and
getting a dog. We thought you were kicking the bucket."

"I'm healthier than ever," I said. "We're here because I want to share
something good with you. It's not just good—it's fabulous."

I took my time before revealing my secret. I wanted to keep them guessing.

"I am a millionaire, and I'm sharing my fortune with you," I squealed. They looked at each other and started laughing hysterically. They laughed so hard they snorted.

"Good one, Mom," Nora teased.

"It's not April Fools, but that is funny," Valerie added.

"I know it sounds outrageous, but it's true," I explained. "My genius idea for the shoes paid off. I sold my shoe business for eight million dollars."

It took an enormous amount of persuasion, but they could see by my face that I wasn't joking. I watched their faces switch from disregard to disbelief. They were suddenly speechless.

"Instead of waiting for you to get it when I pass on, I want to give it to you now so I can enjoy watching you enjoy it."

Their disbelief turned to shock, then to tears. They stumbled over their words, wiped their eyes, and jumped up to hug me.

"Valerie and Nora," I announced. "I'm giving you each three million dollars. I'm giving Julia one million dollars. And I'm giving the last million dollars to charities of my choice."

The next part would be met with mixed reactions.

"But there are a few conditions. You can't get your three million unless Julia agrees to take her million. I know her well enough to know she'll refuse to take it. So it's up to you to convince her. If she won't take her share, you won't get yours."

The girls laughed nervously over the challenge.

"I want Julia to be rewarded for her devoted friendship our whole lives," I said. "She can do whatever she wants with the money."

"So she doesn't have to keep it?" Valerie asked.

"She can give it all away if she chooses, but she has to accept it," I replied. "The second condition is this: To whom much is given, much is required."

"I'm not sure what you mean," Nora said.

"Of the three million dollars you both receive, I want you to give away one million. Choose people who are in need, pick good charities, or find causes that are meaningful to you. Our money is not to be buried. It's to be used for the good of others. I want to impart lessons of generosity and looking out for those less fortunate. This money can change lives—not just yours, but others. And you must invest a portion to save for retirement."

"Mom, this is beautiful," Valerie said. "I love this idea."

"We just have to convince Julia," Nora added. "Can we call her now?"

"Let's do it!" I said, pulling out my phone. "I bet you a million bucks she won't take it."

"I'll bet you three million she does," Valerie laughed.

Julia answered right away, and the three of us sang her an off-key rendition of "Happy Birthday" on speakerphone. She laughed at the thoughtfulness.

"Hello, my fellow birthday girl," I said. "I've got Nora and Valerie here with me. We're out to dinner in New York City. We're celebrating that I completed another trip around the sun. They want to share something with you."

"Hello, all!" Julia replied. "Wow. New York City! What's up?"

"Mom just surprised us with something," Nora started. "And you're part of it."

"Let me guess," Julia said. "She's finally moving to one of the Blue Zones."

"You're thinking much too small," Valerie baited.

"She's moving to all of them?" Julia joked.

"Better. Mom is loaded—and I don't mean on wine. And I mean LOADED. She just dropped a bomb on us. She's giving Nora and me three million dollars apiece."

Julia screamed excitedly through the phone.

"And she's giving you...wait for it...ONE MILLION DOLLARS!" Valerie screamed.

"Shut the fudge up! You're kidding me?" Julia squealed.

"We're not."

"Colette, I love how generous you are," Julia said, regaining her composure. "But I cannot accept this money. Give my share to the girls."

"Nope. You HAVE to take the money," Valerie said.

"Sorry, I won't. I can't," Julia said. Her voice was firm.

"Yes, you will."

"No, I won't."

"Julia, unfortunately, there is a stipulation," Nora explained. "We can't get our share unless you take yours."

"What? Colette, no! You have to give the girls my portion. What am I to do with a million dollars at this point in life?"

"Julia, the agreement is the girls only receive their share of the money if you accept yours. I'm staying out of this. You all have to work it out," I said. I listened to the three of them banter back and forth relentlessly until Julia finally acquiesced.

"Oh my goodness, Nora and Valerie," Julia said. "I would never withhold you receiving this money, so yes, I'll accept it if that's the caveat. Colette, do I have to keep it?"

"It's yours to do with whatever you want. You can give it to Carolann or a stranger on the street. You can even buy another overpriced retirement condo," I teased.

After helping Julia pick her chin up off the ground, we hung up and spent the remainder of our evening drinking champagne. I ordered an expensive bottle to celebrate. Nora and Valerie brainstormed ways they wanted to use the money. They would pay off debt, buy homes for their kids, and travel. For tithing, they discussed creating a foundation jointly. They also wanted to give money to their friends who struggled financially. They talked about spontaneous acts of kindness and randomly giving out one-hundred-dollar bills to strangers. They had all kinds of creative ideas. This was what I wanted. Nothing was greater than watching my daughters care for others around them.

"Mom, what are you going to do with your portion?" Valerie asked me.

"Well, after I pay this 700-dollar food bill, I'll tip the waiter nicely," I said. "I'll give him a 50 percent tip instead of the standard 20 percent."

"How about you give him a 100 percent tip?" Nora suggested.

"You know what, I will," I agreed. "I love that you already have a philanthropic spirit within you. I can't wait to watch how you bless others."

What a peak moment in my golden years. I felt like the wealthiest person on the planet to be able to live large and give freely. This was the legacy I'd pass down to my children—to do good for others, changing the world one dollar at a time.

• • • • • • • • •

**JULIA, 89**

I was now eighty-nine years old. I was a mother, grandmother, and great-grandmother. My family members were the most significant people in my life. Colette's family was as precious to her as mine was to me. Colette was now a great-grandmother, too. The generations beneath us kept multiplying. The farther down the family tree we looked, the more distant our families became. Our daughters grew up together, but our grandkids barely knew each other, and our great-grandkids had never met.

With the frantic pace of their lives and everyone living scattered across the country, our families had never gotten together with all the spouses, kids, grandkids, and great-grandkids. I proposed we bring everyone together for one big family reunion at my retirement community. Colette loved the idea, and she flew her entire family in.

Everyone came, despite hectic schedules. It was a house party of twenty-nine. It included Colette's daughters and their husbands (including Dr. K, whom she eventually married). Plus, her four grandkids and their spouses and eight great-grandkids. In addition, my daughter Carolann, her husband, my granddaughter Ayden, her husband, and her three boys joined us.

I rented two extra condos for the week so we could all be together. Since it was an 55+ community, they had strict rules about young visitors, but they made exceptions from time to time. I was thrilled they made this special allowance for me.

Our week was filled with sun and fun. The weather was spectacular. We couldn't have planned it more perfectly. Our daughters and their husbands golfed, our grandkids played pickleball, and our great-grandkids splashed in the pools. Colette and I lounged under umbrellas in awe of the generations we had produced. These were our families!

If I had only one last wish in life, it was this—being surrounded by my treasured loved ones. Colette's family was my family, too. We weren't related by birth, but we shared something closer than blood ties.

Over the course of the week, my grandkids and great-grandkids became fast friends. And our daughters grew closer. Colette and I made sure everyone became more tightly knit. We didn't say it, but we understood that she and I were the glue holding our families together. We were old women. Who knew how much time we had left? We wanted to ensure our families stayed bonded. And we wanted a photograph to capture this moment in time.

On the last day of our vacation (which went way too fast), I asked everyone to meet at the center courtyard for a group photo. I invited Michael too, but he graciously declined. He said this was exclusively for Colette and me and our families.

I hired a professional photographer, who earned every penny trying to get twenty-nine people to smile, not blink, look at the camera, pay attention, stand straight, and everything else to get an almost perfect shot. Inevitably, someone missed a cue. We roared in laughter at the effort required. It was like herding cats.

The photographer wrapped up the group pictures and snapped candid photos of us engaging, laughing, and being playful. To make it as authentic as possible and capture genuine emotions, he asked Colette what her most embarrassing moment was. She had more than one, and the photographer clicked away as we laughed wildly. He asked me to reveal something I hadn't shared before. Of course, I told the story of getting arrested on my seventieth birthday. My secret was out!

"How was I not aware of this? And to think you know someone well. I don't know you at all, Julia," Colette teased.

The photographer then asked Colette and me to each share one pearl of wisdom we could impart to our families.

"It's hard to narrow it down to one," Colette said. She pulled one of her great-granddaughters close to her side. The photographer kept getting photos as our families smiled.

"Life is far from perfect," Colette reflected. "The sooner you accept life will not go according to plan, the easier life becomes. I resisted aging my whole life. But I should've abandoned the fight against aging sooner because being old is much better than you anticipate. I learned those valuable lessons because of the graceful way Julia has lived her life."

Tears flooded Colette's eyes.

"Julia, what wisdom do you want to share?" the photographer asked me.

I got up from where I was sitting, settled next to Colette, and took her hands in mine. "Life is really, really short," I said. "Time is of the essence, so don't waste your life on insignificant things. Instead, focus on the small joys in the journey. Find the nuggets of gold scattered across your path daily. God leaves them there for you to find. And be thankful. Gratitude is the antidote to worrying and is key to a blessed life. I'm most grateful for Colette in my life."

The tears now flowed freely down my cheeks, too.

"Also, be sure to do significant things now. Forgive now. Say I love you now. Choose happiness now." I looked directly at Colette. "Right now, I want to say, Colette, you are the most precious gift I was ever given. I don't know what I did to deserve your friendship, but you are one class act. I couldn't imagine doing life without you."

The photographer perfectly seized that sacred moment of our friendship. And when the photos were printed, it was my favorite—a black and white portrait of Colette's weathered hand cupped in mine. I framed it and put it on my nightstand. I had the large group family photo enlarged. I hung it above my mantel.

I had a full life because it was full of those I loved.

# Nonagenarians

## Ages 90 – 99

# C

**OLETTE, 90 (GOING ON 19)**

As the airplane door flew open and the rush of wind blew into the cabin, I looked with terror at the pilot. There was no turning back now. I was tethered to my skydiver, ready to take the jump of my life. The pilot gave me a thumbs up. Mine likely wasn't the first face of dread he'd ever given the green light to. The nauseating butterflies churned in my stomach. I broke into a cold sweat and felt it bead up on my back.

The pilot gave the thumbs up a second time. My tethered savior and I rocked back and forth on the edge of the plane, then jumped. The wind rushed wildly past me as we free-fell at a breakneck speed. I wondered how long we'd plummet before meeting our seemingly imminent death. We were wildly nose-diving a hundred miles an hour down, down, down to Earth.

Then my skydiver pulled the ripcord. The parachute gave a fierce tug, and we instantly slowed. The intense speed and hollering noise disappeared. Everything became silent as we floated weightlessly downward. The free fall lasted only briefly, but it felt like an eternity.

It was magical to see the world from this perspective. The earth looked like a patchwork quilt. I could only see the broad landscape, not the details of it. It was beautiful and peaceful. The freedom of what I was experiencing gave me a sense that I could do anything. Pure adrenaline was flowing through my veins. I was on the joyride of my life. Even at ninety years old, I felt life's possibilities become more open to me. I was on top of the world, literally. As we approached the earth, the weight of gravity pulling on us felt harsh. And then, in a matter of moments, it was over. It was a bumpy landing.

The entire dive was a metaphor for life. I felt sad that the real ride of life was nearly over. My life had been full of excitement and fear, and adventures. It was bumpy much of the time. And it went by so very quickly. In the blink of an eye, I was closing in on the final chapter. As a kid, people tried to tell me it would go fast. I didn't believe it. Now that I was here, it saddened me that as time passed, I didn't stop and notice the landscape around me more often—take in the experiences and cherish every moment.

I wished I had enjoyed the journey more instead of worrying about getting to the destination as quickly as possible. I wished I had tried to slow down by appreciating the larger context of life—like the view this skydive showed me—and not fixating on the minor annoyances. The trivial quandaries didn't matter, and I came to understand that's what most things are. You can let them pile up in your head or brush them off like dirt on a shoe.

This was the trip of a lifetime. It was times like this I'd always remember. So often through the years, I'd say that about some memorable moment. But later, I wouldn't remember the moment, just that I'd said it. Today was a time that I will *always* remember.

Skydiving was on my bucket list for my ninetieth birthday. And my goal was achieved. I had flown to Florida to see my dream come true, hoping Julia would join me. She refused. She said her wish was to see her ninety-first birthday.

I lay in the field motionless. I didn't want the experience to end. I took it all in, looking up to the sky where I just returned from.

"Are you okay?" my tethered savior asked me.

"Yes, I'm just not ready for it to be over," I said with melancholy. After another minute, he pulled me up off the ground. Suddenly, camera bulbs flashed as a journalist took pictures. The local *Gazette* was running a story about my thrill ride. The reporter rushed over to me, pushing the camera and microphone into my face.

"What's your age?" the reporter asked.

"I'm ninety years bold."

"How was the jump?"

"Fun and terrifying, surreal and invigorating, all at once," I said breathlessly, adrenaline pouring out of me. I was laughing and smiling and shaking, trying to absorb the madness of what I'd just done.

"Why did you do this at ninety?"

"Why not?" I answered. "Age doesn't have anything to do with it. It's all about your spirit."

"How do you live a meaningful life at this age?"

"Don't listen to what society says about old people," I replied. "You can stay young at heart as long as you choose to."

"What's the secret to your longevity?" The questions kept coming.

"Whiskey and cigars," I joked. "In truth, there is no secret. It's all about when the good Lord wants to take me. I'm just lucky."

"What do you want to say to young people who are watching?"

"As I descended, I felt sad that I hadn't taken more risks in life. If I could do it again, I'd try more things. I encourage young people to push themselves to take risks."

"Will you jump again?"

"Absolutely not! I peed my pants enough."

I had done it. I completed the things on my bucket list. And I was only ninety. I'd have to fill another bucket of dreams.

· · · · · ● ● ● · · ·

## JULIA, 91

"Hello," I answered, responding to the call on my cellphone.

"Julia, where are you?" Colette yelled through the other end.

"I'm driving."

"Where? Don't you know everyone's looking for you?"

"They are? Why?" I asked, confused.

"Because you've been missing. You've been gone for hours, and Michael put out a missing person's report on you."

"Oh no."

"Oh yes. Where are you?"

"I'm not sure. I left to get groceries and got lost, I guess. I've been driving around, trying to figure out how to get back. But it's been a nice little road trip."

"Why didn't you call someone?"

"I couldn't locate my cellphone."

"How'd you find it now when I called?"

"I felt the vibration. I must've put it under the phone books I'm sitting on to prop me up," I explained. I had shrunk in height considerably in the last ten years, and now I needed two thick phone books under me to see over the steering wheel.

"And you didn't feel it vibrating the hundred other times people called?"

"I guess not."

"Julia, your missing person photo has been all over the TV today. People are searching for you."

"Holy crow's feet! That's not good. I need to find the nearest road sign, and then you can help me figure out where I am," I said. I knew I was in serious trouble. "Oh, wait. I see a sign that reads, *Welcome to Georgia*."

"Georgia! Do you realize you've driven to another state?" Colette yelled in anger.

"I do now. Let me turn around at the next exit," I said. I haphazardly crossed three lanes of traffic on the highway to get off the exit ramp. I heard several cars blasting their horns. There must be a crazy driver on the road. I better keep an eye out for it.

"Do you know how to get back?" Colette asked.

"I'm not sure. It's getting dark, and you know I don't like to drive in the dark."

"Then I'll guide you home," she suggested.

For the next five hours, Colette helped me navigate the highways back to my house. I drove well under the speed limit and stayed in the passing lane. If someone didn't like how slow I was moving, they could go around me on the right. Geepers, they were driving fast. Much faster than me. Many people honked and waved fingers and shouted things out of their windows—such Southern hospitality.

I finally pulled into my driveway, exhausted. Two police officers were there. It was after dark, and the lights in the house were blazing bright.

I stayed on the cellphone with Colette and took a deep breath. Michael and the officers were waiting for me inside. Carolann was on Michael's phone. This was going to be an interrogation. I knew I was in serious trouble.

"We need to have a conversation," Carolann said. Her voice was tense. "Hand over your keys to the officers. We hate to do this to you, but you're not allowed to drive anymore."

This didn't feel like a conversation. It was an intervention. They were taking my keys from me. Was this an adult grounding?

"When will I get the keys back?" I asked.

"You won't," Carolann said. "You're done driving."

"You're not safe to drive anymore," Michael said.

"And I can't risk you getting into an accident, or worse, dying like my parents," Colette explained.

"But I've got a lot of tread left in these old tires of mine," I argued.

"Maybe you have tread left in your life, but not in driving," Carolann said.

"How am I supposed to get anywhere?" I cried. "I'm going to lose all my freedom and independence."

"We'll figure it out and set up all the rides you need," Michael offered.

"And we're taking you to a doctor to look into the cause for today's huge lapse in your judgment and memory. Your decision-making continues to deteriorate and..." Carolann's voice trailed off as she began to cry.

"I got lost. So what?" I said, trying to make an excuse for her accusations.

"Mom, it's more than that. You've been forgetting too much lately. You forget appointments. You forget people's names," Carolann said.

"Your forgetfulness is jeopardizing your life, like when you left the stove on," Michael said.

"I don't remember leaving the stove on," I said, perplexed. That was probably not the best answer to give. I had better keep my mouth shut. I wasn't helping my situation.

I perked up to the voices on the TV in the background. The announcer said something about a "ninety-three-year-old missing woman found safe." They were talking about me.

"We're very concerned about your well-being, and we want to ensure your safety," Colette said. "You're not taking this seriously."

"But I am safe," I insisted. "Forgetfulness isn't a death sentence."

"You're safe right now, but what if you hadn't come home?" Carolann urged.

"I'll go to a doctor. But I'm fine," I persisted, fooling no one, including myself. "You'll see. He'll say I'm okay to drive. I just got a little lost today. But there's no need to take my keys away. Besides, I have a spare set."

"Then we'll disable your car," one of the police officers interjected. "You are not safe on the road in our community."

I was fine. Why didn't anyone believe me? This was the beginning of the end. I had always feared having my keys taken from me. And today was the day I dreaded most in life. I was losing my independence and having my child parent me.

I went to bed, grieving that a huge piece of my freedom was being taken from me. I wept at the harsh reality. But I was to blame. I clung to my independence, even if it compromised my safety. At least it wasn't an accident. I wouldn't have been able to live with myself if I had injured someone.

But I also believed it was just a one-time incident and the doctor would give me an all-clear to continue driving. I needed my freedom. I wouldn't stop driving. I would get my keys back. I lived in denial from that day forward.

• • • • • • • • • •

## COLETTE, 93

I was a crumpled mess on the kitchen floor. I had fallen and couldn't get up. "For Pete's sake! This is like a real-life commercial for an emergency response button," I said aloud to Leo. He licked my face as I remained helpless.

I laughed hysterically. It wasn't funny; it was shock from the fall. Because I was a stubborn old mule and refused to ever ask for help, I was trapped on the floor after falling. How did I end up here? It was stupid. I didn't want to bother anyone to come over and retrieve the flashlight stored on the top shelf of the kitchen cupboard. An ice storm was waging war outside, and the power got knocked out. I had needed a flashlight to see. But I was determined to get it myself and not bother anyone, especially when driving was treacherous. It was no good to be dependent upon anyone. I felt I was doing this in the best interest of my family.

I had climbed onto a kitchen chair and reached up to retrieve the flashlight when I lost my balance and fell. I had tried to catch my fall, but Leo got underfoot and made the situation worse. The landing was hard, and instant pain seared through my hip. And here I was. It had been an hour since I fell. At first, I laughed. But as time passed, I cried. I didn't know how long I'd be stranded in the dark, growing colder with each passing moment.

I inched my way over to my phone on the counter but couldn't reach it. I didn't have the upper body strength to lift myself off the floor. The pain in my hip was excruciating. I had injured myself badly. My rescue was within five feet of me, yet I couldn't reach the one thing that would save me from the prison I found myself in. I wasn't behind bars or chained; my prison became the kitchen floor. I would be released only when someone came looking for me. My pride in not wanting to ask for help had led to this imprisonment.

I was an old lady, and I hated the limitations that came with it. I hated being needy and relying on others. I still hadn't learned the life lesson to ask for and accept help. Being ninety-three meant leaning on others without fearing I'd be put in a nursing home. I worried I'd have to move to an old folks' home if I showed vulnerability. It was scary to think about losing my independence as I got older. As children, we depended on our parents for everything. But there's something unnatural about having to depend on our kids. They're supposed to depend on us. If only they knew what it felt like to ask for help for the most trivial things, like finding a flashlight. I used to climb up on the roof of the house and dislodge the ice jams in the winter. I could jump up on the counter to get something from the highest shelf in the pantry and jump back down. Now I couldn't even retrieve a flashlight. I loathed that my body was feeble and my balance unsteady.

"Lord, I promise if I'm rescued, I'll ask for help in the future," I prayed. I didn't use my Jesus calling card often, but today I needed it. "Don't leave me here to die."

My cellphone rang. Wow, I guess I had a direct phone line to God. I knew a family member was calling to check on me during the power outage. I was so grateful I had people to watch over me. But being trapped on the linoleum, I couldn't answer it, and the ringing continued.

Soon after, I was rescued by my granddaughter Taylor. My plea to heaven worked. Who knows how long I would've been stuck there if it weren't for family. Taylor called an ambulance. We agreed I needed to be taken to the hospital.

"Please, just don't put me in a nursing home," I pleaded as the paramedics strapped me to the gurney and hoisted me into the ambulance. "This didn't happen because I'm unsafe living at home. This happened because of pride."

They looked at me with pity. "Don't worry, ma'am; we're not the ones to decide if you need a nursing home," the EMT said, trying to reassure me. I didn't feel reassured.

• • • • • • • •

## JULIA, 94

"You've got Alzheimer's Disease," the doctor announced casually as if it was some ordinary diagnosis. I wondered how often he blew up someone's life with those words. He paused to let this information sink in for me. "Dementia occurs in seven stages, and you're in the moderately severe stage."

"What comes next?" I asked.

"Following this stage is severe decline and then very severe decline," he explained.

"I mean, what comes next for me? What should I do now?

"I would recommend you carry on living your life."

"I feel like life is coming to a screeching halt. This is a death sentence."

"*Life* is a death sentence," he said. "Reframe how you look at it. You can still enjoy a quality life. You fast-forward it. Accomplish what you always wanted to do, except at a faster pace, because your time and memory are limited. Some days will be better than others. Embrace the good days and make the most of them."

"I don't understand how this happened. I tried to do everything right. I ate well. Exercised. Kept my brain sharp. Slept eight hours a night," I explained baffled.

"We don't know what causes Alzheimer's," he said. "Maybe you would've been diagnosed years earlier if you hadn't taken care of your health."

I sat in the exam room, paralyzed. Michael was at the appointment with me. He asked questions and took notes while I tuned them both out. I didn't want to hear the prognosis. I already knew the outcome from watching patients earlier in my career. My mind would slowly shut down, and then my body would follow. It was 100 percent fatal.

I needed my husband, Jack. He was always with me at important appointments like this. Yet, today of all days, he didn't show up. I was angry that he skipped out. He needed to hear this for himself. I would certainly let him hear it when I got home. "How's Jack going to take this news?" I said, breaking down into sobs.

"Your husband's no longer here. Don't you remember?" Michael asked, nervously looking at the doctor.

"I know he's not here right now. That's the problem. Who's going to tell him?"

"I meant he's not alive anymore," he said. "He's been gone for years."

I looked at him, confused. That's right. Jack had been gone for years. I don't know how I could have forgotten that. I felt like I lived with brain fog that didn't clear out. It was a terrifying feeling to forget things that shouldn't be forgotten.

"Sorry, sometimes I get things mixed up," I apologized.

"Don't be sorry. It's because of dementia caused by Alzheimer's," the doctor said.

"I'm the one who owes Colette a hot fudge sundae," I said.

"What do you mean?" Michael asked, perplexed. He assumed it was the dementia talking. But I knew what I was talking about.

"Years ago, I read that one in two people over eighty-five develop Alzheimer's. Colette and I took a bet as to which one of us it would be. I placed my bet it would be her. I owe her a hot fudge sundae."

"I don't think she'll want it," Michael said.

"But I owe her. I owe her so much. I want to repay her for everything she's done for me before I forget," I sobbed.

"We'll figure it out," he reassured me, squeezing my hand.

We left the doctor's office with more prescriptions to add to the cocktail of drugs I was already taking for high blood pressure and diabetes.

Alzheimer's was now added to the list of afflictions. The doctor explained that while there was no cure, medication might slow it. It wasn't likely, but he said it was worth a try.

I had a deteriorating brain that wouldn't remember this conversation in years, months, or even days from now. I was staring death in the face. With this diagnosis, my mind wouldn't even comprehend when death approached. Of course, I always knew I would die someday, and I often wondered how. Now I knew. I would slowly lose my mind and not understand death when it arrived. I would die without even knowing it. What a blessing for me and a curse for my family.

That night Michael and I cried during our regular bedtime pillow talk. I had never seen him cry before. It touched my heart that he shed tears for me.

"Please don't let me forget you," I begged him.

"I will try to help you remember," he promised, kissing my forehead and wrapping his arms around me before we fell asleep. I embraced this familiar routine of ours. I didn't know how many more nights with him I had left to remember.

• • • • • • • • • •

## COLETTE, 95

Due to my fall, I eventually had to have a total hip replacement and ongoing therapy to strengthen my atrophying muscles. I was admitted to a rehabilitation center for short-term care. I had been there for the past ninety-nine days. Tomorrow was day one hundred, and Medicare was kicking me out. They stopped paying on day 101. Insurance determined if I was ready to return home rather than my actual ability. I would be discharged and receive in-home physical therapy. I was ready to be in the comfort of my home again and to see Leo. I missed him. A young female doctor met with me before I was released.

"Falls are the leading cause of fatal and nonfatal injuries in the elderly," she explained in a slow sing-song voice. "Do you understand what I mean by fatal and nonfatal?"

I nodded my head. She talked to me in overly simplified terms like I was a child.

"If we want to live independently, we must be more careful. I'll need you to exercise and, most importantly, ask for help. Do you need me to write this down for you?"

"I think I'm smart enough to follow along," I snapped. I didn't appreciate the way she patronized me.

"Of the 300,000 older adults who fracture a hip annually, 20 to 30 percent die within a year. I don't want you to be a statistic, Colette. You must carefully follow the plan I'm putting in place for you."

"Of course," I said. "I'll do anything." *I'll do anything to get out of being patronized by you*, I thought.

"It includes wearing this," the doctor said, pulling an emergency call pendant out of her pocket. She slipped it over my head, acting as if I couldn't do it for myself.

"Except for that," I said.

"But you said you'd do anything. That includes wearing it. You'll have to push the button if you fall down. Do you want me to show you how to push the button?" she asked as if I was a toddler. I hated elderspeak. It was so condescending.

"I made a stupid mistake by climbing up on that stupid chair," I explained.

"Well, if we ever make another stupid mistake again, we'll be protected with this PERS. PERS means personal emergency response system," she continued with the baby talk, using the word we, not you. There was no "we" in any of this. I hoped I had never talked to older adults the way she did to me.

It was hideous—an ugly, plastic little box on a rope. The device insinuated I was an unsafe elderly lady, unsteady on her feet, which I wasn't. The doctor demanded I wear it and joked that if I didn't, she'd return me to this rehab facility to live forever. I wasn't sure if she was kidding, but I didn't want to find out. I decided to wear the emergency call button as prescribed. She explained it was even an upgraded deluxe version—the crème de la crème of PERS—so when I left my house, I could call for help if I fell in a store or parking lot. Not only was it bad enough that I'd have to wear it at home, but I would also have to wear it in public. This was not an upgrade.

"I'm never going to need it," I said. "I promise I won't have any more falls."

"I hope you're right," she said, patting me on the arm. "But just in case, we're now protected. Think of it as life insurance. We may never need it, but if we do, we're covered."

"Does it come in a nicer color than beige or a bling version?"

"If you'd like to add some bling on it, dearie, go right ahead," the doctor said. "I think that would be cute for you to do."

I needed to do something to camouflage this hideous device. That would be my first project when I got home. I'd have a rhinestone emergency call button to match my bedazzled marshmallow puff shoes. If I was going to be sporting medical devices, at least I would do it in style.

My discharge for tomorrow couldn't come soon enough. When the nursing shifts changed, two young RNs came into my room to check my chart. They chatted and laughed with each other, completely disregarding me. They only saw me as a frail old lady with no value lying in bed, wearing an emergency call button. They saw only what their eyes wanted to see. They wrote notes in my chart and, without acknowledging me, left the room. I grabbed my chart and wrote my own notes in it:

*I am invisible to them. They don't see me.*

*They didn't see me as a starry-eyed child who had big dreams for her life.*

*They didn't see me as a young woman who primped to be youthful and beautiful.*

*They didn't see me as a passionate wife with a husband to love.*

*They didn't see me as a pregnant mom praying for a bright future for her children.*

*They didn't see me as a career woman who yearned to be successful and leave her mark.*

*They didn't see me as a single mom who cried, hoping she was raising her kids well.*

*They didn't see me as a retiree who slowed down to enjoy the fruits of her labor.*

*They didn't see me as a first-time grandmother touched by unconditional love.*

*They didn't see me as a loyal friend who laughed like them with my best friend.*

*I was each of those things. I AM each of those things.*

*They don't see what lies beneath the surface... And that is where the beauty is.*

I closed my chart, hoping someone would care enough to read it and *see* me.

•••••••••••

## JULIA, 97

"Jack wants to kick me out of my home. Please don't let him do this to me," I begged Colette over the phone. "You've got to stop him."

"Not so sure... fine on your own," Colette said, her words breaking up.

"What? You need to speak up. I don't understand you."

"Julia, you need to... hearing aids... turn up!" Colette shouted at me.

"What?"

"HEARING AIDS!" Colette yelled louder through the phone.

"I don't remember where I put them," I answered.

"Well... not going to... or help your case," Colette muttered.

"What?"

"LOOK AROUND!" she hollered. "HOLD ON. I'M CALLING MICHAEL."

I wasn't exactly sure what Colette said on the other end of the phone because I couldn't hear well anymore. But I assumed she'd be over immediately to help me find my hearing aids. She only lived twenty minutes away. I watched out the front window for her to arrive. Instead, a strange man walked in the door.

"Who are you? What are you doing here?" I yelled. I threw a couch pillow at him to scare him away.

"Julia, it's me, Michael. I'm here to help you. I'm talking on the phone with Colette. We're trying to help you."

"Where's Colette?" I asked. "Why isn't she here?"

"She's in Michigan, Julia," he said. "You're in Florida."

*What was I doing in Florida?* I wondered. I looked around to figure out where I was. I think it was my home. I was embarrassed it was in such disarray. I didn't know how it got so messy. Dishes were piled up in the sink. Medication bottles were scattered throughout. I was humiliated that this stranger saw it in this condition. He was rummaging around the house, looking for something. I didn't trust him.

"Get out, or I'm calling the police!" I yelled. I threw another pillow at him.

"I found your hearing aids in the fridge and ketchup in the medicine cabinet," he said. "I think you got them mixed up. Put these in so you can hear." He handed the hearing aids to me, but I was confused about how to use them. I fumbled with them until he assisted me. He turned the volume up, and I could hear again.

This man was talking to Colette on the phone. Why? Did he know her?

"Colette, she needs to return to Michigan to be close to family. This isn't what I signed up for," the man said. "Her family needs to bring her back home. Her home is in Michigan, not here." I couldn't hear Colette's response, but the stranger gave me the phone to talk to her.

"Julia, I know you don't want to hear this, but I don't think you can live on your own anymore," Colette said. "The Alzheimer's is getting worse, and you're not able to care for yourself."

I couldn't make sense of what she was telling me.

"It will be like the blind leading the blind or, in our case, the aged caring for the aged. But I've got a solution if you're in agreement," Colette said. "Move back up to Grand Rapids and live with me. I need the companionship, and you need someone to care for you."

"You want me to live with you?" I asked.

"Yes, like back in our college days. I know I'm a terrible roommate. I promise I won't throw you out like I did that college kid who lived with me. I'm a headstrong old mule, as you know, and I like things my way, but I'll try to do better," Colette suggested.

"You would do that for me?" I broke down in tears.

"Of course. It won't be perfect, but we can watch over each other. I can bring in help, too—someone to bathe you and manage your medications. If you need other care, we'll have family nearby to help. I don't want you to go to assisted living right now. But you do need someone to take care of you."

"But this strange man in my home says I need to be institutionalized."

"Well, today, you're well enough to stay with me. We'll figure out things later if we come to that fork in the road. But I promise I'll take good care of you."

I cried at Colette's proposition. I didn't know where she lived, but I'd live with her anyway.

"So, what do you think? Shall we be roomies again and bring you back to Michigan?" she asked.

I nodded my head through the tears. "Yes, let's be roommates. It'll be like old times."

"Or new times," Colette said. "Who says it has to be old?"

The man standing in my house was crying. I didn't know why. He walked over to me and gave me a big hug. He kissed me on my forehead and wiped tears from his eyes.

"Goodbye, Julia. I will miss you," he said. And he walked out the door.

I wondered how he knew my name.

· · · · ●·●· · · ·

## COLETTE, 99

"Colette, where are the flowers?" Julia asked anxiously as I got her dressed for the day. I completed the daily routine by tying on her floral deck shoes. She said they were her favorites. At least they were today. Tomorrow she might select a different pair as her favorite. Every day was different. But for today, this was her preference.

"Julia, we live in Michigan. It's December. There aren't flowers in Michigan in December."

"Mmm," Julia said, petting Leo on her lap. He often stayed close by her side. He was therapeutic for her. "When are we going to see them in Florida?"

"Not today. Do you want a cup of coffee? I'm making myself some."

"Uh-huh. Why aren't there any flowers on the ground?"

"We don't live in Florida," I answered again.

"But it's June. We're supposed to have flowers in June."

"It's December, sweetie. And we'd have flowers in December if we lived in Florida. But we live in Michigan."

"When are we going home to the flowers?"

"Not today. Do you want sugar?"

"For what?"

"For your coffee. You still want coffee, don't you?"

"Yes, that would be lovely."

I shuffled around the kitchen with my cane. It helped me to stay steady on my feet after my fall and hip surgery. I pulled two coffee mugs out of the cupboard. I had wised up and lowered everything in my cabinets to be within reach. I lit the tea kettle for hot water, and after a few minutes, it began to whistle.

Julia started to scream. I pulled the kettle off the stove and hustled back to her to see what was happening. "The train is scaring me," she hollered.

"It's not a train. It's the tea kettle whistling," I explained, trying to calm her. She was so confused. It broke my heart to see her like this.

"I'd like a cup of coffee. Would you make me some?" Julia asked, returning to her previous state of mind as quickly as the fear came on.

"Of course, dear."

"Why aren't there any flowers?" Julia asked once again.

Repeat, repeat, repeat. It was the same rotating set of questions every day. I couldn't help her remember any more than I could teach a three-year-old Einstein's theory of relativity. It was dementia reaching its peak and erasing her memory. But I answered just the same—with love and patience. I didn't shame her by rudely snapping, "I've already told you for the hundredth time," which would be easy to do. It was exhausting answering the same questions over and over. Sometimes I didn't answer. And sometimes I wanted to yell, "How many times do I have to tell you?" So often, I was out of patience. But I wasn't going to belittle her. I wouldn't yell at her if she had a heart disease, and I refused to yell at her with a brain disease. I honored her by answering every recurring question with respect. I wanted to maintain her dignity.

I returned to the kitchen and slowly poured the steaming water into the mugs. My hands were so weak that lifting the heavy pot to pour the water was difficult. I needed to be careful of the boiling water so I didn't spill it and burn myself. My frail wrist shook uncontrollably as I poured. I shuffled back to the stove and set the kettle back on the burner. I scooped instant coffee into the cups and stirred in the sugar. I dropped an ice cube into Julia's cup to cool it so she wouldn't scald her lips on the steaming water. She wouldn't remember to drink it carefully, and she'd get burned. I didn't want that to happen to her.

"What time is it?" Julia called.

"It's coffee time," I said. It was 9:00 in the morning, but she no longer understood what time meant.

"I don't care for any coffee," Julia said, quickly changing her mind.

"Sure, you do."

I knew it was the confusion of dementia, and I'd still deliver coffee to her. I slowly carried the cups and saucers into the living room.

"Have just a sip. You'll enjoy it," I said. I placed the cup on the seat of her walker, positioned in front of her.

"This smells like Abuela's house," Julia said, slowly taking a sip and smiling.

"What do you mean?" I asked, surprised by the unexpected memory and her ability to recognize the coffee from her childhood.

"When I visit Abuela, she drinks this coffee. It smells like her house."

I found it remarkable she could remember the way her grandmother's house smelled and yet could ask the same questions over and over and remember none of it. The doctors explained long-term memories were stored deeper in the files of her brain, and she'd remember those more than short-term memories. He also helped me understand when she recalled a memory that it was lucidity. She'd have periods of being lucid even as the disease progressed. Though the recall became further and further apart, it was special to me when she'd share a memory buried deep within the confines of her mind.

"Abuela has coffee after every meal. She makes it for me, too. She gives me pan dulce sometimes, too. I love pan dulce."

"I know you do. I have some here. Would you like some?"

"That would be nice."

I inched myself to the edge of my rocker and used my cane to give me the added boost to get up. It took a few attempts to hoist myself out of the seat. I shuffled back to the kitchen and opened the cupboard to get the pastries. I placed them on a plate for her. I returned to the living room with pan dulce in hand.

"I don't care for any," Julia said, staring blankly at the plate.

"I bet you'll enjoy one," I replied, handing it to her. "And you'll like it with your coffee. Keep sipping."

Julia slowly raised the sweetbread to her lips and took a small bite, crumbs landing on her blouse, resting there for as long as she sat. A drop of coffee also spilled down her chin, landing next to the crumbs on her blouse. "This is good. It tastes like Abuela's house," she said.

"Isn't it wonderful that you can remember the love of Abuela?" I asked.

"She is such a kind woman," Julia replied.

"Yes, she was."

"Do you know her?"

"I did," I answered.

"How do you know her?"

"You and I were best friends when we were little girls, and Abuela would make me coffee sometimes. And she'd give me sweetbread, too."

"Oh, that's lovely," Julia said. "You seem like a very nice woman. No wonder Abuela made you coffee and sweets."

I smiled, tears welling up in my eyes because she didn't recognize me. Within the last few months, Julia had forgotten who I was. That was hard to accept, no matter how much I tried to prepare for it. I hoped during her periods of lucidity that she'd recall me and the friendship we'd enjoyed for nine decades. But she no longer remembered who I was.

Until a couple of years ago, before Alzheimer's strangled her memory like a weed choking out a flower, we still enjoyed the blooms of our friendship. Her mind now had deteriorated to this current state. I knew it would get to the point where I couldn't take care of her anymore. She wouldn't be able to eat or drink on her own. As it was, I had home health care aides coming in daily to assist with her toileting and bathing. But we promised each other we'd be at each other's side until the very end. I'd hang on to her as long as I could. I wiped the tears streaming down my face as I pushed out the thoughts of us being separated. I couldn't bear the idea of living without Julia.

"Would you like to listen to some music?" I asked.

"Mmmmm..." Julia began to hum.

I turned on a playlist from the music collection of our younger years. It was a compilation that Julia and I had listened to repeatedly until our minds went numb.

"Oh, Colette, I love this song," Julia suddenly said, reaching deep within her memory bank to recall my name. The music had lit a fuse in her mind like the scent of the coffee. It was as if a lightbulb had turned on, and a memory sparked.

"We sure had fun, didn't we?" I said.

"We had the best of times," she agreed. "I couldn't have asked for a better friend. You're precious to me."

"Aww, Julia, I feel the same," I replied. "I don't know what I did to deserve a friend like you because I was a lot to handle."

Julia laughed. "Act your age, chica," she said suddenly.

"Not your shoe size," I finished.

I was on the verge of sobbing, with the two of us saying our signature sign-off. We sure were a dynamic duo. This would likely be the last time we'd exchange those delightful words. She closed her eyes and smiled, listening to the music streaming in the background. It was such a gift to have her memory rise to the surface so unexpectedly. She recalled my name and our friendship. That was priceless.

She peacefully enjoyed the music. And then the lucid moment evaporated as quickly as it appeared. "Why aren't there any flowers?" Julia asked again, returning to the blank slate in her mind.

The day came when I could no longer care for Julia. Due to Alzheimer's, she became a sundowner. She got increasingly agitated at night. She would wake up and wander the house. She became so confused and disoriented, keeping me up all night. It was wreaking havoc on me because I wasn't getting sleep. She couldn't feed herself anymore, and I couldn't help her any longer. I requested nurse aides come in more frequently. But the timing of her bowels and hunger didn't work in tandem with the schedule of when the aides came.

Julia stopped communicating, and I didn't know how to meet her needs. I couldn't take care of her anymore. It was hard to accept my limitations and break my promise that I wouldn't place her in a nursing home. Julia used to tell me that people in nursing homes rarely got visitors. I refused to let that happen to Julia. But since I drove very little nowadays, especially in the winter, I couldn't visit her often. My heart was crushed to send her away, but this was the end of the road. Julia's body was shutting down, and I couldn't help her. I knew I would soon follow in the death and dying process. It was the saddest day of my life. She and I would be separated.

"I can't do this anymore," I cried to Julia's daughter, Carolann, when I finally called her for help.

"You did it far longer than anyone expected. You're a saint," Carolann said.

"Where will she go?" I asked. I requested Carolann move her to an exceptional nursing home.

"There's a lovely Green House nearby that she would've appreciated back in the day when she worked in nursing care," Carolann suggested.

"A greenhouse?" I laughed. "That sounds about right for a withered prune like her."

"Not that kind of greenhouse," Carolann clarified. "It's an alternative to traditional nursing homes. Instead of an institutional setting, Green Houses provide small residential-like buildings, like a home."

"But it's still a nursing facility?"

"Yes. A cluster of these Green Houses together form a nursing home," she explained. "They provide exceptional care. She'll be well taken care of."

I smiled. "Not as good as what I did."

"Of course not. But they'll come close," Carolann reassured.

I sobbed the day Julia was picked up. It felt like my heart was splitting in two, and she was taking one half with her. Carolann collected a few articles of clothing and toiletries for her. The house sat deafeningly quiet when all the hustle and bustle of moving her out was over. Dead silent. There was a void, and I was completely alone, except for the companionship of my dog. An ocean of tears poured out, leaving me drained and empty. I couldn't live in total isolation like this. We weren't meant to be alone. We were created as social beings. Why did old age have to lead to this? Weren't there enough people we'd impacted in our lives that they shouldn't leave us abandoned? Once again, I was an orphan. At ninety-nine years old, I was all alone. My loved ones were living their own busy lives, as I had when my parents and grandparents got old. It was the pattern of life.

I sat bored and depressed. I'd pet Leo and watch a car drive by occasionally on the snow-covered road. The window in my living room became my view to the outside world—which was covered in a fresh blanket of snow. The trees were empty and lifeless. The cold and barren winter mirrored my mood. I was so lonely. Julia often said this was Mother Nature's way of paring down elderly people's lives. The minimization of the material world helped people detach and prepare for the spiritual world. I felt myself detaching. I yearned for something far greater than this. I had a void in my heart that nothing in this life could fill. It was time to transition, and I felt it in my soul.

But while I waited for the end of the journey, I prayed someone would visit me. It was nearly three weeks later when my granddaughter Taylor and my great-grandson stopped over. Taylor brought me groceries and offered to clean my house. My great-grandson asked me to play a board game. He set up the Game of Life. I smiled, recalling when Julia and I played this for hours as kids. I hadn't played it since childhood. I reviewed the rules and laughed that the conditions for becoming the winner were still the same—to get a high-paying job and stash away as much money as possible before you die.

*There's so much more to life*, I thought to myself. It took me a long time to discover the best things in life had nothing to do with things but with the relationships I nurtured.

"Let me get you a treat," I said to my great-grandson after the game ended with him being crowned the millionaire tycoon. I hobbled to the kitchen to find something in the pantry. I didn't store an abundance of food these days, but I found a box of graham crackers.

My great-grandson gobbled down the crackers, sitting contentedly on my lap. Like me, he was in no rush to move along in life. But a middle-aged person's life was too busy and frantic. Why were adults always in such a rush? Why did they forget the pure joy of just sitting in each other's company? Middle-aged adults lost it temporarily, but I believed they'd get it back when they reached elderhood. They would rediscover what they once lost.

Young children understood this connection with the elderly. The two generations appreciated the reward of just being. Just sitting, talking, and playing, and not trying to race to the next obligation. I began telling a story to my great-grandson. He was eager to listen, and I had so much I wanted to share.

"Grandma, we have to get going," Taylor said, cutting me off. "We'll be back soon."

I sighed. "Please don't be strangers. Come visit more often."

"I'll try, Grandma," Taylor said. "I'm busy with work and family and managing hectic schedules. You remember how it used to be."

It made me sad to accept that my family was too busy for me. I felt insignificant, feeling I wasn't important enough for them to want to visit. Couldn't
they carve time out of their lives to see me more? I wanted to pass down all
the wisdom and experience I had accumulated in nearly one hundred years.
But I realized the secrets I learned would be buried with me. As the African
proverb goes, "When an elder dies, a library burns to the ground."

Taylor leaned in to kiss me on my cheek. She nodded for my great-grandson
to give me a kiss, too. He gave me a wet, juicy smooch and jumped off my lap.
When he reached the door, he turned back, ran into my arms, and gave me
a giant squeeze. It felt so good to be touched by someone, to have human
interaction. I yearned for it.

The door closed. They were gone, and I was alone once again. I returned
to my prison of isolation. I was so grateful for this short visit to break up the
monotony of boredom and captivity. I didn't know how long it would be
before I had another visitor.

As the days passed, I returned to my routine of watching TV, filling out
crossword puzzles, and staring at the snow pile up. I had lost my appetite
and didn't feel like eating. I knew I was starting to lose weight and strength.
I was beginning to die of loneliness. This is what my life had amounted to.
The once precocious little girl, vibrant teen, ambitious career professional,
loving mom, doting grandmother, and active woman inside of me was now
a frail elderly woman living an empty, meaningless existence. I was a prisoner
in my own home. What was the point of longevity if I didn't have the quality
of life to go along with it? I was an old woman now, with more years behind
me than in front of me. I didn't have much purpose left.

"I have to figure out a way out of this!" I cried aloud to no one but myself.
I was desperate to end the isolation.

Deep down beneath the layers of what looked like an old, feeble woman
was once a spunky young lady. I was still young at heart, but it was clouded
by loneliness. "What's your inner age?" I could hear Julia ask me, as she had
through the years.

"Today I feel 199," I said wistfully. I had never felt so old before.

Julia's and my one-hundredth birthdays were a week away. I wanted to be
reunited with her to celebrate a century of life together, but I couldn't just
drive to the nursing home where Julia was and ask for a room as if it were a

hotel. I needed a plan. For days I thought of ways to break out of this prison and end my misery—a real Shawshank redemption for an elderly woman. And then the big idea came to me. My perfect escape.

I scheduled my jailbreak on the eve of our one-hundredth birthdays. I would make my escape just before the stroke of midnight so I could be reunited with Julia exactly at the start of our milestone birthday.

I didn't want to go out looking frumpy. As Grandmother Imelda used to say, "Never leave the house in tattered underwear." I wasn't going to go out with those, either. I wore my finest attire and dressed up like a prom queen. I put on my favorite shimmery teal cocktail dress. I shuffled through my jewelry box and found my favorite diamond earrings. I slipped on a gold necklace and a bracelet to match. I added a turquoise ring. The last thing to complete my outfit was beautiful shoes. I rummaged around my closet and pulled out a favorite pair of high heels—purple polka dots with a bow. I had saved them over the years despite not wearing them after breaking my foot.

"Maybe the shoes would be too much—too suspicious," I said aloud. "To heck with it, it's my bon voyage party, and I'll wear whatever I damn well please."

I crammed my feet into the pumps. I hobbled with my cane over to the full-length mirror to admire myself. My thin gray hair pulled back in a bun, deep wrinkles, brown spots, fat ankles, and sagging boobs reflected. I closed my eyes and envisioned myself as a young girl swirling before the mirror in my bedroom. I remembered how beautiful I was then. I opened my eyes. And then I saw myself. I saw the beautiful woman I was today at nearly one hundred years old, with all the tell-tale signs of being old. I was as beautiful today as I was then. I just happened to be aged. But age had nothing to do with it. I admired myself in the mirror. I was and am beautiful.

"Okay, Colette, are you ready for this?" I said aloud. I nodded to my reflection as I shuffled slowly in my high heels back to the kitchen and turned on the stove for tea.

And then I did it. I put my plan into motion. I pressed the emergency call button I wore draped around my neck. I promised the doctor I would never need it. And in a sense, that was still true. I just needed it now for a different reason. The respondent called out through the transmitter. "Colette, are you okay? Do you have an emergency?" the man asked.

"Yes, I've fallen. I need help getting up," I lied, pouring hot water into my finest teacup one last time. I added a tea bag to steep. I knew I wouldn't use this china after today. I wouldn't need anything from my home to go with me.

"We'll send someone over there shortly to help you. I'll call your family members listed as emergency contacts," the man's voice echoed through the transmitter. "Is the house unlocked?"

"Yes," I said, hobbling to the door to unlock the bolt. I didn't want them to break down the door. "How long will it be before someone rescues me?" I inquired. I returned to my rocking chair, balancing the cup of tea and a plate of cookies, careful not to spill on my silk dress.

"We'll have someone there in twenty to thirty minutes. The road conditions aren't great with the snow coming down, but we'll get there."

"Thank you," I said, trying my best to sound desperate. "Please hurry."

"You'll be okay," he said.

"Yes, I know."

I sat in my chair and nibbled cookies and sipped tea. I lifted Leo onto my lap. He was an old dog. He was more than fifteen years old in human years, which meant he was around eighty-five in dog years. He had lived a long life, too. He was long in the tooth and was on the verge of needing to be put out of his misery. It would happen sooner rather than later, and I didn't have the heart to do it. So I'd have one of my daughters take him to the vet where he could enter doggy Heaven. I held him in my lap and stroked his fur. I told him what a loyal dog he was and thanked him for providing the companionship I'd needed over the years. My tears soaked his fur. He looked at me with sad eyes. He sensed I was leaving him.

I knew that after I got picked up by the paramedics, I'd never return home. I was okay with that. It was part of the plan. Being with Julia was far more valuable than staying in the home I had so fiercely clung to all my life. My home represented my independence. I had always declared I would never go into a nursing home, but it was worth it to be with my best friend. I chuckled, remembering I swore on Imelda's grave that I'd never go into a nursing home. Ha! She would be rolling over in her grave now.

I finished my tea and cookies just before the paramedics arrived. As the ambulance pulled into the driveway, I carefully moved down to the floor and positioned my body in a contorted, fallen shape. I arranged my dress nicely. The paramedics and my daughters rushed in to save me.

"Colette?" they yelled.

"I'm in the living room. Help!" I cried in the most panicked voice I could muster.

As they checked me over for broken bones, the paramedics discussed what to do next. I overheard one of them speak into his walkie-talkie, calling me a LOLINAD. I knew this was a rude term for "little old lady in no acute distress."

Nora and Valerie were understandably more upset than the paramedics, and they deemed me too unsafe to live at home any longer. They were angry that I had been wearing stilettos around the house.

"Bet the shoes caused her to fall. They're too high for someone her age," the paramedic commented. *If only they knew,* I thought.

They all whispered, wondering if I might even have dementia—to be adorned in the fancy dress, jewelry, and high heels at nearly midnight like I was going to a ball.

Nora and Valerie decided it was best to place me in a nursing home. I pretended to argue against a nursing home unless it was with Julia. They agreed to transfer me to her Green House. My plan worked perfectly. I was going to be reunited with my best friend. The paramedics lifted me onto the gurney and began to wheel me away. And then I remembered Granny Smith's hat.

"Wait. Please don't forget my hat," I said.

I told Nora and Valerie where to dig it out from the back of my coat closet. They found it and placed it on my stomach for me to hold on to. I didn't want to leave Granny Smith's hat behind. It meant more to me than any other material item I had accumulated in life.

The paramedics carefully wheeled me through my house. I cried as I looked at the various rooms. I was never going to return. I would never see my home again. But my tears weren't just sadness. They were also joy. By giving up my home, I would be reunited with Julia. All my life, I vowed I would never leave my home. But my friendship and deep bond with Julia were far more powerful than my fear of moving into a nursing home.

They wheeled me out the back door. In the cold of the night, the icy air slammed against my skin. The arctic wind and fluffy snowflakes swirled around me, chilling my bones. The snow crunched beneath the gurney's wheels.

As the ambulance slowly backed out of the driveway, the headlights and flashers illuminated my yard. I caught one last glimpse of my house—the garden where tulips and daffodils poked through in the spring, the side porch that provided shade from the summer heat, the oak trees that dropped leaves in the fall, and the big picture window that provided the best view for a winter wonderland.

This was life—seasons in their finest form. I now could understand that every stage of life has its season. And this was my final season. By evolving and transforming throughout my life, like the seasons, I had collected vast wisdom and resourcefulness. I had just used one hundred years of acquired street smarts and keenness to set myself free. I was going home to Julia.

# Centenarians
## Ages 100 – 109

## COLETTE, 100

Having executed my masterful plan, I was exactly where I wanted to be—in the nursing home where Julia was. It was precisely midnight, the beginning of a new century of our lives. I insisted that I be placed in the same room with her. My request was granted. I was going to be reunited with my lifelong dear friend. A month had passed since I last saw her when she was moved out of my home.

When I was wheeled into Julia's room, I was overcome by a mix of emotions to see her again. I missed her so much. She was asleep, so she didn't know I was there. She wouldn't have known it was me anyway. I asked the nurse aide to help me onto the bed so I could lay next to her. As I wrapped my arm around Julia's shrunken frame, I could feel how thin and skeletal her body had become. She was a bag of bones under the knit blanket. Her wiry white hair was thin and sparse. Her skin—thin and transparent like crepe paper—was gray, almost a shade of death. She looked frailer and more withered than I remembered. Aside from her shallow breathing, she looked like she was already gone.

Seeing her like this, I remembered visiting Gramps in the nursing home. I was terrified of the people who were there. Now I was one of them. What had I been so afraid of? It struck me that I, too, was like Gramps—a young person trapped in an old body. I was a decrepit shell with a vibrant spirit

stuck inside, yearning to still shine through. We, old folks, looked different from how we did in our youth. Yet the life energy within us stayed
the same throughout our lives. That same spirit inside me as a young girl
still existed in me as an old woman. It was a revelation only discovered
when arriving at this destination of oldness. Maybe that's wisdom. We
can't explain what we know at this age. We can only experience it.

I knew I was nearing the end of my life. It might be days, or weeks, or
months. But my time was now limited, and I had one foot in the grave.
And like a child excited for recess, I was waiting for the bell to ring so I
could play in God's divine playground, where I'd be forever young.

*What's the point of it all?* I asked myself. I thought back on the cosmetic work I had done years before. I believed it was to stay beautiful for
the people in my life. But I didn't need any of it. My loved ones didn't
care what I looked like on the surface. Now that I was one hundred, all
my possessions, exterior beauty, and superficial belongings disappeared.

As I reflected, I now realized the point of life is to discover our purpose—to feel our lives mattered and that we made a difference and to
achieve a lifetime of fulfillment and meaning. Did I do that? I believe so.
I had no regrets. I had lived my life to the fullest. I did my best, even if it
wasn't perfect. I thought I would've had more time, yet I was now one
hundred years old. I had been gifted with many more years than almost
everyone I knew. I only wished I had slowed down and enjoyed each step
of the journey more. I should've "stopped and smelled the roses" more
often, as Mr. Patrick, my elementary school principal, had tried to instill
in me decades ago.

When I woke later in the morning, I realized I had fallen asleep next
to Julia. It was still our birthday, the winter solstice—the shortest day
of the year, but we were long-living lassies. We were now genuine antiques—aged to one hundred—validated as having a high value because
of considerable age. We had become centenarians. It was a milestone
I had hoped to reach, but I hadn't known what it would feel like. I
didn't feel one hundred. It was just a number. My inner age felt decades
younger, even now. I still felt like the young bride, the proud new mom,
and the jubilant first-time grandmother. All the things that made me feel
young and alive then still gave me that feeling today.

For our one-hundredth birthdays, the staff threw Julia and me a party. Aides got Julia dressed and transferred her into a wheelchair so she could join. We were wheeled into the gathering place. Residents and our families greeted us and broke into song, crooning "Happy Birthday." One hundred candles glowed on the cake. I attempted to blow out all of them. It took a few tries and help from my daughters, but I did it.

I opened gifts from the staff—rhinestone tiaras for both of us—which they placed on our heads. My family surprised me with red sparkly bejeweled Spry Shoes—a pair for Julia and me. I marveled at the thoughtful gift. The staff switched out Julia's and my slippers and replaced them with the sparkling shoes. I felt like Cinderella!

We also received a special certificate from the White House, acknowledging our one-hundred-year milestone. A nurse presented it to me, and everyone snapped pictures.

"Well, look at that. I actually lived to see the day that something good came out of the White House," I joked, recalling Julia's success in standup comedy. I also had a funny bone in my body—even if it was osteoporotic. But I still had it, nonetheless.

Julia sat slumped over in her wheelchair, unaware of her surroundings. She wasn't coherent to know I was right beside her celebrating this magnificent milestone. But her spirit knew I was there. And she would be pleased we were together for our one-hundredth birthdays. We were both surrounded by everyone we loved and who loved us.

In the end, all we hope for is love—the love of someone who has stood by our side in life and walked with us through the ups and downs in the hills and valleys. Nothing else matters if we don't have someone special to love and to love us in return. And when all else has been removed from our lives, we simply want to have someone we love next to us, holding our hand.

Suddenly and unexpectedly, Julia reached over and took my hand in hers.

# Acknowledgements

To my remarkable kids, Tyler, Aidan, and Ava, whom I've had the honor to parent. Without you, I wouldn't have had the courage to take risks, straighten my crown when life trips me up, and fiercely defend what's good and right. You give me purpose every day to fight for the important things in life. Because of you, I am the woman I am today. You are my greatest teacher.

Tyler, thank you for first making me a mom. Unfortunately, you were the guinea pig when I navigated parenthood as a young, inexperienced mother (I'm so sorry I made you eat asparagus). Despite my shortcomings and without a parent manual to guide me, you turned out to be an exceptional man. You are intelligent and accomplished and I'm so proud of you!

Aidan, thank you for being my beacon of hope. You were the gem that came from the fruit of waiting. Life is often a game of waiting and you taught me the lesson of perseverance. Your fun, outgoing personality is contagious and your hard work is to be celebrated. You are the glue that holds people together!

Ava, thank you for being such a sweet, gentle young woman. You have more confidence at your age than I ever had as a teenager. And you also make far more responsible choices than I did. You are the kindest person I know, and your happiness and optimism never waiver. You are beautiful on both the inside and out!

To my mom, dad & stepmom—Carol, Patrick & Noralie—who give me great insight into how to age well. You are rocking out your retirement years with vigor and liveliness You have sheltered me, inspired me, and provided for me from childhood to adulthood. I hope I'm still jet-setting and driving convertibles and sports cars when I'm your age.

To the love of my life, Brian, who was an early champion of my book. I took a leap of faith to let you read the first pages before anyone. Giving you my manuscript was as exhilarating as giving you my heart. You encouraged me over cups of coffee and glasses of wine when I began writing my earliest chapters. You are my wisest teacher and biggest supporter, and you patiently let me run countless ideas by you. Thank you for having my back and loving me so well.

To my closest girlfriends—Lisa Novosad, Lyn DenBraber, Susan Culver, Lynda Kasperski, Becky Sedam, Erin Collings, Diane Knapp, Liz Eardley, Kim Bradshaw, Patti VanMeurs, Tori Gillesse, Sarah Wonser, Cheri Brenner and many others along the way. You all have taught me the definition of authentic friendship. We've shared lots of tears and laughter during many different seasons of life. You are all such beautiful women.

To my lifelong BFF, Karen Farhat-Hendricks, whom I've shared a friendship with since we were toddlers and carries the torch for Julie, whom the book is dedicated to. Julie, Karen, and I were like the Three Musketeers. Karen, you are the keeper of my every secret. Our friendship is rare and priceless. No matter how much time passes, we pick up where we left off. The stories between us are as countless as shoes in the world.

To my sister, Paula Garvin. We have walked through highs and lows together. And I'm so grateful for our friendship and our same laughing style. Nobody in the world makes me laugh like you.

To all the early readers of my manuscript—Bob Israels, Terri DeBoer, Jo DeMarco, Anne Ellermets, Shelley Irwin, Paige Rubleksi, Lisa Novosad, and Kelly Moeggenborg—who endorsed me with your kind words and gave me the confidence that this book didn't suck.

To Tyler Feuerstein, Arlene DiVita, Deb Stanley, and Kathie Blackmore, who helped edit the manuscript and made sure every t was crossed and i dotted. You were diligent in helping me perfect it.

To Ammie Bouwman, Stephan Ruthenberg, Victoria Galindo, and Frank Gutbrod, who all contributed in various ways to the completion of this project.

And to God, who has provided abundantly for me. Though life has definitely not gone according to plan I couldn't have written my story better, even with all the heartbreaks and joys woven together. He rebuilds my life time and again into beauty from ashes.

# To My Readers

Dear Friends,

Thank you for reading *Not Your Shoe Size*. This book was a passion project that took me seven years to complete (a lot of life happened, and shoes were worn during that time). I wrote it to help women be confident in themselves, especially when they become older and feel invisible. You are not invisible! My hope is if you were inspired by the story, here's how you can help me on my journey.

Please leave me an honest review on Amazon.com and/or Goodreads. com. Your opinion means a lot to me and I read every single review, which keeps me connected to my readers. Reviews are critical to the success of authors.

Finally, recommend this book to others and start a book club with your BFFs. You can download the book club kit at www.jenniferdivita.com . There's nothing like a good read, good friends, and a glass of wine at the same time. There are fun, insightful questions to ponder. I also provide a number of activities to encourage you to age with zeal. You can enjoy it with friends or by yourself.

Warmly,

Jennifer DiVita

P.S. I have two new books in the works. One is a novelette that offers the final vignettes and a few more laughs peeking in on the lives of Colette and Julia. The second book tackles a different social issue that women face with multi-viewpoints and new quirky characters. I promise it's sure to delight! Be sure to sign up for my newsletter at www.jenniferdivita.com and follow me on Facebook to watch for them.

Happy Reading!

To enhance the enjoyment of *Not Your Shoe Size*,
download the Book Club Toolkit.
Visit www.jenniferdivita.com or use the QR code below to easily access the
toolkit. You can enjoy this with friends or on your own.

Jennifer DiVita (aka Jennifer Feuerstein) is an influencer in positive aging. She works for AARP and is a TV talk show host, writer, and sought-after speaker. She was named one of the "50 Most Influential Women in W. Michigan" and uses her voice to share the upside of going down over the hill. Her expertise (plus her own mid-life gaffes and extensive shoe collection) inspired her to write *Not Your Shoe Size* to encourage women to love the skin they're in, no matter what age.

www.JenniferDiVita.com
Facebook.com/JenniferDivitaBooks
Visit my website here: